LIE GROUPS
FOR
PHYSICISTS

THE MATHEMATICAL PHYSICS MONOGRAPH SERIES

A. S. Wightman, Editor
Princeton University

Freeman Dyson (*Institute for Advanced Study*)

SYMMETRY GROUPS IN NUCLEAR AND PARTICLE PHYSICS

Robert Hermann (*Argonne National Laboratory*)

LIE GROUPS FOR PHYSICISTS

George W. Mackey (*Harvard*)

THE MATHEMATICAL FOUNDATIONS OF QUANTUM MECHANICS

Roger G. Newton (*Indiana*)

THE CUMPLEX *j*–PLANE

R. F. Streater (*Imperial College of Science and Technology*)
A. S. Wightman (*Princeton*)

PCT, SPIN AND STATISTICS, AND ALL THAT

LIE GROUPS

FOR

PHYSICISTS

ROBERT HERMANN
Argonne National Laboratory

W. A. BENJAMIN, INC.
New York   Amsterdam
1966

LIE GROUPS FOR PHYSICISTS

*The final manuscript was received July 7, 1965; this
volume was published January 3, 1966*

W. A. BENJAMIN, INC.
NEW YORK, NEW YORK 10016

CONTENTS

LIE GROUPS
FOR
PHYSICISTS

CHAPTER 1

INTRODUCTION

In these lectures I shall give some of the qualitative, geometric background of Lie group theory that is not readily found in a direct manner in the standard treatises, e.g., Chevalley (1946), Helgason (1962), Jacobson (1962), or Pontrjagin (1939). I shall assume that the readers are physicists interested in the possible applications of Lie group theory to elementary-particle theory, and that they have already made some sort of beginning toward studying the subject. Most proofs will be omitted or sketched. In general, there is a great need for expositions of modern mathematics for physicists and engineers which only present the most important ideas. This book was written in that spirit.

I shall emphasize the theory of homogeneous spaces of Lie groups (particularly the theory of symmetric spaces), since apparently this is the side of the theory that is least known to physicists, and there are many ideas here that might be useful if they were better known. It is strongly recommended that Helgason's book, *Differential Geometry and Symmetric Spaces*, be consulted for the details that I have omitted. The book by Auslander and Mackenzie, *Introduction to Differentiable Manifolds*, is recommended as useful background for the more elementary general background on manifolds and Lie groups. In addition, much of the "fine structure" of Lie group theory, particularly that which involves topology and the classification of semisimple Lie algebras, will be omitted.

On the other hand, I have refrained from trying to make this report more *immediately* accessible to physicists, by using the primitive, but ingenious, notations that now seem to be standard in the physics literature. As long as the only Lie groups that appeared in physics were of the very simple type [e.g., $SO(3)$, $U(2)$], mathematicians could not really complain too strongly; however, it has been found in mathematics that the more abstract coordinate and basis-free methods developed in the last twenty years are very powerful when dealing with the more complicated Lie groups that seem to be creeping into physics [e.g., $SU(3)$ and $SU(6)$], and physicists who want to push on in these directions will find themselves needlessly wasting much time and effort if they do not learn the "modern" tricks.

1

I shall concentrate then on those general principles of "geometric" Lie group theory that I believe to be relevant to physics, rather than attempting to duplicate the material that is now traditional in expositions of Lie groups for physicists. For example, the expositions by Behrends et al. (1962), Boerner (1963), Dynkin (1950), Hamermesh (1962), Mathews and Walker (1964), Racah (1951), Salam (1963), and Wightman (1960) can be recommended to the physicist reader as background. As a geometer, I have a strong preference for coordinate-free methods. While the technicalities of manifold theory will be used as little as possible, the reader should at least be familiar with the theory of linear vector spaces as it is used in recent mathematical literature, i.e., in a way independent of bases, and with emphasis on "mapping" ideas. It will be assumed that the reader is familiar with the tensor product, and with such basic ideas as "invariant subgroup," "Lie algebra," etc. For example, the book by Kastler (1961) will be useful to physicists as a bridge between the physicist's and mathematician's versions of linear algebras.

It is a great pleasure to express my thanks to the many people who have helped me in this interdisciplinary endeavor. My conversations with L. Brown, N. Burgoyne, J. Cook, Y. Dothan, M. Gell-Mann, M. Hamermesh, W. McGlinn, L. Michel, J. Moyal, Y. Ne'eman, and B. Sakita have been particularly helpful. I am indebted to W. Givens, W. Miller, and R. Sachs, who arranged on short notice my stay in the uniquely stimulating environment of Argonne National Laboratory. Doris Haight has been a great help as typist. Some of the preliminary work on this material was done under grant from the Mathematics Division of the Air Force Office of Scientific Research. The work was performed in part under the auspices of the U.S. Atomic Energy Commission.

CHAPTER 2

LIE GROUPS AS TRANSFORMATION GROUPS

Groups first arose as transformation groups on spaces. If M is a space, a transformation of a space, denoted, say, by g, is a one-to-one map of M onto itself. If p is a point of M, gp will denote the transform of p by g. Two such maps, say g_1 and g_2, can be composed, to obtain the product g_1g_2:

$$(g_1g_2)p = g_1(g_2p).$$

This product, together with the inverse g^{-1} (i.e., $g^{-1}p$ is that point q such that $gq = p$), give a group structure to the set of transformations. Of course, groups can also be considered as abstract objects, denoted by such letters as G, H, L, etc. Exhibiting such a group as a set of transformations of M, with the "abstract" group operations agreeing with the "geometric" operations on transformations, defines G as a *transformation group on M*. Another way of putting this is to say that exhibiting G on a transformation group on M amounts to exhibiting a map $G \times M \to M$ satisfying an obvious set of conditions. [The image of $(g, p) \in G \times M$ is just gp, the transform of p by g.]

We shall be interested in the cases where G is a Lie group, M is a differentiable manifold, and the action of G on M is given in local coordinates by differentiable functions. (To define a Lie group one must impose on an abstract group the condition that it also is a differentiable manifold, and that the group operations are differentiable in the local coordinates.) There are a series of basic definitions associated with such a group action on M.

1. Let p be a point of M. The set of $g \in G$ that leave p fixed, i.e., satisfy $gp = p$, forms a subgroup of G, called the *isotropy group* of G at p, denoted by G^p.

2. The set of points of M that can be reached by applying elements of G to a single point $p \in M$ is called the *orbit* of G at p, denoted by Gp.

G *acts transitively* on M (or M is a *homogeneous space* of G) if $Gp = M$ for at least one $p \in M$. (It follows then that this is so for every point of M.) Clearly, G acts transitively on every orbit.

3

If G acts transitively on M, M can essentially be reconstructed knowing G and G^p, for one point p in M. In general, if H is a subgroup of a group G, we can construct the *coset* space G/H. An *element* of G/H is a subset of G of the form gH, for *one* $g \in G$. G can be made to act as a group of transformations on G/H: g_0 applied to the coset gH is by definition the coset $g_0 gH$. Note now that $M = Gp$ can be identified with G/G^p: Since $gG^p p = gp$, the map $G(p) \rightarrow M$ "passes to the quotient" to define a map $G/G^p \rightarrow M$ that, it is readily verified, is one-to-one and onto.

Hence the study of homogeneous spaces can, in principle, be reduced to the study of coset spaces G/H, where H is a subgroup of G, hence to the study of pairs (G, H) consisting of a Lie group G and subgroup H. In turn, many of the properties of such pairs can be deduced from algebraic properties of pairs $(\mathbf{G}, \mathbf{H})$ consisting of a Lie algebra $\mathbf{G}$ and subalgebra $\mathbf{H}$. Finally, note that the identification of M with G/G^p really does not depend on the point $p \in M$ chosen: If q is another point of M, and if G acts transitively, there is a $g \in G$ with $gp = q$. Then $G^q = gG^p g^{-1}$; i.e., G is a conjugate subgroup of G. It is clear that the coset spaces corresponding to conjugate subgroups are basically the same.

Example 1

M = Minkowski space, = G/H, where G = the Poincaré group (i.e., the inhomogeneous Lorentz group); H = the homogeneous Lorentz group.

Recall the notation for the "classical groups." $GL(n, R)$ and $GL(n, C)$ are the groups of invertible $n \times n$ real and complex matrices. $SL(n, R)$ and $SL(n, C)$ are those (invariant) subgroups consisting of elements of $GL(n, R)$ and $SL(n, C)$ which have determinant 1. The Lie algebra (see Chapter 3 for its definition) of $GL(n, R)$ and $GL(n, C)$ consists of *all* $n \times n$ real and complex matrices. The Jacobi bracket relation for matrices, say α and β, is the commutator $[\alpha, \beta] = \alpha\beta - \beta\alpha$. $O(n, R)$ is the subgroup of $GL(n, R)$ consisting of orthogonal matrices. $O(n, C)$ is a subgroup of $GL(n, C)$ in a similar way. $SO(n, R) = SL(n, R) \cap O(n, R)$, the *rotation group*. $SO(n, C) = SL(n, C) \cap O(n, C)$. $Sp(n, C)$ is the subgroup of $SL(2n, C)$ that leaves invariant a given nondegenerate skew-symmetric form. $U(n)$ is the unitary subgroup of $GL(n, C)$. $SU(n) = U(n) \cap SL(n, C)$. All these groups, except $O(n, R)$, are connected. All are semisimple, except $GL(n, R)$ and $GL(n, C)$, and $U(n)$.

Example 2

$P_n(R)$ and $P_n(C)$, real and complex projective spaces of n real and complex (respectively) dimensions. (n complex dimensions means $2n$ real dimensions.) For example, $P_n(C)$ is constructed as follows: Start with

C^{n+1}, the space of $(n+1)$ complex variables. A point of C^{n+1} is then an $(n+1)$ tuple $z = (z_1, \ldots, z_{n+1})$ of complex numbers.

Set up an equivalence relation on the nonzero elements of C^{n+1} in the following way. Two vectors z and z' are equivalent if there is a nonzero scalar λ such that $z = \lambda z'$. A "point" of $P_n(C)$ is then an equivalence class of such vectors. [If C^{n+1} is regarded more abstractly as a complex vector space, a "point" of $P_n(C)$ can be regarded as a one-dimensional linear subspace of C^{n+1}.] A function $z \rightarrow f(z)$ (not necessarily holomorphic, of course) on C^{n+1} can then be regarded as a function on $P_n(C)$ if it is homogeneous of zeroth degree, i.e., if $f(\lambda z) = f(z)$. The coordinate functions $z_1, \ldots, z_{n+1}$ are not, of course; hence they are not actually functions on $P_n(C)$. In classical language, they are "homogeneous coordinates" for $P_n(C)$. However, genuine functions on $P_n(C)$ can be constructed by taking rational functions in $z_1, \ldots, z_{n+1}$. For example,

$$y_i = \frac{z_i}{z_1} \qquad (2 \leqslant i \leqslant n+1).$$

These are "inhomogeneous coordinates" for $P_n(C)$. Note that they are not defined everywhere on $P_n(C)$, but just on the set of points arising from vectors z whose first component is nonzero (in classical language, on the complement of the "hyperplane at infinity" defined by $z_1 = 0$). There is a topological reason for this: $P_n(C)$ is a compact topological space, hence does not have a coordinate system that is defined everywhere. On the other hand, functions such as

$$f_{ij}(z) = \frac{z_i \bar{z}_j}{z_k \bar{z}_k}$$

are defined everywhere on $P_n(C)$. (Let indices $i, j, k, \ldots$ have the range from 1 to $n+1$, and adopt the summation convention.) Note however that they are not holomorphic ("complex analytic") functions of z.

Now we can exhibit $P_n(C)$ as a homogeneous space of $GL(n+1, C)$. Consider an element α of $GL(n+1, C)$ as an $(n+1 \times n+1)$ matrix (α_{ij}). Let α act on C^{n+1} by the rule

$$(\alpha z)_i = \alpha_{ij} z_j.$$

Note that if $z' = \lambda z$, $\alpha z' = \lambda \alpha z$ also; hence α "passes to the quotient" to define a transformation on $P_n(C)$. We leave it to the reader to show that the action of $GL(n+1, C)$ is transitive on $P_n(C)$; i.e., any pair of one-dimensional subspaces of C^{n+1} can be mapped into each other by a suitably chosen linear transformation.

Let us determine the isotropy subgroup H of $GL(n+1, C)$ at a point

$P_n(C)$, for example, the point determined by the vector $z^0 = (1, 0, \ldots, 0)$. The matrix α leaves this point fixed if there is a scalar λ with

$$\alpha z^0 = \lambda z^0;$$

i.e.,

$$\alpha_{ij} z_j^0 = \lambda z_i^0,$$

or

$$\alpha_{i1} = 0 \qquad \text{for } i > 1,$$
$$\alpha_{11} = \lambda.$$

Thus, H is the subgroup of $GL(n+1, C)$ determined by the condition

$$\alpha_{i1} = 0 \qquad \text{for } i > 1.$$

$GL(n+1, C)$ does not act "effectively" on $P_n(C)$. Let us pause to explain what this means in general. Consider a group G that acts as a transformation group on a space M. The set of $g \in G$ which acts as the identity transformation, i.e., such that

$$gp = p \qquad \text{for all } p \in M,$$

forms a subgroup L of G. In fact, it is an invariant subgroup of G. For any other $g_0 \in G$,

$$(g_0 g g_0^{-1})(p) = g_0 g g_0^{-1} p = g_0 g_0^{-1} p = p;$$

i.e., $g_0 g g_0^{-1} \in L$. The quotient group G/L can then be formed. Since L acts as the identity on M, the action of G "passes to the quotient" to define an action of G/L on M. G/L acts *effectively* on M; i.e., each element of G/L that is not the identity element of the abstract group does not act as the identity on M.

Return now to the case $M = P_n(C)$. $\alpha \in GL(n+1, C)$ acts as the identity if

$$\alpha_{ij} z_j = \lambda(z) z_i \qquad \text{for all } z \in C^{n+1}.$$

This forces

$$\alpha_{ij} = \lambda \delta_{ij},$$

i.e., α is a diagonal matrix. Another way of looking at it is to note that the diagonal matrices form the center of $GL(n+1, C)$; i.e.,

The quotient of $GL(n+1, C)$ by its center acts on $P_n(C)$. The quotient group is sometimes called the projective or collineation group, since it acts effectively on $P_n(C)$.

We can also consider $SL(n+1, C)$, the group of matrices of determinant 1. It, too, acts transitively on $P_n(C)$. Its center is now discrete, in fact, forms the multiples $\lambda \delta_{ij}$ of the identity matrix, with $\lambda^{n+1} = 1$. Thus, the center is the cyclic group with $n+1$ elements, sometimes denoted by Z_{n+1}. The quotient $SL(n+1, C)/Z_{n+1}$ can then also be identified with the projective group which acts effectively on $P_n(C)$. The subgroup $SU(n+1)$ also acts transitively on $P_n(C)$. The center of $SL(n+1, C)$, namely Z_{n+1}, belongs to $SU(n+1)$. For example, it is an interesting fact that it is precisely the representations of $SU(3)/Z_3$ that occur as symmetries of the strongly interacting particles. The subgroup of $SU(n+1)$ that leaves a point $P_n(C)$ fixed can readily be identified with $U(n)$, so that $SU(n+1)/U(n) = P_n(C)$.

$P_n(R)$ can be dealt with in a similar way by using the real instead of the complex numbers in these constructions.

Example 3

S_n, the n-sphere, $= SO(n+1, R)/SO(n, R)$. Here we start off with R^{n+1}, the space of $(n+1)$-triples of real numbers $x = (x_1, \ldots, x_{n+1})$. S_n is the set of x's with $x_1^2 + \cdots + x_{n+1}^2 = 1$. The matrix groups $SO(n+1, R)$ and $O(n+1, R)$ both act transitively on S_n. The computation of the isotropy subgroup at one point is left to the reader.

CHAPTER 3

LIE ALGEBRAS AND THE CORRESPONDENCE BETWEEN SUBGROUPS AND SUBALGEBRAS

Let G be a Lie group. A *one-parameter subgroup* of G is a mapping $t \to g(t)$ of the real numbers in G that is a homomorphism between the additive group of the real numbers and G; i.e., it satisfies

$$g(t_1 + t_2) = g(t_1)g(t_2).$$

Let ρ be a linear representation of G by linear automorphisms of a (finite-dimensional) vector space V. Thus, for each $g \in G$, $\rho(g)$ is an invertible linear transformation $V \to V$; the rules to be satisfied can be summed up by saying that the map $G \times V \to V$, defined by $(g, v) \to \rho(g)(v)$, defines G as a transformation group on V. Alternatively, of course, one may say that ρ is a homomorphism from G to the group of linear automorphisms of V. To each one-parameter group $t \to g(t)$, we have a one-parameter group $t \to \rho(g(t))$ of linear transformations of V, for which one can find an "infinitesimal generator" α, which is also a linear transformation: $V \to V$ (not necessarily invertible, however).

On the one hand, α can be obtained from the one-parameter group: For $v \in V$,

$$\alpha(v) = \frac{d}{dt} \rho(g(t))(v)\bigg|_{t=0}.$$

On the other hand, the one-parameter group can be reconstructed from α: For $v \in V$, $\rho(g(t))(v)$ is the solution of $dv/dt = \alpha v$, with $v(0) = v$, or, explicitly,

$$\rho(g(t))(v) = \exp(t\alpha)v = \sum_{j \to 0}^{\infty} \frac{(t\alpha)^j}{j!}(v).$$

Thus, we have set up a correspondence between the set of one-parameter subgroups of G and certain linear transformations of a vector space. The linear transformations of a vector space V form a vector space; α_1 and α_2 can be added:

$$(\alpha_1 + \alpha_2)(v) = \alpha_1(v) + \alpha_2(v) \qquad \text{for } v \in V.$$

In addition they form a Lie algebra: The *Jacobi bracket* $[\alpha_1, \alpha_2]$ can be defined as the commutator:

$$[\alpha_1, \alpha_2](v) = \alpha_1\alpha_2(v) - \alpha_2\alpha_1(v) \qquad \text{for } v \in V.$$

Can we define "addition" and "Jacobi bracket" *directly* in terms of one-parameter groups? The key is in the following "perturbation formulas":

$$\exp(t(\alpha_1 + \alpha_2)) = \lim_{n\to\infty} \left[\exp\!\left(\frac{t}{n}\,\alpha_1\right)\exp\!\left(\frac{t}{n}\,\alpha_2\right) \right]^n,$$

$$\exp(t([\alpha_1, \alpha_2])) = \lim_{n\to\infty} \left[\exp\!\left(\frac{t}{n}\,\alpha_1\right)\exp\!\left(\frac{t}{n}\,\alpha_2\right)\exp\!\left(\frac{-t}{n}\,\alpha_1\right)\exp\!\left(\frac{-t}{n}\,\alpha_2\right) \right]^{n^2}.$$

This suggests that we use these formulas so as to make the set of one-parameter subgroups into a Lie algebra. In fact, we can define the "addition" and "Jacobi bracket" of two one-parameter such groups, $t \to g_1(t)$ and $t \to g_2(t)$, as follows.

The one-parameter groups corresponding to addition and brackets are, respectively,

$$t \to \lim_{n\to\infty} \left[g_1\!\left(\frac{t}{n}\right)g_2\!\left(\frac{t}{n}\right) \right]^n,$$

$$t \to \lim_{t\to\infty} \left[g_1\!\left(\frac{t}{n}\right)g_2\!\left(\frac{t}{n}\right)g_1\!\left(\frac{-t}{n}\right)g_2\!\left(\frac{-t}{n}\right) \right]^{n^2}.$$

Now, there is no a-priori guarantee that these limits exist, or that they define one-parameter subgroups, or that they satisfy the algebraic conditions needed to show that these form a Lie algebra. These facts can be proved however, and we shall assume them. This Lie algebra will be called *the* Lie algebra of G, and will be denoted by **G**. (Actually, in the proof one must detour around this definition and use the manifold structure of G to identify **G** with the set of left-invariant vector fields on G.)

Elements of **G** will be denoted by such letters as $X, Y, \ldots$. We are thinking of them as "infinitesimal generators" of the one-parameter groups of G. (The old name for Lie algebra, "infinitesimal group," is very descriptive at this point.) To keep this in mind, it is convenient to *denote* the one-parameter group "generated" by X as $t \to \exp(tX)$. This agrees with the facts recalled above for linear transformation groups, of course. In fact, if $\rho\colon G \to A(V)$ is a linear representation on a vector space V, then $X \to \alpha = \rho(X)$ defines a transformation of **G** into the Lie algebra of linear transformations of V. One sees from the remarks above that this correspondence is a Lie algebra homomorphism; i.e., sums and brackets go into sums and brackets.

Further, we shall define a map from **G** to G, called the *exponential map* and denoted by exp: $\mathbf{G} \to G$: exp assigns to $X \in \mathbf{G}$ the point $\exp(X)$, i.e., the value at $t = 1$ of the one-parameter group generated by X. One can prove that $\dim \mathbf{G} = \dim G$, and that the map exp has, relative to local coordinates in $\mathbf{G}$ and G, a nonzero Jacobian in the neighborhood of 0. This means that the Euclidean coordinates of $\mathbf{G}$ can be introduced as a coordinate system in a neighborhood of the identity of G. These are called *canonical coordinates*. In general, we do not have $\exp(\mathbf{G}) = G$; i.e., every element of G does not necessarily lie on a one-parameter subgroup. However, if G is connected, every element of G can be written as the product of such elements.

The importance of the Lie algebra lies in the fact that, if G is connected, many of its algebraic properties mirror more complicated group-theoretic properties of G. For example, $\mathbf{G}$ is Abelian, i.e., satisfies

$$[\mathbf{G}, \mathbf{G}] = 0\dagger \qquad \text{if and only if } G \text{ is Abelian as a group.}$$

Another such example is the correspondence between subgroups of G and subalgebras of $\mathbf{G}$. Let H be an *arcwise-connected subgroup* of a Lie group G; i.e., H is a subgroup of G in the algebraic sense, and every element of H can be joined to the identity element by a curve lying in H. Let $\mathbf{H}$ consist of the infinitesimal generators of those one-parameter groups of G that lie in H; i.e., $\mathbf{H} = \{X \in \mathbf{G}: \exp tX \in H \text{ for } -\infty < t < \infty\}$. Another theorem of Lie group theory can now be stated:

$\mathbf{H}$ *is a subalgebra of* $\mathbf{G}$; *i.e.,* $[\mathbf{H}, \mathbf{H}] \subset \mathbf{H}$ *and* $\mathbf{H} + \mathbf{H} \subset \mathbf{H}$.

(This was not a priori obvious, since H is not necessarily a *closed* subset of G.)

Conversely, any such subalgebra arises in this way from such a subgroup. Then, there is a one-to-one correspondence between arcwise-connected subgroups of G and subalgebras of $\mathbf{G}$. Finally, any such subgroup H has a Lie group structure of its own for which $\mathbf{H}$ is its Lie algebra.

The following theorem, the *closed subgroup theorem*, is very useful:

Let H be a subgroup of G in the algebraic sense that forms a closed subset of $\mathbf{G}$. Let H^0 be the subset of those elements of H that can be joined to the identity by a curve in H. Then, H^0 is an invariant subgroup of H, which is itself a closed subset of H

---

† In general, if $\mathbf{K}$ and $\mathbf{L}$ are the subsets of a Lie algebra, $[\mathbf{K}, \mathbf{L}]$ denotes the set of all elements of the form $[X, Y]$, for $X \in K$, $Y \in L$.

(and of G), and the quotient group H/H^0 is discrete. H^0 is called the connected component of H.

For example, consider the group $O(n)$ of real orthogonal matrices, considered as a subgroup of $GL(n, R)$. Since the matrices in $O(n)$ are defined by algebraic conditions (namely $\alpha^t\alpha = I$), it is a closed subset of $GL(n, R)$. The connected component is $SO(n)$, the rotation group. The Lie algebra of $GL(n, R)$ is the set of all $n \times n$ real matrices. The subalgebra corresponding to $SO(n)$ is composed of the skew-symmetric $n \times n$ real matrices. $O(n)/SO(n)$ is Z_2, the cyclic group with two elements. Similarly, $U(n)$, the group of all unitary matrices, is a subgroup of $GL(n, C)$ (defined by the condition that $\alpha^t\bar\alpha$ $(= \alpha\alpha^*) = I$). It is connected; its Lie algebra is the set of all skew-Hermitian matrices; i.e., $\alpha + {}^t\bar\alpha = 0$. (Physicists usually consider its Lie algebra as the set of $i\alpha$, with α a Hermitian matrix.)

Now, let σ be an automorphism of G; i.e., σ is a map $G \to G$ such that $\sigma(g_1 g_2) = \sigma(g_1)\sigma(g_2)$ for $g_1, g_2 \in G$. If $t \to g(t)$ is a one-parameter subgroup, then so is the transform of the group by ρ, namely $t \to \sigma(g(t))$. Then, σ permutes the one-parameter subgroups, i.e., defines a transformation, which we shall also denote by σ, on $\mathbf{G}$. It is readily verified that σ also preserves the Lie algebra operations we have defined on $\mathbf{G}$; i.e., σ defines a *Lie algebra automorphism* of $\mathbf{G}$. We can sum up these remarks in the formula

$$\sigma \exp(tX) = \exp(t\, \sigma\, (X)).$$

Now every $g \in G$ defines an automorphism of G, namely the *inner automorphism* by g, denoted by Ad g:

$$\text{Ad } g(g') = gg'g^{-1} \qquad \text{for } g' \in G.$$

The set of automorphisms of G itself forms a group, denoted by Aut(G). (The group operation is just composition of maps.) Similarly, the automorphisms of $\mathbf{G}$ form a group, denoted by Aut($\mathbf{G}$). The map $g \to$ Ad g defines a homomorphism of G into Aut G.

By the above remarks, Ad g also is a Lie algebra automorphism of $\mathbf{G}$; i.e.,

$$g \exp Xg^{-1} = \exp(\text{Ad } g(X)) \qquad \text{for } X \in \mathbf{G}, g \in G.$$

Theorem 3–1

The Lie algebra of Aut($\mathbf{G}$) is the set of derivations of $\mathbf{G}$. (A derivation of $\mathbf{G}$ is a linear map $D: \mathbf{G} \to \mathbf{G}$ such that $D([X, Y]) = [D(X), Y] + [X, D(Y)]$ for $X, Y \in \mathbf{G}$.) The Lie algebra of the subgroup of Aut **G** corresponding to the image of G, i.e., Ad(G), is the set of inner derivations.

(An inner derivation is a map of **G** of the form $Y \to [X, Y]$ for a fixed $X \in \mathbf{G}$. We denote it by Ad X. That it is a derivation follows from the Jacobi identity.)

Proof:

Suppose $t \to \sigma(t)$ is a one-parameter group of automorphisms of **G**. Let D be the map: $\mathbf{G} \to \mathbf{G}$ defined by

$$D(X) = \frac{d}{dt} \sigma(t)(X) \Big|_{t=0} \cdot$$

To prove the derivation property, note that

$$
\begin{aligned}
D([X, Y]) &= \frac{d}{dt} \sigma(t)([X, Y]) \Big|_{t=0} \\
&= \frac{d}{dt} [\sigma(t)(X), \sigma(t)(Y)] \Big|_{t=0} \\
&= \left[\frac{d}{dt} \sigma(t)(X) \Big|_{t=0}, Y \right] + \left[X, \frac{d}{dt} \sigma(t)(Y) \Big|_{t=0} \right] \\
&= [D(X), Y] + [X, D(Y)].
\end{aligned}
$$

Conversely, suppose that D is a derivation. In particular, it is a linear transformation. It generates a one-parameter group $t \to \exp(tD) = \sum_{j=0}^{\infty} (tD)^j / j!$ of linear transformations of **G**. We leave it to the reader to show that the derivation property of D implies that this is a group of Lie algebra automorphisms.

Now, suppose $\sigma(t) = \text{Ad}(\exp(Xt))$, for $X \in \mathbf{G}$; i.e., $t \to \rho(t)$ is a one-parameter group of inner automorphisms. Let $Y \to D(Y)$ be the corresponding derivation.

$$
\begin{aligned}
D(Y) &= \frac{d}{dt} \text{Ad}(\exp(Xt))(Y) \Big|_{t=0} \\
&= \lim_{t \to 0} \left[\text{Ad}\left(\exp(Xt)\left(\frac{Y}{t} \right) - \frac{Y}{t} \right) \right] \cdot
\end{aligned}
$$

$\text{Ad}(\exp(Xt))(Y)$ is the generator of the one-parameter group

$$s \to \exp(Xt) \exp(sY) \exp(-Xt).$$

$$
\begin{aligned}
\exp\left[s\left(\text{Ad}(\exp Xt)\left(\frac{Y}{t} \right) - \frac{Y}{t} \right) \right] \\
&= \lim_{n \to \infty} \left[\exp Xt \exp \frac{sY}{tn} \exp(-Xt) \exp \frac{-sY}{tn} \right]^n \\
&= \lim_{n \to \infty} \left[\exp Xt \exp \frac{sY}{n} \exp(-Xt) \exp\left(\frac{-sY}{n} \right) \right]^{n/t} \cdot
\end{aligned}
$$

Let t go to zero.   We can suppose that it goes to zero through values
$t = 1/n$; i.e.,

$$\lim_{t \to 0} \exp\left[s\left(\mathrm{Ad}(\exp Xt)\left(\frac{Y}{t}\right) - \frac{Y}{t}\right)\right]$$

$$= \lim_{n \to \infty} \left[\exp \frac{X}{n} \exp \frac{sY}{n} \exp\left(\frac{-X}{n}\right)\exp\left(\frac{-sY}{n}\right)\right]^{n^2}$$

$$= (\text{by the "definition" of } [X, Y] \text{ given above}) \exp([X, sY]) = \exp(s[X, Y]).$$

This shows that $D(Y) = [X, Y]$.

CHAPTER 4

SEMISIMPLE LIE ALGEBRAS

Having recalled the basic facts concerning the relation between Lie groups and Lie algebras, we turn to some important qualitative facts about semisimple Lie groups. (We shall not be concerned at all with the detailed structure and classification of the semisimple Lie groups.)

Let $\mathbf{G}$ be a Lie algebra. $\mathbf{G}$ is *semisimple* if it has no nonzero *Abelian* ideals. (An ideal is a subspace, say $\mathbf{I} \subset \mathbf{G}$, with $[\mathbf{G}, \mathbf{I}] \subset \mathbf{I}$.) *Cartan's criterion* is very important: To state it, introduce the real-valued, symmetric bilinear form on $\mathbf{G}$, $(X, Y) \to B(X, Y)$, in the following way: $B(X, Y)$ is the *trace* of the linear transformation

$$\text{Ad } X \text{ Ad } Y \text{ of } \mathbf{G}, \qquad \text{for } X, Y \in \mathbf{G}.$$

(For $X \in \mathbf{G}$, Ad X is linear transformation which takes $Z \in \mathbf{G}$ into $[X, Z]$.)

$B(\ ,\ )$ is called the *Killing form*. It is closely related to the *Casimir operator* that physicists know well, e.g., in representations of $SO(3, R)$. To see this, introduce a basis $(X_1, \ldots, X_n)$ of $\mathbf{G}$. Introduce indices $1 \leqslant i, j, \ldots \leqslant n$ and the summation convention. The numbers (C_{ijk}) such that

$$[X_i, X_j] = C_{ijk} X_k$$

are the *structure constants* of the Lie algebra with respect to the basis.

The matrix of Ad X_i with respect to this basis is (C_{ijk}), $1 \leqslant j, k \leqslant n$. Thus, the trace of Ad X_i Ad X_l, which is $B(X_i, X_l)$, is $C_{ijk} C_{lkj}$, which is of course also the matrix (as $1 \leqslant i, l \leqslant n$) of the quadratic form $B(\ ,\ )$.

Cartan's Criterion:

$\mathbf{G}$ is semisimple if and only if the form $B(\ ,\ )$ is nondegenerate, i.e., the determinant of the matrix $(C_{ijk} C_{lkj})$ is nonzero.

We shall not give the proof here. As an example of its application, we *will* prove the following theorem.

Theorem 4–1

$\mathbf{G}$ is semisimple if and only if it is the direct sum of ideals that are simple as Lie algebras.

Proof:

A Lie algebra is simple if it has no nontrivial ideals at all. If **G** itself is simple, we are through. Suppose then that **G**$_1$ is a nontrivial ideal. By taking **G**$_1$ as an ideal of minimal dimension we can suppose that **G**$_1$ is simple. Let **G**$_2$ be the orthogonal complement of **G**$_1$ in **G**, i.e.,

$$\mathbf{G}_2 = \{X \in \mathbf{G}\colon B(X, \mathbf{G}_1) = 0\}.$$

Several independent lemmas about the Killing form for arbitrary Lie algebras are needed.

Lemma 4–2

For $X, Y, Z \in \mathbf{G}$, $B([X, Y], Z) + B(Y, [X, Z]) = 0$.

Proof:

Let $W \in \mathbf{G}$.

$$\begin{aligned}\mathrm{Ad}([X, Y])(W) &= [[X, Y], W] \\ &= [X, [Y, W]] - [Y, [X, W]]\end{aligned}$$

(by the Jacobi identity); hence

(4–1) $\mathrm{Ad}([X, Y]) = \mathrm{Ad}\,X\,\mathrm{Ad}\,Y - \mathrm{Ad}\,Y\,\mathrm{Ad}\,X.$

Then

$\mathrm{Ad}([X, Y])\,\mathrm{Ad}\,Z + \mathrm{Ad}\,Y\,\mathrm{Ad}[X, Z]$
$= (\mathrm{Ad}(X)\,\mathrm{Ad}\,Y - \mathrm{Ad}\,Y\,\mathrm{Ad}\,X)\,\mathrm{Ad}\,Z + \mathrm{Ad}\,Y(\mathrm{Ad}\,X\,\mathrm{Ad}\,Z - \mathrm{Ad}\,Z\,\mathrm{Ad}\,X).$

Then

$B([X, Y], Z) + B(Y, [X, Z])$
$= \mathrm{trace}(\mathrm{Ad}(X)\,\mathrm{Ad}\,Y\,\mathrm{Ad}\,Z) - \mathrm{trace}(\mathrm{Ad}\,Y\,\mathrm{Ad}\,X\,\mathrm{Ad}\,Z)$
$+ \mathrm{trace}(\mathrm{Ad}\,Y\,\mathrm{Ad}\,X\,\mathrm{Ad}\,Z) - \mathrm{trace}\,\mathrm{Ad}\,Y\,\mathrm{Ad}\,Z\,\mathrm{Ad}\,X$

That this is zero follows from the law

$$\mathrm{trace}(\alpha\beta) = \mathrm{trace}(\beta\alpha).$$

Lemma 4–3

If **G**$_1$ is an ideal of **G**, then the Killing form of two elements of **G**$_1$ relative to **G** is equal to the Killing form relative to **G**$_1$ applied to these elements. (However, this is not so if **G**$_1$ is merely a subalgebra of **G**.)

Proof:

Choose a basis (X_i) of $\mathbf{G}$ such that $(X_i, \ldots, X_p)$ is a basis of $\mathbf{G}_1$. Let $(\mathrm{Ad}\ X\ \mathrm{Ad}\ Y)(X_i) = \alpha_{ij}X_j$. Then, since $\mathbf{G}_1$ is an ideal, $\alpha_{i,p+1} = 0 = \cdots = \alpha_{i,n}$. Then $B(X, Y) = \alpha_{ii} = \sum_{i \leqslant p} \alpha_{ii}$, which is equal to trace of $(\mathrm{Ad}\ X\ \mathrm{Ad}\ Y)$ restricted to $\mathbf{G}_1$.

Now we can finish the proof of the theorem.

$$\mathbf{G}_2 \text{ is an ideal of } \mathbf{G}.$$

This follows from Lemma 4–2: For $X \in \mathbf{G}_2$, $Y \in \mathbf{G}$,

$$B([X, Y], \mathbf{G}_1) = -B(X, [Y, \mathbf{G}_1]) = B(X, \mathbf{G}_1) = 0;$$

hence $[X, Y] \in \mathbf{G}_2$.

$$\mathbf{G} \text{ is the direct sum of } \mathbf{G}_1 + \mathbf{G}_2.$$

First, every element of X of $\mathbf{G}$ can be written as the sum of elements of $\mathbf{G}_1$ and $\mathbf{G}_2$. For, let $(X, \ldots, X_p)$ be a basis of $\mathbf{G}$ such that

$$B(X_i, X_j) = 0 \qquad \text{for } i \neq j,\ 1 \leqslant i \leqslant p,$$
$$B(X_i, X_i) \neq 0.$$

(By Lemma 4–3, the Killing form restricted to $\mathbf{G}_1$ is nondegenerate, since $\mathbf{G}_1$ is simple in its own right. Hence, such a basis exists.)   Consider

$$X - \sum_{i=1}^{p} \frac{B(X, X_i)}{B(X_i, X_i)} X_i = Y.$$

Then $B(Y, X_i) = 0$ for $1 \leqslant i \leqslant p$; hence $B(Y, \mathbf{G}_1) = 0$ and $Y \in \mathbf{G}_2$; i.e., X is written as the sum of elements from $\mathbf{G}_1$ and $\mathbf{G}_2$.

Now we show that $\mathbf{G}$ is a direct sum of $\mathbf{G}_1$ and $\mathbf{G}_2$. All that remains to be proved is that $\mathbf{G}_1 \cap \mathbf{G}_2 = (0)$. Suppose otherwise; i.e., $X \in \mathbf{G}_1 \cap \mathbf{G}_2$. Then $B(X, \mathbf{G}_1) = 0$. Since $\mathbf{G}_1$ is simple, Lemma 4–3 implies that $B(\ ,\ )$ restricted to $\mathbf{G}_1$ is nondegenerate, which implies that $X = 0$.

$$\mathbf{G}_2 \text{ is semisimple.}$$

By Cartan's criterion, to prove that $\mathbf{G}_2$ is semisimple we must show that its Killing form is nondegenerate. By Lemma 4–3, it suffices to show that $B(\ ,\ )$ restricted to $\mathbf{G}_2$ is nondegenerate. Suppose otherwise; i.e., there is a $X \in \mathbf{G}_2$ with $B(X, \mathbf{G}_2) = 0$. But, also, $B(X, \mathbf{G}_1) = 0$, where $B(X, \mathbf{G}) = 0$, implying $X = 0$, since $B(\ ,\ )$ *itself* is nondegenerate.

If $\mathbf{G}_2$ is simple, we are through; if not, choose an ideal in $\mathbf{G}_2$ of minimal dimension and proceed in the same way. Now, an ideal of $\mathbf{G}_2$ is an ideal of $\mathbf{G}$, since $[\mathbf{G}_1, \mathbf{G}_2] = 0$. Eventually, this process must end by exhibiting

G as the direct sum of ideals which are mutually perpendicular with respect to the Killing form.

This finishes the proof of the theorem.   We have gone into detail, because it offers a good example of the simplicity and power of using "intrinsic" methods that are independent of basis.   The following theorem offers another good example of this.

Theorem 4–4

Every derivation of a semisimple Lie algebra is inner.

Proof:

Let $D(\mathbf{G})$ be the set of derivations of **G**. $D(\mathbf{G})$ is made into a Lie algebra by defining

$$[D_1, D_2] = D_1 D_2 - D_2 D_1.$$

[This agrees with the Lie algebra operation obtained by considering $D(\mathbf{G})$ as the Lie algebra of Aut(**G**).]

Lemma 4–5

The set of inner derivations is an ideal in $D(\mathbf{G})$.

Proof:

Let $D \in D(\mathbf{G})$, $X, Y \in \mathbf{G}$.

$$\begin{aligned}
[D, \operatorname{Ad} X](Y) &= D(\operatorname{Ad} X(Y)) - \operatorname{Ad} X D(Y) \\
&= D([X, Y]) - [X, D(Y)] \\
&= [D(X), Y] + [X, D(Y)] - [X, D(Y)] \\
&= [D(X), Y];
\end{aligned}$$

hence $[D, \operatorname{Ad} X] = \operatorname{Ad}(D(X))$, which shows that

$$[D(\mathbf{G}), \operatorname{Ad}(\mathbf{G})] \subset \operatorname{Ad}(\mathbf{G}).$$

Let $B(\ ,\ )$ be the Killing form of $D(\mathbf{G})$.   By Lemma 4–3, $B(\ ,\ )$ restricted to Ad **G** is the Killing form of **G**.   (Note that the homomorphism $\mathbf{G} \to \operatorname{Ad} \mathbf{G}$ is an isomorphism — for the kernel of this homomorphism would be an ideal of **G** which commutes with every element of **G**, i.e., would be Abelian, contradicting the definition of semisimplicity for **G**. In general, the kernel of the homomorphism $\mathbf{G} \to \operatorname{Ad} \mathbf{G}$ is the *center* of **G**.)

Suppose that $D \in D(\mathbf{G})$, but $D \notin \operatorname{Ad} \mathbf{G}$.   As we have seen, by subtracting off elements of Ad **G**, we can suppose that

$$B(D, \operatorname{Ad} \mathbf{G}) = 0.$$

For $X \in \mathbf{G}$, D, $D_1 \in D(\mathbf{G})$, we have

$$\text{Ad } D \cdot \text{Ad}(\text{Ad } X)(D_1) = [D, [\text{Ad } X, D_1]]$$
$$= -[D, \text{Ad } D_1(X)] = -\text{Ad}(DD_1(X)).$$

Then, $\text{Ad } D \text{ Ad}(\text{Ad } X)(D(\mathbf{G})) \subset \text{Ad } \mathbf{G}$. Hence, $\text{Ad}(\text{Ad } X)\text{Ad } D$ acting in $\text{Ad } \mathbf{G}$ must have trace zero. But, for $Y \in \mathbf{G}$,

$$[\text{Ad } X, [D, \text{Ad } Y]] = [\text{Ad } X, \text{Ad } D(Y)].$$

Now, for $Z \in \mathbf{G}$,

$$\begin{aligned}[\text{Ad } X, \text{Ad } D(Y)](Z) &= \text{Ad } X \text{ Ad}(D(Y))(Z) - \text{Ad}(D(Y))\text{Ad } X(Z)\\
&= [X, [D(Y), Z]] - [D(Y), [X, Z]]\\
&= [[X, D(Y)], Z] + [D(Y), [X, Z]] - [D(Y), [X, Z]],\\
&\quad \text{using the Jacobi identity,}\\
&= \text{Ad } X \text{ Ad}(D(Y))(Z);\end{aligned}$$

hence

$$[\text{Ad } X, \text{Ad}(D(Y))] = \text{Ad } X \text{ Ad}(D(Y)).$$

This implies that

$$B(X, D(Y)) = 0 \qquad \text{for all } X \in \mathbf{G}.$$

Since $\mathbf{G}$ is semisimple, $D(Y) = 0$. Since Y is arbitrary in $\mathbf{G}$, $D = 0$, contradicting that $D \notin \text{Ad } \mathbf{G}$.

Corollary to Theorem 4–4

If $\mathbf{G}$ is a semisimple Lie algebra, then $\text{Ad } G$ (the group of inner automorphisms of $\mathbf{G}$) is the connected component of $\text{Aut}(\mathbf{G})$. In particular, $\text{Ad } G$ is an invariant subgroup of $\text{Aut}(\mathbf{G})$, and $\text{Aut}(\mathbf{G})/\text{Ad } G$ is a *discrete* group. (In fact, it can be proved that $\text{Aut}(\mathbf{G})/\text{Ad } G$ is a finite group that can be computed by an algorithm once one knows the Dynkin diagram of $\mathbf{G}$.)

CHAPTER 5

COMPACT AND NONCOMPACT
SEMISIMPLE LIE ALGEBRAS

DUAL SYMMETRIC SPACES

For this chapter, let **G** be a semisimple Lie algebra. The Killing form is a quadratic form on **G** that is intrinsically associated with the Lie algebra structure. Like any quadratic form, it can be reduced to "canonical form"; i.e.,

$$-X_1^2 - \cdots - X_p^2 + X_{p+1}^2 + \cdots + X_n^2.$$

The number p is an invariant of the quadratic form. It turns out to be an important invariant of the Lie algebra as well, namely the dimension of the "maximal compact subalgebra" of **G**. We now turn to an explanation of this fact. First, it is necessary to study the algebras for which $p = n$, i.e., the semisimple algebras for which the Killing form is negative definite.

Theorem 5–1

Let G be a compact Lie group (not necessarily semisimple) and let ρ be a linear representation of G by transformations of a finite-dimensional complex vector space **V**. Let ρ also denote the "infinitesimal" representation obtained of **G** by linear operators on **V**. Then for $X \in \mathbf{G}$, $\rho(X)$ has only pure imaginary eigenvalues and has a diagonal matrix with respect to a suitable basis of **V**. [Another way of putting this is to say that $\rho(X)$ is completely reducible; i.e., if V_1 is a subspace of V with $\rho(X)(V_1) \subset V_1$, then there is a direct sum decomposition $V = V_1 \oplus V_2$ with $\rho(X)(V_2) \subset V_2$.] Further, the Killing form of **G** is negative semidefinite; i.e.,

$$B(X, X) \leqslant 0 \qquad \text{for all } X \in \mathbf{G}.$$

Proof:

Suppose $\rho(X)$ has an eigenvector v with eigenvalue λ; i.e.,

$$\rho(X)(v) = \lambda v.$$

19

Suppose λ is not pure imaginary; i.e., $\lambda = \lambda_1 + i\lambda_2$, with $\lambda_2 \neq 0$. Suppose, for example, that $\lambda_1 > 0$. Then

$$\rho(\exp tX)(v) = e^{\lambda t}v = e^{\lambda_1 t}(e^{i\lambda_2 t}v).$$

Hence $\rho(\exp tX)(v) \to \infty$ as $t \to \infty$. But $\rho(G)$ is a *compact* group of linear transformations; hence $\rho(G)(v)$ is *compact* as a subset of V, hence is bounded. This is a contradiction.

Now, by "integration over G," V has a positive definite Hermitian inner product which is invariant under G. This means that with respect to a suitable basis of V, $\rho(G)$ is represented by a group of unitary matrices. Hence $\rho(\mathbf{G})$ is represented by skew-Hermitian matrices; i.e., for $X \in \mathbf{G}$, $\rho(X)$ is a *normal* operator. It is well known then (the "spectral theorem") that $\rho(X)$ can be diagonalized.

Finally, apply this to the case where ρ is the adjoint representation of G by inner automorphisms on $\mathbf{G}$. Then, Ad X, for $X \in \mathbf{G}$, has pure imaginary eigenvalues. Hence Ad X Ad X has nonpositive real eigenvalues, hence has nonpositive trace. But the trace is just $B(X, X)$.

Theorem 5–2   *(Weyl's Theorem)*

Let G be a semisimple connected Lie group. (A group is semisimple if its algebra is semisimple.) Then, G is compact if and only if the Killing form on $\mathbf{G}$ is negative definite.

Proof (incomplete):

Combining Theorem 5–1 with the fact that the Killing form is definite for a semisimple group, we see that for a compact semisimple group the Killing form is negative definite.

Conversely, suppose the Killing form is negative definite. Consider the adjoint group (Ad G) of inner automorphisms of $\mathbf{G}$. Since it leaves invariant the Killing form, which is negative definite, by a suitable choice of basis the adjoint group consists of orthogonal matrices. [The following fact is left to the reader to prove as an exercise: If σ is an automorphism of $\mathbf{G}$, then σ leaves invariant the Killing form; i.e., $B(\sigma(X), \sigma(Y)) = B(X, Y)$ for $X, Y \in \mathbf{G}$.] The condition that a linear transformation of $\mathbf{G}$ be an automorphism is expressed by algebraic relations; hence Ad G is a *closed* subgroup of orthogonal matrices, hence is compact itself.

These remarks constitute the easy part of the theorem. Now to finish the proof, it is necessary to show that G itself is compact. We have seen that there is a homomorphism $G \to$ Ad G, and that it is a local isomorphism; i.e., the kernel is a discrete subgroup of G. Knowing that Ad G is compact, we must show that this kernel is finite, which we cannot do here since topological techniques which would take too long to explain must be used. (For example, one proof proceeds by showing that the first Betti number of Ad G vanishes, and that the fundamental group of a compact connected manifold is finitely generated.)

The most remarkable fact about the Weyl theorem from the qualitative point of view is that an algebraic property of the Lie algebra, i.e., negative definiteness of the Killing form, forces a topological condition on the group, i.e., compactness.

Now, return to a general semisimple Lie algebra $\mathbf{G}$. We say that $\mathbf{G}$ is of *compact type* if the Killing form is negative definite. Otherwise, it is of *noncompact type*.

Theorem 5–3   (*Cartan's Theorem*)

$\mathbf{G}$ has a direct-sum decomposition of the form $\mathbf{G} = \mathbf{K} \oplus \mathbf{P}$, satisfying

(5–1) $\mathbf{K}$ is a subalgebra; i.e., $[\mathbf{K}, \mathbf{K}] \subset \mathbf{K}$; Ad $\mathbf{K}$ leaves $\mathbf{P}$ invariant; i.e., $[\mathbf{K}, \mathbf{P}] \subset \mathbf{P}$; $[\mathbf{P}, \mathbf{P}] \subset \mathbf{K}$.

(5–2)   The Killing form B of $\mathbf{G}$ restricted to $\mathbf{K}$ is negative definite, restricted to $\mathbf{P}$ is positive definite.

Further, if $\mathbf{K}'$ is any subalgebra of $\mathbf{G}$ such that the Killing form of $\mathbf{G}$ restricted to $\mathbf{K}'$ is negative definite, then there is a $g \in G$ such that Ad $g(\mathbf{K}') \subset \mathbf{K}$; i.e., $\mathbf{K}'$ is conjugate under an inner automorphism to a subalgebra of $\mathbf{K}$.

We shall not give the proof here. Unfortunately, the existing proofs in the literature are rather long, since they use the detailed structure theory of semisimple Lie algebras. We shall give some examples below to convince the reader that Theorem 5–3 expresses in general, qualitative form some facts that he already knows in special cases.

Some further remarks will enhance the theorem's usefulness.

If K is a compact subgroup of G, then $B(\ ,\ )$ restricted to $\mathbf{K}$ is negative definite.

Proof:

By Theorem 5–1, Ad X, for $X \in \mathbf{K}$, has pure imaginary eigenvalues; hence (Ad X Ad X) has nonpositive eigenvalues, hence trace (Ad X Ad X) = $B(X, X)$ is $\leqslant 0$. Suppose it equals zero. Then all eigenvalues of Ad X are zero. By Theorem 5–1 again, Ad X is completely reducible, hence

Ad X itself is zero; i.e., X commutes with all elements of **G**. This forces X to be zero, since **G** is semisimple.

In general, we shall say that a subalgebra **K** of a Lie algebra **G** is a *symmetric subalgebra* of **G** if **G** admits a decomposition $\mathbf{G} = \mathbf{K} \oplus \mathbf{P}$, satisfying the commutation relations given by (5–1). If K is a subgroup of a Lie group G we will say that K is a symmetric subgroup and G the coset space G/K *symmetric space* if **K** is a symmetric subalgebra of **G**. To explain the name "symmetric," define a linear map $s\colon \mathbf{G} \to \mathbf{G}$ by the conditions

$$(5\text{–}3) \qquad\qquad \begin{aligned} s(X) &= X && \text{for } X \in \mathbf{K} \\ &= -X && \text{for } X \in \mathbf{P}. \end{aligned}$$

Conditions (5–1) are readily seen to be *equivalent* to the condition that s define an automorphism of **G**. Conversely, if s is a symmetric automorphism of **G** (i.e., if $s^2 = $ identity), then **K** and **P** can be *defined* by (5–3) and it is readily seen that (5–1) results.

Given such a symmetric space, denoted, say, by $(\mathbf{G}, \mathbf{K}, \mathbf{P})$, one can define a new symmetric space $(\mathbf{G}^*, \mathbf{K}, \mathbf{P}^*)$ by a sort of "analytic continuation" process. First, define $\mathbf{G}_c$ as the set of all combinations $\{X + \sqrt{-1}\,Y\colon X, Y \in \mathbf{G}\}$. $\mathbf{G}_c$ is the "complexification" of **G**. We shall mainly consider $\mathbf{G}_c$ as a real Lie algebra of twice the real dimension of **G**, although it may also be considered as a complex Lie algebra of the same complex dimension as the real dimension of **G**. Consider the following subset of $\mathbf{G}_c$:

$$\mathbf{G}^* = \mathbf{K} + \sqrt{-1}\,\mathbf{P}.$$

Because of the commutation relations (5–1), it is readily verified that $\mathbf{G}^*$ is a new *real* Lie algebra, and **K** is a symmetric subalgebra of it. Further, if $\mathbf{P}^* = \sqrt{-1}\,\mathbf{P}$, then $(\mathbf{G}^*, \mathbf{K}, \mathbf{P}^*)$ satisfies the commutation relations (5–1), hence defines a *new* symmetric space G^*/K. It will be called the *dual* symmetric space to the one G/K with which we began. One should note that, as a global object, G^*/K does not bear any obvious relation to G/K, and we shall see in fact that they can be remarkably different spaces.

Note that $B(\ ,\ )$, the Killing form of **G**, restricted to **P** has *opposite sign* to $B^*(\ ,\ )$, the Killing form of G^*, restricted to $\mathbf{P}^*$ [i.e., $B(X, X) = -B(\sqrt{-1}\,X, \sqrt{-1}\,X)$]. On the other hand, $B(\ ,\ )$ and $B^*(\ ,\ )$ restricted to **K** are the same.

Return now to the situation considered in Theorem 5–3. As stated there, the decomposition $\mathbf{G} = \mathbf{K} \oplus \mathbf{P}$ is unique up to an inner automorphism, and will be called the *Cartan decomposition of* **G**. In this situation, we shall denote $\mathbf{G}^* = \mathbf{K} + \sqrt{-1}\,\mathbf{P}$ by $\mathbf{G}_\mu$. By the above remark, the Killing form of $\mathbf{G}_\mu$ is *negative definite*, here $\mathbf{G}_\mu$ is of compact type G_μ, and G_μ/K are compact. $\mathbf{G_\mu}$ will be called the *unitary real form* (of $\mathbf{G}_c$) corresponding to $\mathbf{G}$. Theorem 5–3 now tells us the following:

> Let $\mathbf{G}$, $\mathbf{G'}$ be *two real semisimple Lie algebras of noncompact type*, with $\mathbf{G} = \mathbf{K} \oplus \mathbf{P}$, $\mathbf{G'} = \mathbf{K} \oplus \mathbf{P'}$, *Cartan decompositions of both.* Then $\mathbf{G}$ and $\mathbf{G'}$ are *isomorphic if and only if* $\mathbf{G_\mu} = \mathbf{K} + \sqrt{-1}\,\mathbf{P}$ *and* $\mathbf{G'_\mu} = \mathbf{K'} + \sqrt{-1}\,\mathbf{P'}$ *are isomorphic (as Lie algebras) by an isomorphism carrying* $\mathbf{K}$ *into* $\mathbf{K'}$. In other words, the semisimple Lie algebras of noncompact type can be classified by classifying the pairs $(\mathbf{G_\mu}, \mathbf{K})$ consisting of a semisimple Lie algebra of compact type, and a symmetric subalgebra $\mathbf{K}$.

There is another way of looking at the construction of the dual symmetric space that will be useful in the examples. Consider the map $s_1\colon \mathbf{G}_c \to \mathbf{G}_c$ defined by

$$s_1(X + iY) = X - iY \qquad \text{for } X + iY \in \mathbf{G}_c = \mathbf{G} + i\mathbf{G}.$$

It is readily verified that s_1 is an isomorphism of $\mathbf{G}_c$ (considered as a *real* Lie algebra), and $\mathbf{G}$ is the fixed set of s_1. Then

$$\mathbf{G^*} \text{ is the set of } Z \in \mathbf{G}_c \text{ with } s_1(Z) = s(Z).$$

[$s(Z)$ is defined by $s(X + iY) = s(X) + is(Y)$; i.e., s is just the extension of the s originally defined on $\mathbf{G}$ to $\mathbf{G}_c$]. Then, if G_c is the group corresponding to $\mathbf{G}_c$, G^* can be defined as the set of g such that

$$s(g) = s_1(g).$$

Example 1

$G = SL(n, R)$, which is of noncompact type. Consider $K = SO(n, R)$. Let us see if it can be exhibited as a symmetric subgroup: If α is an $n \times n$ matrix, the condition that it be orthogonal is

$${}^t\alpha = \alpha^{-1} \qquad \text{or} \qquad ({}^t\alpha)^{-1} = \alpha.$$

Then let $s(\alpha) = ({}^t\alpha)^{-1}$.

$$\begin{aligned} s(\alpha_1\alpha_2) &= {}^t(\alpha_1\alpha_2)^{-1} = ({}^t\alpha_2{}^t\alpha_1)^{-1} = {}^t\alpha_1{}^{-1}{}^t\alpha_2{}^{-1} \\ &= s(\alpha_1)s(\alpha_2), \\ s^2(\alpha) &= ({}^t(({}^t\alpha)^{-1}))^{-1} = {}^t({}^t\alpha) = \alpha. \end{aligned}$$

Thus, s satisfies all required conditions. At the Lie algebra level,

$$s(X) = -{}^tX$$

(considering $\mathbf{G}$ as the set of $n \times n$ real matrices of trace zero). Then $s(X) = X$ for $X \in \mathbf{K}$; i.e., $-{}^t X = X$, or

$$X \text{ is } \textit{skew-symmetric}.$$

$X \in \mathbf{P}$ if $s(X) = -{}^t X = -X$, or ${}^t X = X$; i.e.,

$$X \text{ is } \textit{symmetric}.$$

Then the decomposition $\mathbf{G} = \mathbf{K} \oplus \mathbf{P}$ is just the decomposition of a matrix into symmetric and skew-symmetric parts. G_c is now just $GL(n, C)$.

$$s_1(\alpha) = \bar{\alpha} \ (= \text{complex conjugate of matrix elements of } \alpha).$$

$\alpha \in G^* \ (= G_u)$ is now determined by the condition that

$$s_1(\alpha) = \bar{\alpha} = ({}^t \alpha)^{-1} \qquad \text{or} \qquad \alpha^{-1} = {}^t \bar{\alpha},$$

which are the conditions for a unitary matrix. Hence

$$G_u = SU(n).$$

The dual, unitary symmetric space to $SL(n, R)/SO(n, R)$ is

$$SU(n)/SO(n, R).$$

Example 2

Let Q be an $n \times n$ real symmetric matrix. We can associate with Q the quadratic form $v \to {}^t v Q v$ on R^n, and the group $SO(Q, R)$ is the set of linear transformations of determinant one preserving this quadratic form. Then a matrix α belongs to $SO(Q, R)$ if and only if

$$ {}^t \alpha Q \alpha = Q.$$

Then $SO(n, R) = SO(Q, R)$ for $Q = $ identity matrix. Let $G = SO(Q, R)$, $K = G \cap SO(n, R)$.
   If $\alpha \in K$, then ${}^t \alpha = \alpha^{-1}$; hence

$$\alpha^{-1} Q \alpha = Q \qquad \text{or} \qquad Q\alpha = \alpha Q \qquad \text{or} \qquad \alpha = Q^{-1}\alpha Q.$$

Let $s = Q^{-1}\alpha Q$. Now we can bring the quadratic form $v \to {}^t v Q v$ to normal form. This means that we can suppose that

$$Q^2 = 1.$$

Then, also, $s^2 = $ identity.
   Now $s(SO(Q, R)) \subset SO(Q, R)$ — for

$$ {}^t(Q^{-1}\alpha Q)Q(Q^{-1}\alpha Q) = Q^t\alpha Q^{-1}QQ^{-1}\alpha Q$$
$$ = Q^t\alpha Q^{-1}\alpha Q = Q^t\alpha Q\alpha Q.$$

If $\alpha \in SO(Q, R)$, then this equals QQQ, which is Q; i.e.,

$$s(\alpha) \in SO(Q, R).$$

Now, let us complexify: $G_c = SO(Q, C)$, i.e., the complex $n \times n$ matrices α satisfying ${}^t\alpha Q\alpha = Q$ [which is isomorphic by a simple change of bases to $SO(n, C)$]$s_1 = \bar\alpha$, complex conjugate. $\alpha \in G_c$ belongs to G_u if and only if

$$s_1(\alpha) = s(\alpha);$$

i.e.,

$$\bar\alpha = Q\alpha Q.$$

Now Q can be taken to have the following form:

$$\begin{pmatrix} -1 & & & & & \\ & \ddots & & & & \\ & & -1 & & & 0 \\ & & & 1 & & \\ & 0 & & & \ddots & \\ & & & & & 1 \end{pmatrix}.$$

Let

$$R = \begin{pmatrix} i & & & & & \\ & \ddots & & & & \\ & & i & & & 0 \\ & & & 1 & & \\ & 0 & & & \ddots & \\ & & & & & 1 \end{pmatrix}.$$

Then $Q = R^2$; $R^{-1} = \bar R$. Hence

$$\bar\alpha = R^2\alpha R^{-2} \quad \text{or} \quad \overline{R\alpha R^{-1}} = R\alpha R^{-1}$$

Consider the transformation $\alpha \to R\alpha R^{-1}$. Now

${}^t(R\alpha R^{-1})(R\alpha R^{-1})$
$= R^{-1}{}^t\alpha R \cdot R\alpha R^{-1}$
$= R^{-1}{}^t\alpha Q\alpha R^{-1}$
$= R^{-1}QR^{-1} = QQ = I$; i.e., the transformation $\alpha \to R\alpha R^{-1}$ is an isomorphism of G_u with $SO(n, R)$. Hence, $SO(n, R)$ is the unitary form of $SO(Q, R)$. Let us see which subgroup of $SO(n, R)$ corresponds to $K = SO(n, R) \cap SO(Q, R)$.

If $\alpha \in K$ or Q, then $\alpha Q = Q\alpha$; hence $R\alpha R^{-1}$ commutes with Q. This implies that $R\alpha R^{-1}$ must be of the form

$$\begin{pmatrix} \cdots & 0 \\ 0 & \cdots \end{pmatrix};$$

i.e.,

$$RKR^{-1} = SO(p, R) \times SO(n - p, R),$$

where p is the number of minus signs in the diagonal of Q.

COMPLETE REDUCIBILITY OF REPRESENTATIONS OF SEMISIMPLE GROUPS

Let ρ be a representation of a Lie group G by linear transformations of a vector space V. ρ acts *irreducibly* if there is no subspace of V [other than (O) and V itself] which is invariant under $\rho(G)$. ρ is *completely reducible* if V is the direct sum of subspaces which are left invariant by $\rho(G)$ and if $\rho(G)$ acts irreducibly in each of these subspaces. Another famous theorem of H. Weyl asserts that if V is finite-dimensional and if G is connected and semisimple, then the representation is completely reducible. In fact, Weyl devised the "unitary trick" and Theorem 5-2 precisely to prove this theorem, which was needed to complete Cartan's classification of the representations of semisimple groups. Although there is now a straightforward algebraic proof available [see Jacobson (1962)], it is an illustrative application of Lie group theoretic reasoning to prove it Weyl's way.

To do so, first one notes that it suffices to consider the case where V is a complex vector space (since the property of being completely reducible is "invariant under complexification"). $\rho(G)$ is then a Lie algebra of linear transformations of V. We can complexify these transformations (i.e., multiply by $\sqrt{-1}$) to obtain a linear representation of $\mathbf{G}_c$, which is complex semisimple Lie algebra. By using the structure theory of complex semisimple Lie algebras, Weyl showed that the maximal compact subalgebra $\mathbf{G}_\mu$ of $\mathbf{G}_c$ is also a real form of $\mathbf{G}_c$; i.e., when it is complexified it too gives $\mathbf{G}_c$. Again, it is readily verified that a Lie algebra of linear transformations is completely reducible if and only if its complexification is completely reducible. Thus we are reduced to the problem of showing that the compact Lie algebra $\mathbf{G}_\mu$ of transformations on V is completely reducible. For this, we can use a "transcendental" method: Let G_μ be the simply connected group whose Lie algebra is $\mathbf{G}_\mu$: By Theorem 5-2, it is compact. The simple connectivity assures us that the representation of $\mathbf{G}_\mu$ arises from a representation of G_μ by linear transformations on V. Now, one can use invariant integration on the group to show that G_μ acting on V leaves invariant a positive definite Hermitian form — hence complete reducibility!

The complete-reducibility property of semisimple groups has many applications in Lie group theory. We shall see one such application in Chapter 10, in the problem of finding the Casimir operators of semisimple Lie algebras. As another, we can re-prove Theorem 4-4, which asserts that all derivations of a semisimple algebra are inner.

Let $\mathbf{G}$ be a semisimple Lie algebra, and let $D(\mathbf{G})$ be the Lie algebra of derivations of $\mathbf{G}$. Since $\mathbf{G}$ has no center, it is imbedded as an ideal in $D(\mathbf{G})$ via the inner derivations. Now, $D(\mathbf{G})$ is also finite-dimensional.

The commutation of a derivation by an inner derivation defines a representation of $\mathbf{G}$ in $D(\mathbf{G})$; hence by complete reducibility there is a subspace $\mathbf{A} \subset D(\mathbf{G})$ such that

$$D(\mathbf{G}) = \mathbf{G} \oplus \mathbf{A}, \ [\mathbf{G}, \mathbf{A}] \subset \mathbf{A}.$$

Since $\mathbf{G}$ is an ideal in $D(\mathbf{G})$,

$$[\mathbf{G}, A] = 0.$$

Then, if $D \in \mathbf{A}$, X, $Y \in \mathbf{G}$,

$$\begin{aligned}
0 &= [\mathrm{Ad}\ X, D](Y) \\
&= \mathrm{Ad}\ XD(Y) - D(\mathrm{Ad}\ X(y)) \\
&= [X, D(Y)] - D([X, Y]) = [D(X), Y].
\end{aligned}$$

Since Y is arbitrary in $\mathbf{G}$, $D(X)$ lies in the center of $\mathbf{G}$. Since $\mathbf{G}$ is semisimple, $D(X) = 0$, hence $D = 0$, since X is arbitrary in $\mathbf{G}$.

As another application of the complete-reducibility theorem, we can prove that a connected noncompact semisimple Lie group cannot admit a faithful finite-dimensional unitary representation, a result that seems to puzzle some physicists. This fact is contained in the following theorem:

If H is a connected semisimple subgroup of the Lie group $G = GL(n, C)$, then H is a closed subgroup. [In particular, if H admits a faithful unitary representation it is a subgroup of $U(n)$, hence compact.]

Proof:

Let $\bar{H}$ be the point set of closure of H on G, i.e., the set of limits of elements of H. It is an application of the formalism of topological group theory and the closed subgroup theorem to show that $\bar{H}$ itself is a Lie group; hence its Lie algebra $\bar{\mathbf{H}}$ contains $\mathbf{H}$ as a subalgebra. Since $\mathrm{Ad}\ H(\mathbf{H}) \subset \mathbf{H}$, we also have $\mathrm{Ad}\ \bar{H}(\mathbf{H}) \subset \mathbf{H}$; hence

$$[\bar{\mathbf{H}}, \mathbf{H}] \subset \mathbf{H}.$$

But by the complete-reducibility theorem, there is a subspace $\mathbf{A} \subset \bar{\mathbf{H}}$ with

$$\bar{\mathbf{H}} = \mathbf{H} + \mathbf{A}, \ [\mathbf{H}, \mathbf{A}] \subset \mathbf{A}.$$

These two facts force $[\mathbf{H}, \mathbf{A}] = 0$.

Suppose now that $\mathbf{A} \neq 0$. Let $X \in \mathbf{A}$. Since $\bar{H}$ is a subgroup of $GL(n, C)$, it is exhibited as a Lie algebra of $n \times n$ complex matrices. By the complete-reducibility theorem, the vector space C^n can be decomposed into the direct sum of subspaces in each of which H acts irreducibly.

Since $\overline{H}$ is the closure of H, $\overline{H}$ also leaves these subspaces invariant. Hence, $\overline{\overline{H}}$ and therefore X, leave these subspaces invariant also. Now, X commutes with the action of H. Since H acts irreducibly, Shur's lemma† implies that X in each of these spaces is a multiple of the identity. Suppose this multiple is different from zero in at least one of the irreducible subspaces. Then the one-parameter group generated by X has a determinant different from one in this subspace. But, since H is a semi-simple group, every element of H has determinant 1. Since $\overline{H}$ is the closure of H, and the determinant is a continuous function on the group, each element of $\overline{H}$ has determinant 1. Contradiction, and $\mathbf{A} = 0$, hence $\mathbf{H} = \overline{\mathbf{H}}$, hence H = connected component of the identity of $\overline{H}$.‡ But, since $\overline{H}$ is a closed subgroup of G, so is its connected component.§ Q.E.D.

COMPLEX SEMISIMPLE LIE ALGEBRAS

Let $\mathbf{G}$ be a Lie algebra over the complex numbers. This means that $\mathbf{G}$ is a Lie algebra over the real numbers, but that it is also permissible to multiply $X \in \mathbf{G}$ by $i = \sqrt{-1}$ so that

$$[X, iY] = i[X, Y] \quad \text{for } X, Y \in \mathbf{G}.$$

Let $B(\ ,\ )$ be the Killing form. Now

$$\begin{aligned}\mathrm{Ad}(iX)\mathrm{Ad}(iY)(Z) &= [iX, [iY, Z]] \\ &= -[X, [Y, Z]];\end{aligned}$$

hence

(5–4)
$$B(iX, iY) = -B(X, Y).$$

Suppose $\mathbf{G}$ is semisimple. Let $\mathbf{K}$ be a maximal compact subalgebra of $\mathbf{G}$ (considering $\mathbf{G}$ as a real Lie algebra, of course). Then, for $X \in \mathbf{K}$,

$$B(X, X) < 0.$$

Hence, $B(iX, iX) > 0$, which shows that iX cannot belong to $\mathbf{K}$. Further, by Theorem 5–3, the dimension of K is equal to the dimension of the largest subspace of $\mathbf{G}$ on which B is negative definite. However, by (5–4), this dimension must equal half of the (real) dimension of $\mathbf{G}$. Then

$$\mathbf{G} = \mathbf{K} + i\mathbf{K}.$$

---

† Shur's lemma asserts that a transformation of a finite-dimensional complex vector space that commutes with every element of an irreducible group of linear transformations on the vector space must be a scalar multiple of the identity.

‡ We use here the following fact: Two connected subgroups of a Lie group that have the same Lie algebra are the same.

§ Fact about topological groups: The connected component of the identity is a closed subgroup.

Of course, we also have

$$[i\mathbf{K}, i\mathbf{K}] \subset \mathbf{K}.$$

This shows that the subspace $\mathbf{P}$ occurring in the Cartan decomposition $\mathbf{G} = \mathbf{K} \oplus \mathbf{P}$ must be equal to $i\mathbf{K}$. $\mathbf{G}$ is the *complexification of* $\mathbf{K}$, and $\mathbf{K}$ is called the *compact real form* of $\mathbf{G}$.

Finally, suppose that $\mathbf{G}'$ is another subalgebra of $\mathbf{G}$ whose complexification is $\mathbf{G}$; i.e.,

$$\mathbf{G} = \mathbf{G}' \oplus i\mathbf{G}'.$$

It can then be proved that, at most choosing a conjugate subalgebra of $\mathbf{G}'$, $\mathbf{K} \cap \mathbf{G}'$ is a maximal compact subalgebra of $\mathbf{G}'$ and a symmetric subalgebra of $\mathbf{K}$. Thus, classifying "real forms" of a complex simple Lie algebra $\mathbf{G}$ is equivalent to classifying the symmetric subalgebras of its compact real form.

CHAPTER 6

CONJUGACY OF CARTAN SUBALGEBRAS AND DECOMPOSITIONS OF SEMISIMPLE LIE GROUPS

For all this chapter, let G be a semisimple Lie group, K a compact symmetric subgroup; i.e., G admits a decomposition $\mathbf{G} = \mathbf{K} \oplus \mathbf{P}$, with

$$\text{Ad } K \, (\mathbf{P}) \subset \mathbf{P}; \quad [\mathbf{P}, \mathbf{P}] \subset \mathbf{K}.$$

Definition:

A *Cartan subalgebra* of the symmetric space G/K is a maximal Abelian subalgebra of $\mathbf{P}$, denoted typically by $\mathbf{A}$. An element $X \in \mathbf{P}$ is a *regular element* if the centralizer† of X in $\mathbf{P}$ is a Cartan subalgebra, i.e., if X belongs to precisely one Cartan subalgebra.

Theorem 6–1

Let X be an element of $\mathbf{P}$. Then, Ad X, considered as a transformation in $\mathbf{G}$, is completely reducible; i.e., a matrix representing it can be diagonalized.

Proof:

If $\mathbf{G}$ is compact, this follows from Theorem 5–1. Suppose then that $\mathbf{G}$ is of noncompact type. Let $\mathbf{G} = \mathbf{K}' + \mathbf{P}'$ be a Cartan decomposition of $\mathbf{G}$. By Theorem 5–3, we may suppose that $\mathbf{K} \subset \mathbf{K}'$.

Lemma 6–2

Let $B(\quad, \quad)$ be the Killing form of $\mathbf{G}$. Then

$$B(\mathbf{K}, \mathbf{P}) = 0 \quad \text{and} \quad \mathbf{P}' \subset \mathbf{P}.$$

† The centralizer of X in $\mathbf{P}$ consists of those elements of $\mathbf{P}$ which commute with X.

Proof:

Let s be the automorphism of **G** such that $s(X) = X$ for $X \in$ **K**, $-X$ for $X \in$ **P**. Since the Killing form is invariant under automorphisms, we have

$$B(X, Y) = B(s(X), s(Y)) = -B(X, Y) \qquad \text{for } X \in \mathbf{K}, Y \in \mathbf{P};$$

hence

$$B(X, Y) = 0.$$

Similarly, $B(\mathbf{K}', \mathbf{P}') = 0$. Hence the Killing form restricted to **K** and **K**' is negative definite (Theorem 5–1), and **P** and **P**' are, respectively, the orthogonal complement of **K** and **K**' in **G** with respect to the Killing form; hence

$$\mathbf{P}' \subset \mathbf{P}.$$

Return to the proof of the theorem. By Theorem 5–3, the Killing form restricted to **P**' is positive definite, hence **K**' is the orthogonal complement of **P**' in **G**. An element $X \in$ **P** can then be written as the sum $Y + Z$, with $Y \in$ **P**', $Z \in$ **K**', hence $Z \in$ **P**. Now $[Y, Z] \in$ **P**'. Since $[\mathbf{P}', \mathbf{P}] \subset$ **K**, we also have $[Y, Z] \in$ **K**. These two relations force $[Y, Z] = 0$. Then Ad Y and Ad Z commute; hence to prove complete reducibility of $\text{Ad}(X)$ it suffices to prove it for Ad Y and Ad Z. Since K' is compact, Theorem 5–1 implies that Ad Z is completely reducible. Ad Y is completely reducible if and only if $\text{Ad}(iY)$, acting in $\mathbf{G}_c$, is completely reducible. But, we have seen that $iY \in G_u$, another Lie algebra of compact type — hence the theorem.

Theorem 6–3

Let **A** be a maximal Abelian subalgebra of **P**. Then **A** contains regular elements.

Proof:

Since **A** is Abelian and each Ad X, for $X \in$ **A**, can, considered as a linear transformation in $\mathbf{G}_c$, be diagonalized, a single basis for $\mathbf{G}_c$ can be chosen in which all Ad X, for $X \in$ **A**, are diagonal matrices. Explicitly, we have a basis $(Y_1, \ldots, Y_n)$ for $\mathbf{G}_c$ such that

$$[X, Y_i] = \lambda_i(X)Y_i \qquad \text{for } 1 \leqslant 1 \leqslant n, X \in \mathbf{A},$$

where $X \to \lambda_i(X)$ are complex-valued linear forms on **A**. Now we have

$$\mathbf{G}_c = \mathbf{K}_c \oplus \mathbf{P}_c \qquad \text{where } \mathbf{K}_c = \mathbf{K} + i\mathbf{K}, \mathbf{P}_c = \mathbf{P} + i\mathbf{P}.$$

The same commutation relations hold for $\mathbf{K}_c$ and $\mathbf{P}_c$ as for $\mathbf{K}$ and $\mathbf{P}$.   Now some of the forms $X \to \lambda_i(X)$ are identically zero, say $\lambda_1, \ldots, \lambda_p$.   Further, if

$$[X, Y] = 0 \quad \text{if } Y = Y' + Y'' \qquad \text{with } Y' \in \mathbf{K}_c, \ Y'' \in \mathbf{P}_c,$$

then $[X, Y'] = 0 = [X, Y'']$ because of the commutation relations between $\mathbf{K}_c$ and $\mathbf{P}_c$.

Since $\mathbf{A}$ is maximal Abelian in $\mathbf{P}$, so is $\mathbf{A}_c = \mathbf{A} + i\mathbf{A}$ maximal Abelian in $\mathbf{P}_c$.   We can relabel the $\lambda_1, \ldots, \lambda_p$ so that

$$Y_1, \ldots, Y_i \in \mathbf{P}_c \qquad Y_{r+1}, \ldots, Y_p \in \mathbf{K}_c.$$

Since $\lambda_1, \ldots, \lambda_p$ are identically zero, $Y_1 \ldots, Y_r$ must belong to $\mathbf{A}_c$.

The rest of the forms, $\lambda_{p+1}, \ldots, \lambda_n$, are not identically zero; hence we can choose at least one element $X \in \mathbf{A}$ on which they are all nonzero. (In fact, such elements are dense in $\mathbf{A}$.)   For such an element X, any element of $\mathbf{P}$ commuting with it must then be a linear combination of the $Y_1, \ldots, Y_r$; i.e., the elements of $\mathbf{P}$ commuting with X must be in $\mathbf{A}$; hence such an X is a regular element.   Q.E.D.

Theorem 6–4

Let $\mathbf{A}$ be a fixed Cartan subalgebra of $\mathbf{P}$, and let $\mathbf{A}'$ be any Abelian subalgebra of $\mathbf{P}$.   Then, there is an element $k \in K$ such that

$$\text{Ad } K(\mathbf{A}') \subset \mathbf{A}.$$

In particular, two Cartan subalgebras of $\mathbf{P}$ are conjugate by a transformation of Ad K.

Proof:

We shall find k by setting up a "minimal principle" to find it.   (This idea was discovered by G. Hunt.   Cartan's original proof was much more complicated.)   Let $B(\ ,\ )$ be the Killing form of $\mathbf{G}$.   We can suppose without loss in generality that $\mathbf{A}'$ is itself a Cartan subalgebra (since any Abelian subalgebra of $\mathbf{P}$ is contained in a maximal one).   Let X and X' be regular elements of $\mathbf{A}$ and $\mathbf{A}'$, whose existence is proved by Theorem 6–2.

Consider the following real-valued function on K:

$$k \to B(\text{Ad } k(X'), X).$$

Let k be an element of K for which this takes on minimum value.   (Since K is *compact*, such an element exists.)   Let $Z \in K$.   Then

$$t \to B(\text{Ad}(\exp tZ) \text{ Ad } k(X'), X)$$

has a minimum value for $t = 0$. In particular, its derivative at $t = 0$ is zero:

$$
\begin{aligned}
0 &= \frac{d}{dt}\, B(\mathrm{Ad}(\exp tZ)\, \mathrm{Ad}\, k(X'),\, X)\Big|_{t=0} \\
&= B([Z,\, \mathrm{Ad}\, k(X')],\, X) \\
&= -B(Z,\, [\mathrm{Ad}\, k(X'),\, X]).
\end{aligned}
$$

Then $[\mathrm{Ad}\, k(X'),\, X]$ belongs to **K**, and is perpendicular (with respect to the Killing form) to every element of **K**. Since the Killing form restricted to **K** is negative definite,

$$[\mathrm{Ad}\, k(X'),\, X]\ \text{must be zero.}$$

Since X is a regular element of **A**, $\mathrm{Ad}\, k(X') \in$ **A**. Now $\mathrm{Ad}\, k(X')$ is also a regular element of $\mathrm{Ad}\, k(\mathbf{A}')$. Since a regular element can only belong to one Cartan subalgebra, we have

$$\mathrm{Ad}\, k(\mathbf{A}') = \mathbf{A}. \qquad \text{Q.E.D.}$$

Theorem 6–5

Suppose that G is a connected Lie group which only has a finite center† and whose Lie algebra is **G**. Let K be the connected subgroup whose Lie algebra is **K**. (It is compact; it might not be if the center of G were infinite.) Let P be the image of **P** in G under the exponential map. Then

$$G = P \cdot K.$$

If **G** is of noncompact type, and $\mathbf{G} = \mathbf{K} + \mathbf{P}$ is a Cartan decomposition, then every element of G admits a unique decomposition as the product of elements of K and P. If G is compact, such a decomposition is "almost unique" in the sense that the elements of G that have an ambiguous representation of this type lie on certain lower-dimensional submanifolds of G.

Since the proof of this theorem involves a rather long excursion into Riemannian geometry, we shall omit it. Instead, we will show that it gives in special cases many of the decomposition theorems exhibiting matrices of one type as the product of matrices of other types that physicists know well.

---

† Recall that for a semisimple Lie group, it is only necessary that the center be discrete. All the classical matrix groups only have finite centers. The simplest exception is the simply connected covering group of $SL(2, R)$. However, this group has no faithful finite-dimensional representation.

Before dealing with the examples, some further remarks will be useful. First, suppose that s is an automorphism of G such that $s^2 = $ identity, $s(X) = X$ for $X \in \mathbf{K}$, $-X$ for $X \in \mathbf{P}$. (The "symmetric" condition requires that s exists as an *automorphism of* $\mathbf{G}$. However, we have seen examples that s is very easily found in practice. s will always exist if G has a trivial center, i.e., is the adjoint group of $\mathbf{G}$.)

Elements of P are called *transvections*, and are denoted typically by τ. Since $\tau = \exp(X)$, for some $X \in \mathbf{P}$, we have the following functional equation for τ:

$$s\tau = s(\exp X) = \exp(s(X)) = \exp(-X) = \tau^{-1}.$$

The following theorem will facilitate finding P in the examples.

Theorem 6–6

Consider the set of all $g \in G$ such that

(6–1) $$s(g) = g^{-1}.$$

P then consists of the set of all such elements g of G that can be joined to the identity element by a curve $t \to g(t)$ such that $s(g(t)) = g(t)^{-1}$ for all t [i.e., P is the connected component containing the identity element of those elements of G satisfying (6–1)].

Again we shall not go into the proof, since it involves some geometric machinery that would make too long a detour. It can be readily checked on the examples.

Now, despite the fact that we have exhibited P as a subset of G, elements of P cannot be multiplied together and (in general) remain in P. However, there is one operation involving the group properties which P admits.

Theorem 6–7

If $\tau \in P$, $g \in G$, then $g\tau s(g^{-1})$ belongs to P.

Proof:

$$s(g\tau s(g^{-1})) = s(g)s(\tau)s^2(g^{-1})$$
$$= s(g)\tau^{-1}g^{-1} = (g\tau s(g^{-1}))^{-1};$$

i.e., $g\tau s(g^{-1})$ satisfies (6–1). Also, $g\tau s(g^{-1})$ can be connected to the identity by a curve satisfying (6–1). For, since G is connected, g can be connected

to the identity by a curve $t \to g(t)$.   By the definition of P, τ can be joined
to the identity by a curve $t \to \tau(t)$.   Then the curve

$$t \to g(t)\tau(t)s(g(t)^{-1})$$

joins $g\tau s(g^{-1})$ to the identity.   Hence, $g\tau s(g^{-1}) \in P$.   Q.E.D.

Note now that each $g \in G$ defines a transformation $\tau \to g\tau s(g^{-1})$ of P.
This defines G as a transformation group on P.   Now the identity e
belongs to P.   Let us compute the isotropy subgroup of G at the identity:

(6–2) $ges(g^{-1}) = e$ i.e. $g = s(g)$.

Now, elements of K, the *connected* subgroup of G generated by $\mathbf{G}$, satisfy
(6–2).   On the other hand, the set of *all* elements of G satisfying (6–2) is
a subgroup of G, containing (and possibly larger than) K.   Let us call
it $K(s)$.   At any rate, it is readily seen that K is the connected component
of $K(s)$; hence $K(s)$ also has $\mathbf{K}$ as its Lie algebra.   The orbit of G at e
is isomorphic (as explained in Chapter 2) to $G/K(s)$.

Theorem 6–8

The orbit of $\mathbf{G}$ acting on P at e fills up all of P; i.e., $\mathbf{G}$ acts
transitively on P, and P is isomorphic (as explained in Chap-
ter 2) to $G/K(s)$.

Proof (partial):

Dimension $(G/K(s)) = \dim \mathbf{G} - \dim \mathbf{K} = \dim \mathbf{P} = \dim P$; i.e., the orbit of G at e has the same dimension as P.   In general this would not
suffice to prove that the orbit fills up P.   (There are transformation
groups acting on spaces nontransistively which have orbits of the same
dimension as the space.)   However, it *can be proved* that $K(s)$ is compact,
and that this implies that the orbit of G at e fills up P.

Now, we have exhibited the coset symmetric space $G/K(s)$ as a *subset*
of G.   As we will see in the examples, this explains why many symmetric
spaces can be exhibited as subsets of matrix spaces.

Having decomposed $G = PK$, we can decompose P and K still further.
First, let $\mathbf{A}$ be a Cartan (i.e., maximal Abelian) subalgebra of P.   Let
$A = \exp(\mathbf{A})$.   If X is a regular element of $\mathbf{A}$, $\tau = \exp(X)$, it can be proved
that A consists of the elements of A that commute with τ, and that can
be joined to the identity by a curve consisting of elements of P that commute with τ.   (This is a good way of determining A in practice.)   Now,

by Theorem 6–3, every element of $\mathbf{P}$ can be written $\text{Ad } k(X)$, for some $X \in \mathbf{A}$. Hence, every element of P can be written

$$\text{Ad } k(\tau) = k\tau k^{-1} \; (= k\tau s(k^{-1})) \qquad \text{for some } \tau \in A;$$

i.e.,

$$P = \text{Ad } K(A).$$

Now, $g \in G$ can be decomposed as

$$\tau k \qquad \text{for } \tau \in P, \, k \in K.$$

τ can be written $k_1 a k_1^{-1}$, for $a \in A$, $k_1 \in K$; i.e.,

$$g = k_1 a k_1^{-1} k.$$

Hence G can be decomposed as

$$KAK.$$

This decomposition can be continued: Let K' be only a symmetric subgroup of K. K can be written $K'A'K'$; here

$$G = K'A'K'AK'AK'.$$

This can be continued if necessary: The result is an algorithm that picks out a finite number of one-parameter subgroups of G such that every element of G can be written as a product in a definite order of elements from these one-parameter groups. As we shall explain later, the simplest case is where $G = SO(3, R)$. There are then three such one-parameter groups, and the result is the description of a rotation by three Euler angles.

We have now finished the discussion of the generalities concerning this type of decomposition of semisimple Lie groups. Note that the method applies whether or not G is compact. Another sort of decomposition (the "Iwasawa decomposition"), which is restricted to the case of noncompact groups, will be discussed in Chapter 7. Now we turn to the examples.

Example 1

$G = SL(n, R)$. Let us continue to denote $(n \times n)$ matrices by such letters as α, β.

Let $s(\alpha) = {}^t\alpha^{-1}$. Then, s is an automorphism, and s^2 is the identity. $\alpha \in K(s)$ if $\alpha = {}^t\alpha^{-1}$; i.e., ${}^t\alpha = \alpha^{-1}$; i.e., α is orthogonal. Hence, $K(s) = SO(n, R)$, which is connected; hence

$$K(s) \text{ also equals } K.$$

Suppose α satisfies (6–1); i.e.,

$$^t\alpha^{-1} = \alpha^{-1};$$

i.e.,

$$^t\alpha = \alpha.$$

α is symmetric.   Since $\det(\alpha) = 1$, we see that if α can be joined to the identity by a curve consisting of symmetric matrices, we must have

   α is a positive-definite symmetric matrix; hence
   $P \ (= SL(n, R)/SO(n, R))$ is the set of positive-definite matrices.
   P is the set of symmetric matrices of trace zero.

   The decomposition $G = PK$ is then just the "polar decomposition" of a matrix as the product of a symmetric positive-definite matrix and an orthogonal one.   The action of G on P goes as follows: g transforms $\alpha \in P$ into.

$$g\alpha s(g^{-1}) = g\alpha\,^t g.$$

Example 2

$G = SL(n, C)$; $s(g) = \alpha^{*-1}$, where

$$\alpha^* = \,^t\bar{\alpha}.$$

$K(s)$ is now $SU(n)$, which is again connected, so that

$$K(s) = K.$$

If $s(\alpha) = \alpha^{-1}$, then $\alpha^* = \alpha$; i.e., α is Hermitian symmetric.   Again, since $\det \alpha = 1$, P is composed of the positive-definite Hermitian matrices. The decomposition $G = PK$ is again the polar decomposition.   The action of G on P is

$$\alpha \to g\alpha s(g^{-1}) = g\alpha g^*.$$

Note that the case $n = 2$ is particularly important for physics. $G = SL(2, C)$ is the twofold covering of the homogeneous Lorentz group, and K covers the "little" subgroup of the Lorentz group, i.e., the group that is responsible for spin.

Example 3

   $G = SO(3, R)$, the rotation group in three variables.   Consider the subgroup $SO(2, R)$, i.e., the group of rotations around one fixed axis.   Let g_0 be any element of $SO(2, R)$ with $g_0^2 = $ identity (i.e., g would be a rotation of 180°).   Let $s = \text{Ad } g_0$.   It is readily seen that $SO(2, R)$ is a maximal subgroup of $SO(3, R)$; hence $s^2 = $ identity, and

$$K = SO(2, R) = K(s).$$

Now, **P** is two-dimensional. It is readily seen that Ad K acting on **P** is the action of $SO(2, R)$ as a one-parameter group of rotations in a plane. Thus, **A** can be taken as any one-dimensional subspace of **P**, and A is a one-parameter subgroup of G. Then

$$G = KAK,$$

which is the "Euler angle" description of G. (Since K and A are one-parameter groups, KAK can be described by three angular variables.) The "dual" noncompact group to G is the Lorentz group acting in a three-dimensional Minkowski space, with two space variables. There is again a decomposition of the form $G = KAK$, described by two angular variables to parametrize two copies of K, and a real variable varying from $-\infty$ to ∞ to describe A. (The difference between the "compact" and "noncompact" cases is that in the former A is compact, i.e., a circle, hence is described by an angular variable, whereas in the latter A is a line.) Again, this decomposition is well known to physicists.

These examples could be continued — say to $G = SO(4, R)$, $K = SO(3, R)$. The "dual" group is then the homogeneous Lorentz group acting on 4-space and leading to further decompositions of it, which is found in the physics literature in the form of very laborious explicit formulas.

Example 4: The Compact Simple Lie Groups

This is not really an "example," but one type of symmetric space that has particularly nice properties. Suppose that K is a compact simple Lie group, and that $G = K \times K$; i.e., G is the direct product of K with itself. Let s be the automorphism of G such that

$$s(k_1, k_2) = (k_2, k_1).$$

The fixed point set $K(s)$ is the diagonal in $K \times K$, i.e., the set of (k, k), for $k \in K$. P is the set of pairs (k_1, k_2) with

$$(k_2, k_1) = s(k_1, k_2) = (k_1^{-1}, k_2^{-1});$$

i.e.,

$$k_2 = k_1^{-1}.$$

Hence P is the set of pairs (k, k^{-1}), which can of course again be identified with K. The action of $K \times K$ on P is

$$(k_1, k_2) \cdot (k, k^{-1}) = (k_1 k k_2^{-1}, k_2 k^{-1} k_1^{-1}).$$

We see that it is equivalent to the action of $K \times K$ on K itself by left and right multiplication. Let us pass to the Lie algebra. **G** can be identified with the set of order pairs (X, Y), $X, Y \in K$. Hence **G** can be written as the direct sum of two *ideals* $\mathbf{G}_1 \oplus \mathbf{G}_2$ that are each isomorphic to $\mathbf{K}$. However, we prefer to identify $\mathbf{K}$ with the diagonal, the set of $X \oplus X$, and $\mathbf{P}$ with the "antidiagonal," the set of $X \oplus (-X)$. Again, Ad K acting on $\mathbf{P}$ is equivalent to Ad K acting on $\mathbf{K}$, if $\mathbf{K}$ is identified with $\mathbf{P}$ as a vector space.

$\mathbf{G}$ is a semisimple Lie algebra of compact type. The dual Lie algebra is

$$\begin{aligned} \mathbf{K} + i\mathbf{P} &= \text{the set of } (X \oplus X) + i(Y \oplus -Y) \\ &= (X + iY) \oplus (X - iY). \end{aligned}$$

This can, in turn, be identified as a *real* Lie algebra with $\mathbf{K}_c$, the complexification of $\mathbf{K}$, considered as a real Lie algebra. Thus we see that K_c can be decomposed as a product of K and the subset $\exp(iK)$.

We invite the reader to look up the classification of symmetric spaces G/K given in Helgason's book and work out the details of these decompositions in all cases.

CHAPTER 7

THE IWASAWA DECOMPOSITION

In this chapter, G will be a semisimple, connected Lie group of *noncompact type* having at most a finite center. Let $\mathbf{G}$ be its Lie algebra, and let $\mathbf{G} = \mathbf{K} \oplus \mathbf{P}$ be a Cartan decomposition of $\mathbf{G}$.

Lemma 7-1

Let X be an element of $\mathbf{P}$. Then Ad X acting in $\mathbf{G}$ is completely reducible and has real eigenvalues. In particular, there is a basis of $\mathbf{G}$ for which Ad X is diagonal.

Proof:

Let $\mathbf{G}_u = \mathbf{K} + i\mathbf{P}$ be the dual Lie algebra of compact type. Then, $\mathrm{Ad}(iX)$ is completely reducible, and has pure imaginary eigenvalues (see Chapter 5). Hence, i Ad $iX = -\mathrm{Ad}\ X$ is also completely reducible and has real eigenvalues. The last statement follows from linear algebra: If a real matrix has simple elementary divisors and real eigenvalues, it can be diagonalized by a real matrix. Q.E.D.

Now, let $\mathbf{A}$ be a Cartan subalgebra of $\mathbf{P}$. Since $\mathbf{A}$ is Abelian, the elements of $\mathrm{Ad}(\mathbf{A})$ can be simultaneously diagonalized. Suppose that $W \in \mathbf{G}$ is an eigenvector; i.e.,

$$[X, W] = \lambda(X)W.$$

The eigenvalues $X \to \lambda(X)$ are linear forms on $\mathbf{A}$, and those that are not identically zero are (counted by multiplicity) called the roots of the symmetric space. W is called a *root vector*.

Suppose that we decompose $W = Y + Z$, with $Y \in \mathbf{P}$, $Z \in \mathbf{K}$. Then

$$[X, Y] + [X, Z] = \lambda(X)(Y + Z);$$

hence

(7–1)
$$[X, Y] = \lambda(X)Z,$$
$$[X, Z] = \lambda(X)Y.$$

Conversely, a pair of elements (Y, Z), with $Y \in \mathbf{P}$, $Z \in \mathbf{K}$, satisfying (7–1), determine a root vector, namely $W = Y + Z$.

40

Let Σ be the set of these roots, considered, of course, as real-valued linear forms on $\mathbf{A}$.   Now, if $\lambda \in \Sigma$, so does $-\lambda$, since

$W = Y - Z$ is a weight vector with weight from $-\lambda$.

This suggests that we split Σ into two parts, Σ_+ and Σ_-, which we can call "positive" and "negative" roots.   The simplest way to accomplish this goes as follows.

Choose a fixed regular element $X_0 \in \mathbf{A}$.   Let us say that a root form λ belongs to Σ_+ if

$$\lambda(X_0) > 0,$$

and that it belongs to Σ_- if $\lambda(X_0) < 0$.

Let $\mathbf{N}^+$ and $\mathbf{N}^-$ be the subspace of $\mathbf{G}$ spanned by root vectors corresponding to roots belonging to Σ_+ and Σ_-, respectively.   If $[X, W_1] = \lambda_1(X)W_1$, and $[X, W_2] = \lambda_2(X)W_2$, then

$$[X, [W_1, W_2]] = (\lambda_1(X) + \lambda_2(X))[W_1, W_2].$$

This shows that $[W_1, W_2]$ is also a root vector (unless it is zero).   This simple remark forces several very important conclusions.   (We deal only with $\mathbf{N}^+$; similar conclusions follow for $\mathbf{N}^-$.)

(7–2) $[C(\mathbf{A}) + \mathbf{N}^+, \mathbf{N}^+] \subset \mathbf{N}^+$

$[C(X)$ denotes the centralizer of $\mathbf{A}$ in $\mathbf{G}$, i.e., the set of $Y \in \mathbf{G}$ such that $[Y, \mathbf{A}] = 0$.   It is a subalgebra of $\mathbf{G}$.]

(7–3) $\mathbf{N}^+$ *is a nilpotent Lie algebra.*

(A Lie algebra, say $\mathbf{L}$, is nilpotent if

$[\mathbf{L}, \mathbf{L}]$ is not equal to $\mathbf{L}$;
$[\mathbf{L}, [\mathbf{L}, \mathbf{L}]]$ is not equal to $[\mathbf{L}, \mathbf{L}]$;

etc., continuing down to the condition

$$[\mathbf{L}, [\mathbf{L}, \cdots [\mathbf{L}, \mathbf{L}] \cdots]] = 0,$$

if the bracket is iterated sufficiently many times.)

For the proof of (7–3) note that the elements of $[\mathbf{N}^+, \mathbf{N}^+]$ are weight vectors for weights that can be written as the sum of two elements of Σ_+. $[\mathbf{N}^+, [\mathbf{N}^+, \mathbf{N}^+]]$ are weight vectors for weights that can be written as the sum of three elements of Σ_+.   Continuing, we eventually get zero, since there are only a finite number of weights in Σ_+.

(7–4) $\mathbf{A} + \mathbf{N}^+$ is a solvable Lie algebra.

(A Lie algebra **L** is *solvable* if

$$\mathbf{L}_1 = [\mathbf{L}, \mathbf{L}] \text{ is not equal to } \mathbf{L};$$
$$\mathbf{L}_2 = [\mathbf{L}_1, \mathbf{L}_2] \text{ is not equal to } \mathbf{L}_1,$$

etc., continuing to the condition that L_j is zero if j is sufficiently large.)
The proof follows from (7–2) and (7–3).

(7–5)   **G** *is a direct sum of the subalgebras* $\mathbf{K} \oplus \mathbf{Z} \oplus \mathbf{N}^+$.

Proof:

Note, by (7–1), that weight vectors cannot belong to either **K** or **P**. Hence, the mapping $\mathbf{N}^+ \to \mathbf{P}$ which assigns to each weight vector in $\mathbf{N}^+$ its projection in **P** is one-to-one. Clearly then,

$$\dim \mathbf{A} + \mathbf{N}^+ = \dim \mathbf{P}.$$

Also, **K**, **A**, and $\mathbf{N}^+$ can have no elements in common. Here

$$\dim(\mathbf{K} + \mathbf{A} + \mathbf{N}^+) = \dim \mathbf{G}.$$

Theorem 7–1   (*The "Iwasawa Decomposition"*)

Let K, A, and N^+ be the connected subgroups corresponding, respectively, to the subalgebras **K**, **A**, and $\mathbf{N}^+$. Then

$$G = KAN^+,$$

and this decomposition of **G** is unique.

We shall not be able to prove this here, because of the detour that would be necessary to develop the necessary geometric tools. We shall be content to compute some examples.

Example 1

$G = SL(n, R)$, $K = SO(n, R)$.
We have seen that **A** can be taken as the Lie algebra of diagonal matrices of trace zero. Let W be a weight vector, and let X be a regular element of **A**, i.e., one with unequal diagonal elements. Suppose, as $n \times n$ matrices,

$$X = (X_{ij}), \; W = (W_{ij}),$$
$$\lambda W = [X, W] = XW - WX = \sum_{k=1}^{n} X_{ik}W_{kj} - W_{jk}X_{kj}.$$

Since X is diagonal, this must equal

$$(X_{ij}W_{ij} - W_{ij}X_{jj}),$$

i.e.,

$$\lambda W_{ij} = X_{ii}W_{ij} - W_{ij}X_{jj} \qquad \text{or} \qquad W_{ij}(\lambda - X_{ii} + X_{jj}) = 0.$$

Now, let us choose X so that

$$X_{jj} - X_{ij} \neq X_{j_1 j_1} - X_{i_1 j_1} \qquad \text{for } (i, j) \neq (i_1, j_1),$$
$$X_{ii} > X_{jj} \qquad \text{for } i > j.$$

Then W_{ij} can be nonzero for *only one* pair (i, j), and for that pair i must be $> j$, since λ is > 0. Then $\mathbf{N}^+$, which is the space of matrices spanned by these matrices, consists in the lower triangular matrices with zero on the diagonal, i.e., of the type

$$\begin{pmatrix} 0 & & 0 \\ & \ddots & \\ * & & 0 \end{pmatrix}.$$

$A\mathbf{N}^+$ is then the group of lower triangular matrices, of the form

$$\begin{pmatrix} * & & 0 \\ & \ddots & \\ * & & * \end{pmatrix}.$$

The Iwasawa decomposition

$$G = KA\mathbf{N}^+$$

is then just that which decomposes a matrix into a product of orthogonal and lower triangular.

Example 2

$G = SL(n, C),\ K = SU(n)$.

We have seen that $\mathbf{A}$ works out to be the space of Hermitian diagonal matrices. Just as in Example 1, $\mathbf{N}^+$ turn out to be the lower triangular matrices, and the Iwasawa decomposition turns out to involve a product of a unitary matrix, a lower triangular, and a real diagonal one.

Example 3

$\mathbf{G}$ is the complexification, $\mathbf{K}_c$, of a compact simple Lie group $\mathbf{K}$. Then $\mathbf{G} = \mathbf{K} + i\mathbf{K}$; i.e., $\mathbf{P} = i\mathbf{K}$ — a maximal Abelian subalgebra $\mathbf{A}$ if $\mathbf{P}$ is of the form $i\mathbf{C}$, where $\mathbf{C}$ is a maximal Abelian subalgebra of $\mathbf{K}$. The centralizer of $\mathbf{A}$ in $\mathbf{G}$ is then $\mathbf{C} + i\mathbf{C}$. The conjugacy of Cartan subalgebras of the symmetric space implies that two maximal Abelian subalgebras of $\mathbf{K}$ itself are conjugate under Ad K.

Let Σ be the set of roots, split up into two parts, Σ_+ and Σ_-, as explained above. The following facts are known, and in fact are standard results one must prove to classify simple Lie algebras.

(a) For $\lambda \in \Sigma$, let G_λ be the space of all $W \in \mathbf{G}$ such that:

(b) If $W_\lambda \in G_\lambda$, and $W_\lambda = X + Y$, with $X \in \mathbf{P}$, $Y \in \mathbf{K}$, then

$$W_{-\lambda} = X - Y \text{ belongs to } G_{-\lambda},$$
$$[W_\lambda, W_{-\lambda}] = 2[X, Y] \in \mathbf{A}.$$

(c) There are a finite number of roots $\lambda_1, \cdots, \lambda_r$ ($r = \dim \mathbf{A}$) in Σ_+ such that any root $\lambda \in \mathbf{A}$ can be written as the sum

$$\sum_{i=1}^{r} m_i \lambda_i \qquad \text{with } m_i \text{ integers.}$$

Then $\mathbf{N}^+$ and $\mathbf{N}^-$ are complex subalgebras of $\mathbf{K}_c$. $\mathbf{C} + i\mathbf{C} + \mathbf{N}^+$ is a maximal solvable subalgebra of $\mathbf{K}_c$.

CHAPTER 8

FINITE-DIMENSIONAL REPRESENTATION OF COMPACT LIE ALGEBRAS

Let **G** be a compact semisimple Lie algebra [recall that this means that the Killing form $B(\ ,\ )$ is negative definite]. Let **C** be a maximal Abelian subalgebra of **G**. (By Chapter 6, two maximal Abelian subalgebras are conjugate under an inner automorphism of **G**.) Let ρ be an irreducible representation of **G** by transformations of a finite-dimensional complex vector space V. As we have seen, all transformations $\rho(X)$, for $X \in$ **G**, can be diagonalized. Since **C** is Abelian, its elements can be simultaneously diagonalized. A real-valued linear form ω on **C** is a *weight* of the representation if it is at a simultaneous eigenvalue for elements of **C**, i.e., if there is a vector $v \in V$ such that

$$\rho(X)(v) = i\omega(X)v \qquad \text{for all } X \in \mathbf{C}.$$

v is called a *weight vector*. Naturally, a basis can be chosen for V consisting of weight vectors.

Let X_0 be a regular element of **A** fixed in advance. A weight ω_m of the representation is a maximal weight if $\omega_m(X_0)$ is equal to the maximal value of $\omega(X_0)$, where ω ranges over all weights. The remarkable property of those maximal weights, discovered by Cartan, is that they serve to characterize the representations. We shall list without proof [see Jacobson (1962)] some of these properties.

1. There is just one maximal weight. Its eigenvectors have multiplicity 1.

2. Two irreducible representations are equivalent if and only if they have the same maximal weight.

3. The tensor product of two irreducible representations of maximal weights ω and ω' has, when decomposed under the action of **G**, precisely one irreducible component of maximal weight $\omega + \omega'$.

The rest of this chapter will be devoted to a description of the maximal weights in terms of the root system of the Lie algebra **G**. First, let us suppose that ρ was originally a representation of **G** by transformations on a real vector space U, and V is the complexification of U; i.e.,

$$V = U + iU.$$

If $\rho(X)(v) = i\omega(X)v$, and if $v = \mu_1 + i\mu_2$, then

$$\rho(X)(\mu_1 + i\mu_2) = i\omega(X)\mu_1 - \omega(X)\mu_2;$$

hence

$$\rho(X)(\mu_1) = -\omega(X)\mu_2,$$
$$\rho(X)(\mu_2) = \omega(X)\mu_1.$$

Conversely, a pair of vectors in U satisfying these conditions determines an eigenvector of $\rho(X)$. It is sometimes more convenient to use this description of the eigenvectors of $\rho(X)$.

Now apply these remarks to the case where ρ is the adjoint representation of G, V is the complexification $\mathbf{G} + i\mathbf{G} = \mathbf{G}_c$ of **G**, and U is **G** itself. The nonzero weights of this representation are called the *roots* of the Lie algebra **G**. Let X_0 be the fixed regular element of **C** chosen above. Let Σ_+ be the set of roots that are positive on X_0.

Associated with each $\lambda \in \Sigma_+$, we then have a pair (Y_λ, Z_λ) (playing the role of μ_1, μ_2) of elements of **G** satisfying, for $X \in \mathbf{C}$,

$$[X, Y_\lambda] = \lambda(X)Z_\lambda,$$
$$[X, Z_\lambda] = -\lambda(X)Y_\lambda.$$

The properties of these elements can be described (without proof here) as follows:

1. $B(Y_\lambda, Z_\lambda) = 0$, where $B(\quad,\quad)$ is the Killing form of **G**.
2. Any other pair Y_λ', Z_λ' of elements satisfy the same condition as a linear combination of the Y_λ, Z_λ.
3. As λ varies over Σ_+, the Y_λ, Z_λ, together with a basis for **C**, give a basis for **G**.

Now,

$$B(Y_\lambda, Y_\lambda) = \frac{B([X, Z_\lambda], [X, Z_\lambda])}{\lambda(X)^2}$$
$$= \frac{-B([X, [X, Z_\lambda]], Z_\lambda)}{\lambda(X)^2} = B(Z_\lambda, Z_\lambda).$$

Hence we can normalize Y_λ and Z_λ, so that

$$-1 = B(Y_\lambda, Y_\lambda) = B(Z_\lambda, Z_\lambda).$$

So normalized, let us define

$$X_\lambda = [Z_\lambda, Y_\lambda].$$

For $X \in \mathbf{C}$,

$$[X, X_\lambda] = [[X, Y_\lambda], Y_\lambda] + [Z_\lambda, [X, Y_\lambda]] = 0.$$

Since $\mathbf{C}$ is maximal Abelian in $\mathbf{G}$,

$$X_\lambda \in \mathbf{C}.$$

Further,

$$B(X, X_\lambda) = B(X, [Z_\lambda, Y_\lambda]) = B([X, Z_\lambda], Y_\lambda)$$
$$= \lambda(X).$$

Hence X_λ is the element of $\mathbf{C}$ corresponding to the linear form λ under the isomorphism between $\mathbf{C}$ and its dual space defined by the Killing form. Put

$$W_\lambda = Z_\lambda + iY_\lambda,$$
$$W_{-\lambda} = Z_\lambda - iY_\lambda.$$

For $X \in \mathbf{C}$,

$$[X, W_\lambda] = -\lambda(X)Y + i\lambda(X)Z = i\lambda(X)W_\lambda,$$
$$[X, W_{-\lambda}] = -i\lambda(X)W_\lambda,$$
$$[W_\lambda, W_{-\lambda}] = -2iX_\lambda.$$

The W_λ and $W_{-\lambda}$ are then elements of the complexified Lie algebra $\mathbf{G}_c$, which are eigenvectors of Ad $\mathbf{C}$. They are called the *root vectors* corresponding to the root $\lambda \in \sum_+$. If λ' is another root, note that

$$[X, [W_\lambda, W'_{\lambda}]] = i(\lambda(X) + \lambda'(X))[W_\lambda, W_\lambda].$$

Hence the bracket of two root vectors is again a root vector if it is non-zero. In fact, one can prove that

$$[W_\lambda, W'_\lambda] \text{ is nonzero if and only if } \pm (\lambda - \lambda') \in \sum_+.$$

Return now to consideration of a general representation ρ of $\mathbf{G}$ by transformations of a finite-dimensional complex vector space V. If $v \in V$ is a weight vector for weight ω, and if λ is a root, note that

$$\rho(X)(\rho(W_\lambda))(v) = i(\lambda(X) + \omega(X))\rho(W_\lambda)(v).$$

Hence, $\rho(W_\lambda)(v)$ is, if nonzero, a weight vector with weight $\lambda + \omega$. In particular, if v_m is a maximal weight vector,

$$\rho(W_\lambda)(v_m) = 0,$$

since otherwise $(\lambda + \omega)$ would be a root and ω would not be maximal. This condition can be stated more neatly as follows. Let $\mathbf{N}^+$ be the complex subspace of $\mathbf{G}_0$ spanned by the root vectors for *positive* roots, λ, i.e., for $\lambda \in \Sigma_+$. We see that $\mathbf{N}^+$ is a nilpotent subalgebra of $\mathbf{G}_c$, and that

$$\rho(\mathbf{N}^+)(v_m) = 0.$$

Conversely, it can be proved that the maximal weight is the only weight vector that is left fixed by $\rho(\mathbf{N}^+)$.

Fix a $\lambda \in \Sigma_+$, and suppose for the moment that only

$$\rho(W_\lambda)(v_m) = 0.$$

W_λ, $W_{-\lambda}$, and X_λ form a three-dimensional subalgebra of $\mathbf{G}_c$ that is isomorphic to the one-dimensional simple Lie algebra, namely the Lie algebra of $SL(2, C)$. Also, this algebra is the complexification of that generated by X_λ, Y_λ, Z_λ in $\mathbf{G}$, which is isomorphic to the Lie algebra of $SO(3, R)$. Physicists know the representation theory of $SO(3, R)$ and $SL(2, C)$ extremely well, of course. These also play the key role in representation theory for $\mathbf{G}$, since $\mathbf{G}$ is built up from the three-dimensional subalgebras associated with each λ, as λ runs through Σ_+. We shall now proceed to the usual determination of the basis for the representation of this three-dimensional subalgebra by applying the "annihilation" operator $(W_{-\lambda})$ to v_m. In fact, put

$$v_1 = \rho(W_{-\lambda})(v_m)$$
$$\vdots$$
$$v_{d-1} = \rho(W_{-\lambda})(v_{d-1})$$
$$\rho(W_{-\lambda})(v_{d-2}) = 0.$$

(Thus, d is the dimension of the subspace of V containing v_m, invariant and irreducible under W_λ, $W_{-\lambda}$, X_λ)

$$\begin{aligned}\rho(X_\lambda)(v_j) &= \rho(X_\lambda)\rho(W_{-\lambda})(v_{j-1}) \\ &= \rho([X_\lambda, W_{-\lambda}])(v_{j-1}) + \rho(W_{-\lambda})\rho(X_\lambda)(v_{j-1}) \\ &= -iB(X_\lambda, X_\lambda)v_j + \rho(W_{-\lambda})\rho(X_\lambda)(v_{j-1}),\end{aligned}$$

$$\begin{aligned}\rho(W_\lambda)(v_j) &= \rho(W_\lambda)\rho(W_{-\lambda})(v_{j-1}) \\ &= \rho([W_\lambda, W_{-\lambda}])(v_{j-1}) + \rho(W_{-\lambda})\rho(W_\lambda)(v_{j-1}) \\ &= -2i(X_\lambda)(v_{j-1}) + \rho(W_{-\lambda})(W_\lambda)(v_{j-1}).\end{aligned}$$

Then, for $j = 1$,

$$\rho(X_\lambda)(v_1) = (-iB(X_\lambda, X_\lambda) + i\omega(X_\lambda))v_1,$$
$$\rho(W_\lambda)(v_1) = 2\omega(X_\lambda)v_m.$$

For $j \geqslant 2$,

$$\rho(X_\lambda)(v_j) = i(\omega(X_\lambda) - j\lambda(X_\lambda))v_j,$$

$$\begin{aligned}
\rho(W_\lambda)(v_j) &= -2i(i(\omega(X_\lambda) - (j-1)\lambda(X_\lambda))v_{j-1} \\
&\quad + \rho(W_{-\lambda})(W_\lambda)(v_{j-1}) \\
&= 2(\omega(X_\lambda) - (j-1)\lambda(X_\lambda))v_{j-1} \\
&\quad + \rho(W_{-\lambda})\rho(W_\lambda)(v_{j-1}) \\
&= 2(\omega(X_\lambda) - (j-1)\lambda(X_\lambda))v_{j-1} \\
&\quad + \rho(W_{-\lambda})(2(\omega(X_\lambda) - (j-2)\lambda(X_\lambda)))v_{j-2} \\
&\quad + p(W_{-g})p(W_g)(v_{j-2}) \\
&= 2(\omega(X_\lambda) - (j-1)\lambda(X_\lambda))v_{j-1} \\
&\quad + 2(\omega(X_\lambda) - (j-2)\lambda(X_\lambda)v_{j-1} \\
&\quad + \rho(W_{-\lambda})^2\rho(W_\lambda)(v_{j-2}) \\
&= v_{j-1}\sum_{k=1}^{j-1} 2(\omega(X_\lambda) - (j-k)\lambda(X_\lambda)) \\
&\quad + \rho(W_{-\lambda})^{j-1}\rho(W_\lambda)(v_1) \\
&= v_{j-1}(2(j-1)\omega(X_\lambda) - j(j-1)\lambda(X_\lambda) + 2\omega(X_\lambda)) \\
&= v_{j-1}(2j\omega(X_\lambda) - j(j-1)\lambda(X_\lambda)).
\end{aligned}$$

Since $v_d = 0$, we can put $j = d$ in the last relation, and since $v_{d-1} \neq 0$, equate the coefficient on the right side to zero:

$$2d\omega(X_\lambda) = d(d-1)\lambda(X_\lambda) \qquad \text{or} \qquad \frac{2\omega(X_\lambda)}{\lambda(X_\lambda)} = d - 1.$$

This is the fundamental relation in representation theory. We can use it to state the following basic result:

Theorem 8–1

The linear form ω on **C** is a maximal weight of a finite-dimensional irreducible representation of **G** if and only if

$$(8\text{–}1) \qquad \omega\left(\frac{2X_\lambda}{B(X_\lambda, X_\lambda)}\right) \text{ is an integer for each } \lambda \in \Sigma_+.$$

This integer is then one less than the dimension of the smallest space containing the maximal weight vector and invariant under X_λ, W_λ, and $W_{-\lambda}$.

We shall not prove here that to each form satisfying these conditions there is an irreducible representation. See Jacobson (1962).

The relation also plays a basic role in the structure theory of semisimple Lie algebras. To see this, apply it to the case where $V = \mathbf{G}_c$ and ρ is the adjoint representation. Suppose that μ is also a root of $\mathbf{G}_c$, and that W_μ is the corresponding root vector. Let a and b be the biggest integers, such that

$$\mu + j\lambda \text{ is a root for } -a \leqslant j \leqslant b.$$

Then $\mu + b\lambda$ is a maximal weight form for the three-dimensional algebra spanned by X_λ, W_λ, $W_{-\lambda}$; the dimension of the corresponding representation (since the weight vector spaces are one-dimensional) is

$$b + a + 1.$$

Then (8–1) takes the form

$$\frac{2(\mu + b\lambda)(X_\lambda)}{B(X_\lambda, X_\lambda)} = b + a,$$

or

$$(8\text{–}2) \qquad \frac{2B(X_\mu, X_\lambda)}{B(X_\lambda, X_\lambda)} = a - b.$$

Let us return now to a general irreducible representation ρ of $\mathbf{G}$. Introduce a *simple root system* for $\sum_+$, i.e., a set of positive roots $\lambda_1, \ldots, \lambda_r \in \sum_+$ such that every $\lambda \in \sum_+$ can be written uniquely as a sum of $\lambda_1, \ldots, \lambda_r$ with nonnegative integer coefficients. (Again, it is one of the basic facts about semisimple Lie algebra that such systems exist, with $r = \dim \mathbf{C}$, called the *rank* of the algebra $\mathbf{G}$.) It can be proved that the condition that a form ω be a maximal weight is

$$(8\text{–}3) \qquad \frac{2\omega(X_{\lambda_j})}{B(X_{\lambda_j}, X_{\lambda_j})} = \text{integer} \qquad \text{for } 1 \leqslant j \leqslant r.$$

This relation exhibits the "lattice" structure of the maximal weights, hence of the irreducible representations of $\mathbf{G}$. In fact, define maximal weights $\omega_1, \ldots, \omega_r$ by the relation

$$(8\text{–}4) \qquad \frac{2\omega_k(X_{\lambda_j})}{B(X_{\lambda_j}, X_{\lambda_j})} = \delta_{jk} \qquad (1 \leqslant j, k \leqslant r).$$

Then every maximal weight can be written as the sum of the $\omega_1, \ldots, \omega_r$ with integer coefficients. The irreducible representations whose maximal weights are the $\omega_1, \ldots, \omega_r$ are the *fundamental representations:* In view of Cartan's theorem that the sum of two maximal weights is a maximal weight of a representation occurring once in the tensor product of the two representations, we see that all representations can be obtained from the fundamental ones by decomposing their tensor products. We can refer the reader for further work on representations from the maximal-weight point of view to Dynkin's articles [(1950), (1957a), (1957b)].

This picture of the structure of the space of irreducible representations of $\mathbf{G}$ or $\mathbf{G}_c$ is due to Cartan (1913a): In determining the fundamental representations explicitly, he discovered one, the spinors, that was not known before.   It is the ultimate goal of the theory of infinite-dimensional representation to "fill in the space" between the finite-dimensional ones.

CHAPTER 9

VECTOR BUNDLES AND
INDUCED REPRESENTATIONS

There is a close relation between the theory of linear representations of a Lie group G and the spaces on which G can act as a transitive transformation group. This is reasonable from a physical point of view also. Lie groups usually enter physics because they appear as transformations on, say, phase space that are "symmetries" of the physical system. The linear representations occurring in physics are not given abstractly but are obtained by decomposing the action of G on such objects as functions, tensor fields, etc., that "live" on the space on which G acts. Admittedly it is not yet clear whether the "internal" symmetries that are appearing among the elementary particles admit such a clear geometrico-physical interpretation, but it certainly would serve as a guide to further research to try to show that they do appear in this way. The aim of this chapter is to describe in general terms the relation between the geometry of homogeneous spaces of Lie groups and linear representation theory. This theory also can be treated with more emphasis on the point of view of functional analysis via the theory of "induced representations," but we believe that the geometric view is more useful to the physicist because it is closer to the sort of intuitive picture of representation theory with which he already works.

Physicists are used to working with the following sort of setup: Consider vector-valued "fields" of the form $x \rightarrow \psi_i(x)$, where x denotes a point of space and i denotes a set of indices. Typically, i will denote a set of tensor and/or spinor indices. Consider a group G that acts on the space variables x, and a mapping $(g, x) \rightarrow A_{ij}(g, x)$ into matrices that act on the vector space denoted by the indices. Then we can transform the fields by letting G act both on the x-variables and on the indices via the mapping, obtaining a transform of the type

$$\psi_i \rightarrow A_{ij}(g, x)\psi_j(g^{-1}x).$$

This type of action of groups on vector or spinor fields can best be understood via the concept of homogeneous vector bundle. This idea can serve to clarify and unify many of the confusing ideas concerning group "invariance" and "covariance" that are floating around in physics literature.

To define a *vector bundle* one must be given two spaces, E and M, and a map π from E *onto* M, such that, for each point $p \in M$, the fiber $\pi^{-1}(p)$ of the map is a real vector space. Thus elements of E can be added if they "lie over" the same element of M in the sense that their image under π is the same point of M. In other words, E is thought of as being linear "vertically" but nonlinear "horizontally" (Fig. 1). However, a new vector space can be constructed by considering the space of cross sections. A *cross section* is a map, denoted, say, by ψ, of $M \to E$ such that

$$\psi(p) \in \pi^{-1}(p) \qquad \text{for } p \in M.$$

Thus ψ assigns a point in the fiber sitting over each point of M. Two such cross sections can then be added by adding their values:

$$(\psi_1 + \psi_2)(p) = \psi_1(p) + \psi_2(p),$$

and multiplied by scalars,

$$(c\psi)(p) = c\psi(p).$$

If we denote the space of cross sections by $\Gamma(E)$, it then is an (infinite-dimensional) vector space over the real numbers, say. [If each fiber is a complex vector space, of course, $\Gamma(E)$ becomes a complex vector space also.]

Now we must see how groups fit in. Consider a group G that acts on E and M in the following way. For $p \in M$, $g \in G$, g maps the fiber $\pi^{-1}(p)$ by a linear transformation into the fiber $\pi^{-1}(gp)$. We can then define a linear transformation, denoted by ρ, of G on cross sections: For $g \in G$, $\psi \in \Gamma(E)$, $p \in M$,

$$\rho(g)(\psi)(p) = g\psi(g^{-1}p).$$

Figure 1

We can now see how this setup gives the one physicists are used to. Suppose $\psi^1, \ldots, \psi^n$ is a set of cross sections such that, for $p \in M$, $\psi^1(p), \ldots, \psi^n(p)$ is a basis of the vector space $\pi^{-1}(p)$. Such a system can be called a *basis* for the cross sections. An arbitrary cross section can then be written

$$\psi = \sum_i \psi_i(p)\psi^i(p),$$

where $\psi_i(p)$ are real-valued functions on M. Thus, cross sections are in one-to-one correspondence with the objects the physicists work with, namely functions on M with indices. Suppose $g \in G$. Then

$$\rho(g)(\psi^i)(p) = A_{ij}(g, p)\psi^i(p).$$

The matrix functions $A_{ij}(g, p)$ thus determine an action of G on the index functions on M. However, the vector-bundle concept is so much clearer and elegant that we shall work with it. It is clearly the right geometric structure with which to make precise and clear the type of arguments physicists use over and over in field theories.

Suppose now that G acts transitively on M; let H be the isotropy subgroup of G at a fixed point $p_0 \in M$, so that M becomes the coset space G/H. In addition, suppose G acts on the vector bundle E sitting over G/H so that its action on the base agrees with the usual action of G on cosets. We shall call such a structure a *homogeneous vector bundle*.

There will be many homogeneous vector bundles associated with a given coset space G/H. We shall now investigate how they are determined. Let U be the vector space $\pi^{-1}(p_0)$. Since H acting on the base leaves p_0 invariant, each $h \in H$ acting on E maps U linearly into itself; i.e., the vector bundle itself determines a linear representation σ of H by linear transformation on the vector space U. We shall see that the homogeneous vector bundles over G/H are in one-to-one correspondence with such linear representations of H. [This explains why we give the action of H on $\pi^{-1}(p_0)$ the "name" σ, while the action of G on E was given no special name. We can think of the bundle as "parametrized" by σ.]

First, let us analyze the space of cross sections $\Gamma(E)$. Each $\psi \in \Gamma(E)$ defines a map $\tilde{\psi}: G \to U$ in the following manner: Suppose $p = gp_0$ is a point of $G/H = M$, with $g \in G$. Define

(9–1) $$\tilde{\psi}(g) = g^{-1}\psi(gp_0).$$

Note that, for $h \in H$,

$$\tilde{\psi}(gh) = h^{-1}g^{-1}\psi(ghp_0) = h^{-1}g^{-1}\psi(gp_0);$$

hence

(9–2) $$\tilde{\psi}(gh) = \sigma(h^{-1})\tilde{\psi}(g).$$

Conversely, suppose that $\tilde{\psi}$ is a map: $G \to U$ transforming via (9–2) under right multiplication by H. We can then assign to $\tilde{\psi}$ a cross section $\psi \in \Gamma(E)$ by the formula

$$(9\text{–}3) \qquad\qquad \psi(gp_0) = g\tilde{\psi}(g).$$

Note that (9–2) is exactly the right transformation law to really guarantee that ψ is a cross section: For

$$(gh)\tilde{\psi}(gh) = g\sigma(h)\sigma(h^{-1})\tilde{\psi}(g) = g\tilde{\psi}(g).$$

We have then proved that

> There is a one-to-one correspondence between cross sections of the vector bundle and maps of G into U satisfying (9–2).

Thus, considering cross sections as maps $G \to U$ satisfying (9–2) gives us a convenient analytic presentation for the space of cross sections. The linear representation σ of G on $\Gamma(E)$ also takes a very convenient form: By definition, for $g_0, g \in G$, we have

$$\rho(g_0)(\psi)(gp_0) = g_0\psi(g_0^{-1}gp_0).$$

But,

$$\begin{aligned} g_0\psi(g_0^{-1}gp) &= g \cdot g^{-1}g_0\psi(g_0^{-1}gp) \\ &= g\tilde{\psi}(g_0^{-1}g). \end{aligned}$$

By (9–1),

$$\begin{aligned} \widetilde{\rho(g_0)(\psi)}(g) &= g^{-1}\rho(g_0)(\psi)(gp_0) \\ &= g^{-1}g_0\psi(g_0^{-1}gp_0); \end{aligned}$$

hence

$$g_0\psi(g_0^{-1}gp_0) = g\widetilde{\rho(g_0)(\psi)}(g).$$

Equating, we have

$$(9\text{–}4) \qquad\qquad \widetilde{\rho(g_0)(\psi)}(g) = \tilde{\psi}(g_0^{-1}g).$$

Thus, in the $\sim$-presentation of $\Gamma(E)$, G acts on $\Gamma(E)$ via ρ in a very simple manner, as a left translation.

We can now throw away explicit use of the vector bundle to define $\Gamma(E)$ directly once σ is given. Start off and define $\Gamma(E)$ as the set of maps $\tilde{\psi}: G \to U$ satisfying (9–2). Define $\rho(g_0)(\tilde{\psi})$ via (9–4). Note directly that $\rho(g_0)(\tilde{\psi})$ also satisfies (9–2).

[*Proof:*

$$(g_0)(\tilde{\psi})(gh) = \tilde{\psi}(g_0^{-1}gh) = \sigma(h^{-1})\tilde{\psi}(g_0^{-1}g)$$
$$= \sigma(h^{-1})\rho(g_0)(\tilde{\psi}).]$$

Starting off with a linear representation σ of H in U, we have defined a representation ρ of G in $\Gamma(E)$. This is called the *representation of G induced by σ*, and is the definition used by Mackey (1963a) and the other workers who use the methods of functional analysis to study group representations.

On the other hand, E itself can be reconstructed from $\Gamma(E)$. Note that the fiber $\pi^{-1}(gp_0)$ can be identified with the quotient of $\Gamma(E)$ by those cross sections $\psi \colon G/H \to E$ that are zero at gp_0. However, if $\psi(gp_0) = 0$, then also $\tilde{\psi}(g) = 0$. Without assuming that E exists, define U_{gp_0} as the quotient of $\Gamma(E)$ by the subspace of those maps $\tilde{\psi} \colon G \to U$ that are zero at g. [Note that if $\tilde{\psi}(g) = 0$, so is $\tilde{\psi}(gh) = \sigma(h^{-1})\tilde{\psi}(g)$; hence U_{gp_0} really only depends on the right coset of G by H.] We can then *define E* as the union of these vector spaces U_{gp_0}, as g runs through G. (This is not the most convenient definition from the point of view of putting a topology and manifold structure on E, but it will suffice for our purposes.) We have now proved that

> There is a one-to-one correspondence between homogeneous vector bundles over a homogeneous space G/H and linear representations of H.

Many of the infinite-dimensional representations of noncompact Lie groups obtained by Wigner, Bargmann, Gel'fand and his co-workers, and Harish-Chandra can be obtained as cross sections of homogeneous vector bundles. Since such bundles can be "parametrized" by representations of H, we may say that this gives a method of "parametrizing" infinite-dimensional representation of noncompact Lie groups.

Finally, it is interesting to arrive at the geometric picture with which we began from a reverse point of view. Suppose that ρ' is a linear representation of a group G by transformations on a vector space V. Suppose that U' is a subspace of V such that $\rho'(H)(U') = U'$, and let U be the quotient vector space V/U'. The representation ρ' restricted to H passes to the quotient to define a linear representation σ of H in $V/U' = U$, which then defines a homogeneous vector bundle $\Gamma(E)$ over G/H. Given $v \in V$, we can define a map $\tilde{\psi}_v \colon G \to U$ by the formula

(9–5) $\tilde{\psi}_v(g) =$ the image of $\rho(g)(v)$ in the quotient V/U'.

It is then quite routine to verify that $\tilde{\psi}_v$ satisfies (9–2), and that the assignment $v \to \tilde{\psi}_v \in \Gamma(E)$ commutes with the action of G on V and $\Gamma(E)$.

Thus, we see that the representations ρ of G which "contain" the given representation σ of H in the sense that V can be split into subspaces $V = U' \oplus U$ which are invariant under H, such that H acts in U via σ, are obtained among the representations of G obtained by decomposing the action of G on $\Gamma(E)$.   Making this precise leads to the *Frobenius reciprocity theorem*, which we shall treat, in part, in Chapter 18.

Of course, in most of the situations in physics this machinery is not really needed in all its complexity.   For example, in many cases E is the product $(G/H) \times U$, so that $\Gamma(E)$ can be considered merely as the vector space of maps of G/H into U.   In other cases E is only the product over certain subsets of G/H, which leads to the physicists' "local" picture of fields as cross sections.   However, many of the complications one finds in the physics literature, due, for example, to spin, are clarified in a vector-bundle context, and the theory can be strongly recommended to physicists as an appropriate mathematical language with which to understand the true nature of the relation between symmetries and fields.   Certainly it can be quite dogmatically asserted that the machinery is absolutely necessary to organize the existing results on infinite-dimensional representations of noncompact groups in a semicoherent framework.   (Unfortunately, even many mathematicians who work on this subject have only realized this in the last few years.)

Example 1: Finite-Dimensional Representation

Let G be a semisimple Lie group, and let $G = KAN$ be an Iwasawa decomposition of G. (Then K is a maximal compact subgroup, A is Abelian, and N is nilpotent.)   Let K_0 be the centralizer of A in K.   Suppose that ρ is a linear representation of G on a real, finite-dimensional vector space V.   By the Lie theorem, AN acting in V has an eigenvector; i.e., there is a $v_0 \in V$ and homomorphism $\lambda: A \to R$ such that

$$(9\text{--}6) \qquad \rho(an)(v_0) = \lambda(a)v_0 \qquad \text{for all } an \in AN.$$

[The "Lie theorem" asserts that every solvable Lie group acting in a finite-dimensional *complex* vector space must have an eigenvector. AN is solvable; hence $\rho(AN)$ acting in the complex vector space associated with V must have an eigenvector.   Since $\rho(N)$ is nilpotent, i.e., has only one as an eigenvector, $\rho(N)$ must preserve this eigenvector.   As we have seen, the method of constructing A from a Cartan decomposition for $\mathbf{G}$ implies that $\rho(A)$ only has real eigenvalues.   Hence $\rho(AN)$ has an eigenvector in V, which is fixed by $\rho(N)$.]
Let $k \in K_0$.   Then

$$\rho(an)(\rho(k)(v_0)) = \rho(ank)(v_0) = \rho(akn')(v_0)$$
$$= \rho(kan')(v_0) = \lambda(a)\rho(k)(v_0).$$

[We need to know that Ad $K_0(N) = N$. This follows from the definition of $\mathbf{N}$ as the subspace of $\mathbf{G}$ spanned by eigenvectors of Ad X, for positive eigenvalues, for a regular element of $\mathbf{A}$.] Hence $\rho(K_0)$ preserves the set of vectors v_0 satisfying (9–6). Let U be a space of vectors satisfying (9–6) on which $\rho(K_0)$ acts irreducibly. Let $H = K_0AN$. ρ restricted to H defines a representation σ of H in U. By the above remarks, if ρ is irreducible, it is contained in a representation obtained by inducing σ from H to G, i.e., by constructing a homogeneous vector bundle associated with σ on G/H. G/H is an interesting sort of space, and occurs in many contexts in the theory of representations. It is one of the *boundary homogeneous spaces* [first so named by Furstenberg (1963)] of G, and its geometric properties will be investigated in more detail in a later chapter. Note now that the Iwasawa decomposition implies that K acts transitively on G/H (here G/H is compact), with isotropy subgroup K_0, so that G/H is also equal to K/K_0.

Example 2: Wigner's Construction

Let G be a Lie group that is a semidirect product of an invariant subgroup T and a subgroup L. [In Wigner's case, G is the inhomogeneous Lorentz (i.e., the Poincaré group), T are the translations, and L the homogeneous Lorentz transformations.] Let α be a representation of T on a vector space U'. (In Wigner's case, U' is a one-dimensional complex vector space, so that α is a character of T.) Let $L(\alpha)$ be the set of all $g \in L$ such that

$$\alpha(g\tau g^{-1}) = \alpha(\tau) \qquad \text{for all } \tau \in T.$$

Let $H = L(\alpha)T$. $L(\alpha)$ is the "little group" corresponding to the representation α. [In Wigner's case, α can be considered as an element of a vector space on which L acts, so that $L(\alpha)$ is the isotropy subgroup of L.] Let β be a representation of $L(\alpha)$ by linear transformations of a vector space U''. Let U be the tensor product $U'' \otimes U'$. We can define a linear representation of σ of $L(\alpha)T$ by linear transformations on U by the formula

$$\sigma(lt) = \beta(l) \otimes \alpha(\tau) \qquad \text{for } l \in L(\alpha), \, \tau \in T.$$

$(\beta(l) \otimes \alpha(\tau))$ denotes the tensor product of the transformations. To see that σ is a genuine representation, note that

$$\begin{aligned}
\sigma(l\tau l'\tau') &= \sigma(ll'\tau'^{-1}\tau l'\tau') \\
&= \beta(ll') \otimes \alpha(\text{Ad } l'^{-1}(\tau)\tau') \\
&= \beta(ll') \otimes (\alpha(\text{Ad } l'^{-1}(\tau)\alpha(\tau'))) = \beta(ll') \otimes \alpha(\tau\tau'),
\end{aligned}$$

since

$$l, l' \in L(\alpha).$$

Wigner now obtains a representation of $G = LT$ by inducing this representation σ from H to G, i.e., by letting G act on the homogeneous vector bundle defined by σ on $G/L(\alpha)T$. Since T is an invariant subgroup, note that T acts as the identity on $G/L(\sigma)T$, i.e., $G/L(\sigma)T$ is just $L/L(\sigma)$. [In Wigner's case, $L(\sigma)$ is the subgroup of the homogeneous Lorentz group which leaves a line of momentum space invariant, so that $L/L(\sigma)$ is a quadric in momentum space. The representation β of $L(\sigma)$ determines the spin of the particle defined by the representation.] However, T acts nontrivially on the fiber of the vector bundle over $L/L(\sigma)$ (this is just the representation α of T with which we started) which is what gives rise to the representation of G in which T acts in a nontrivial way.

Of course, this is not Wigner's way of looking at these representations. Using the Dirac notations, the wave functions are functions $\psi(p, s)$ of the momentum vector $p = (p_0, \ldots, p_3)$ and the discrete spin variables s, with p restricted by

$$p^2 = m^2.$$

But this quadric is just $L/L(\sigma)$: ψ is just a local presentation of a cross section of a bundle over this homogeneous space. An analogous situation that is somewhat easier to understand intuitively arises in the representation of $SO(3, R)$. The vectors of the representation space can either be considered "abstractly," parametrized by eigenvalues of a maximal Abelian algebra of operators of the representation, or "explicitly" as functions on the sphere, i.e., as spherical harmonics.

It is an important problem for physics to be able to describe Wigner's representation in a way that exhibits how the representation reduces under L. Several remarks along these lines can be given at this stage. Let us describe the representation ρ of G induced by a representation of σ in a slightly different way. An element of V can be described as a map f: $L \rightarrow U$ [since a map f: $G \rightarrow U$ such that $f(gh) = \sigma(h^{-1})f(g)$ is determined by its restriction to L]. Then

$$\rho(\tau)(f)(g) = f(\tau^{-1}g) = f(gg^{-1}\tau^{-1}g) = \sigma(\mathrm{Ad}\ g^{-1}(\tau))f(g)$$
$$\rho(l)(f)(g) = f(l^{-1}g) \qquad \text{for } \tau \in T, g, l \in L.$$

Suppose, for simplicity, that U represents the complex numbers (i.e., α is a *character* of T), β is the identity representation, and T is Abelian. Thus, V is just the set of complex-valued functions on L; these formulas tell us that T is represented by multiplication by functions, while L is represented by left-translation of these functions. In terms of functional analysis, this representation is the one in which the operators corresponding to T are as predicted by the "spectral theorem." In particular, they have no point spectrum.   If one attempted to write them by means of the Dirac notations, the eigenvectors would be delta functions.

The action of L on V is just left translation, i.e., the "regular representation." Suppose that (f_u) are functions on L that transform under a given representation $(\alpha_{uv}(l))$ of L under left translation on L. (u and v may be continuous indices, if L is noncompact.)   Then

$$f_u(l_g^{-1}) = \sum_v \alpha_{uv}(l)gf_v(g)$$

for $l, g \in L$.   The family of functions $g \to \sigma(\text{Ad } g(\tau))$, indexed by $\tau \in T$, are functions on L that transform under left translation by L like the representation of Ad L on $\mathbf{T}$.   Thus the products

$$g \to \sigma(\text{Ad } g^{-1}(\tau))f_u(g)$$

transform under left translation by L like the tensor product of these two representations.   The explicit formulas for these products would then involve the Clebsch-Gordan coefficients for the two representations.   For compact groups this makes the explicit description of the decomposition within the realm of practicality, since the description of the decomposition of left translation (the Peter-Weyl theorem) and the decomposition of tensor products are "known" (although they can only be carried out explicitly in a few simple cases).   For general noncompact groups L, even semisimple ones, what is known about the regular representation is only in very general form, and the decomposition of tensor products is not too well known either.   However, in some respects the description may be simplified if L is noncompact.   We shall examine this in more detail in Chapter 12.

MULTIPLIER AND UNITARY REPRESENTATIONS

Suppose that G is a Lie group, H a subgroup, and σ a representation of H on a vector space U. Let E be the corresponding vector bundle over G/H. We can obtain more representations of G by providing "multipliers" to the action of G on the cross sections of E. In fact, suppose $m(g, p)$ for $p \in G/H$, $g \in G$, a linear transformation on the vector space $\pi^{-1}(p)$. If $f \colon G/H \to E$ is a cross section, then we can use the multipliers $m(\ ,\ )$ to transform f by $g_0 \in G$ in the following way:

(9-7) $$\rho(g_0)(f)(p) = m(g_0, p)g_0 f(g_0^{-1}p).$$

Let us find the conditions that the system of multipliers satisfy in order that $g_0 \to \rho(g_0)$ be a genuine representation of G; i.e., $\rho(g_0 g_1) = \rho(g_0)\rho(g_1)$ for $g_0, g_1 \in G$.

$$\rho(g_0 g_1)(f)(p) = m(g_0 g_1, p)g_0 g_1 f(g_1^{-1} g_0^{-1} p)$$
$$= \rho(g_0)(\rho(g_1)(f))(p)$$
$$= m(g_0, p)g_0(\rho(g_1)(f)(g_0^{-1} p))$$
$$= m(g_0, p)g_0(m(g_1, g_0^{-1} p)g_1 f(g_1^{-1} g_0^{-1} p)).$$

The condition is thus seen to be

$$(9\text{–}8) \qquad\qquad m(g_0 g_1, p) = m(g_0, p)g_0 m(g_1, g_0^{-1} p)g_0^{-1}.$$

It is also useful to see how the multipliers act on the representation of cross sections as maps $\tilde{f} : G \to U = \pi^{-1}(e)$. Now,

$$\tilde{f}(g) = g^{-1} f(ge) \qquad \text{where } e \text{ is the identity coset of } G/H.$$
$$\rho(g_0)(f)(g) = g^{-1}(\rho(g_0)(f)(ge))$$
$$= g^{-1}(m(g_0, ge)g_0 f(g_0^{-1} ge))$$
$$= g^{-1} m(g_0, ge)gg^{-1} g_0 f(g_0^{-1} ge)$$
$$= g^{-1} m(g_0, g^{-1} e)g\tilde{f}(g_1^{-1} g).$$

Hence

$$\rho(g_0)(\tilde{f})(g) = \tilde{m}(g_0, g)\tilde{f}(g_0^{-1} g) \qquad \text{where } \tilde{m}(g_0, g) = g^{-1} m(g_0, g^{-1} e)g.$$

This determines the multiplier representation in this presentation.

Typically, such systems of multipliers are used to construct unitary representations of G in case the homogeneous space G/H does not have a volume element invariant under the action of G. Suppose that dp is a volume element on G/H; i.e., if $p \to \alpha(p)$ is a real-valued function on G/H, the integral $\int \alpha(p) \, dp$ is defined. Let $(p, g) \to J_g(p)$ be the Jacobian of the transformation $p \to gp$; it is characterized by the relation

$$\int \alpha(gp)J_g(p) \, dp = \int \alpha(p) \, dp.$$

Now, suppose that ρ is a multiplier representation of G on cross sections of a homogeneous vector bundle E over G/H. Suppose that, for $p \in G/H$, each vector space $\pi^{-1}(p)$ is a complex vector space and has a unitary inner product $<\ ,\ >$, with associated norm $\|\ \|$, which is preserved under the action of G. (Another way of putting this condition is to require that the linear representation σ of H on the vector space U which defines the bundle be a *unitary* representation.) Then, if $f \in \Gamma(E)$, we can define the norm of f in the following way:

$$\|f\|^2 = \int \|f(p)\|^2 \, dp.$$

This norm makes $\Gamma(E)$ (after completion) into a Hilbert space. Let us look for the condition that ρ be a unitary representation:

$$\|\rho(g)(f)\|^2 = \int \|m(g, p)gf(g^{-1}p)\|^2 \, dp$$
$$= \int \|m(g, gp)gf(p)\|^2 J_g(p) \, dp$$
$$= [\text{using } (9\text{-}8)] \int \|m(g^{-1}, p)^{-1}f(p)\|J_g(p) \, dp$$
$$= \|f\|^2,$$

provided

(9–9) $J_g(p)^{-1/2}m(g^{-1}, p)$ is a unitary transformation of the vector space $\pi^{-1}(p)$.

Summing up, we have shown that the linear representation constructed from the multiplier system $m(\ ,\ )$ and the vector bundle E is unitary if (9–9) is satisfied. For example, the multipliers of the following form give a class of unitary representations.

(9–10) $m(g, p) = J_{g^{-1}}(p)^{1/2+si}$ where s is any real number.

Finally, we shall indicate a general procedure (discovered by Bargmann, Gel'fand, and Neumark in special cases) for obtaining certain families of unitary representations of semisimple Lie groups. This method may be considered as a generalization of Wigner's method for constructing representations of the Poincaré group that we described above.

Let G be a Lie group, and let L and K be closed subgroups of G such that

$$G = KL,$$

and such that each element of G admits a unique continuous product representation of this form. (K is not necessarily a compact subgroup here; we choose this notation because in the applications we have in mind it will be a maximal compact subgroup of a semisimple Lie group G, and L will be AN^+, where $G = KAN^+$ is an Iwasawa decomposition for G.) Let α be a representation of L by linear transformations. Let $K(\alpha)$ be the set of all elements $k \in K$ that have the following property: For all elements $l, l' \in L$, $k' \in K$, that are related by

$$lk = k'l',$$

we have $\alpha(l) = \alpha(l')$.

Theorem 9–1

$K(\alpha)$ is a closed subgroup of K. If H is defined as $K(\alpha)L$, then H is a closed subgroup of G. If β is a linear representation of $K(\alpha)$, then the following formula defines a linear representation σ of H:

$$\sigma(kl) = \beta(k) \otimes \alpha(l) \qquad \text{for } k \in K(\alpha), \, l \in H,$$

provided $\beta(k) = \beta(k')$ whenever k and k' are related as follows: $lk = k'l$ for some $l, l' \in L$.

Proof:

First we show that $K(\alpha)$ is closed under the inverse operation. Suppose that $k \in K(\alpha)$, and that

$$lk^{-1} = k'l'.$$

Then $l'k = k'^{-1}l$; hence $\alpha(l) = \alpha(l')$ since $k \in K(\alpha)$, which proves that $k^{-1} \in K(\alpha)$.

Next, prove that $K(\alpha)$ is closed under products, which will show that it is a subgroup. Suppose $k, k_1 \in K(\alpha)$, and we have a relation of the form

$$lkk_1 = k'l'.$$

Then

$$lk = k'l'k_1^{-1}.$$

Suppose $l'k_1^{-1} = k''l''$. Then

$$lk = k'k''l''.$$

Since $k \in K(\alpha)$, we have $\alpha(l) = \alpha(l'')$. Since $k_1^{-1} \in K(\alpha)$, $\alpha(l') = \alpha(l'')$; hence $\alpha(l) = \alpha(l')$. This proves that $kk_1 \in K(\alpha)$.

Next we prove that $H = K(\alpha)L$ is a subgroup of G. Consider a product of the form

$$klk_1l_1 \qquad \text{with } k, k_1 \in K(\alpha); \; l, l_1 \in L.$$

Suppose that $lk_1 = k'l'$. We shall prove that $k' \in K(\alpha)$, which will suffice to prove that $klk_1l_1 \in H$. Suppose then that

$$l''k' = k''l_1'.$$

But, $k' = lk_1l'^{-1}$; hence

$$l''lk_1l'^{-1} = k''l_1 \qquad \text{or} \qquad l''lk_1 = k''l_1l'.$$

Therefore,

$$\alpha(l''l) = \alpha(l_1 l') \qquad \text{since } k_1 \in K(\alpha).$$

But, since $k_1 \in K(\alpha)$, we also have $\alpha(l) = \alpha(l')$. Since α is a representation of L,

$$\alpha(l'') = \alpha(l_1),$$

which proves that $k' \in K(\alpha)$.

We leave it to the reader to show that H and $K(\alpha)$ are closed subgroups. We shall finally prove that the last formula defines a linear representation of H.

$$\sigma(klk_1 l_1) = \sigma(kk'l'l_1),$$

where k' and l' are defined by

$$lk_1 = k'l'.$$

We have seen that $k' \in K(\alpha)$. Then

$$\sigma(klk_1 l_1) = \beta(kk') \otimes \alpha(l'l_1).$$

Since $\beta(k') = \beta(k_1)$ and $\alpha(l') = \alpha(l)$, we see that

$$\sigma(klk_1 l_1) = \sigma(kl)\sigma(k_1 l_1),$$

which shows that σ is a representation.   Q.E.D.

Thus we can now induce the representation σ from H to get a representation of G. We shall discuss the properties of these representations in greater detail later. Note how this reduces to Wigner's construction in case L is an invariant subgroup of G. For then, if

$$lk = k'l',$$

we have $k'l' = k \cdot k^{-1}lk$.

Since Ad $k^{-1}(L) = L$, and since the decomposition of each element of G as KL is unique, we have

$$k' = k \qquad l' = \text{Ad } k^{-1}(l).$$

Hence β can be any representation of $K(\alpha)$, and $K(\alpha)$ is the set of all $k \in K$ such that $\alpha(\text{Ad } k(l)) = \alpha(l)$ for all $\alpha \in L$.

A final remark can be made regarding the motivation for this construction. We are interested in irreducible representations. It is a very difficult problem, not yet completely elucidated, to decide when induced representations are irreducible. However, we can see one obvious necessary condition. Suppose, in general, that G is a group and that H is a

subgroup.   Let σ be a linear representation of H by linear transformations on a vector space U.   Consider the induced representation ρ.   Now,
note that ρ is *not* irreducible in case the following condition is satisfied:

> There is a subgroup H' of G that contains H such that the
> representation σ can be extended to a representation of H' by
> linear transformations on the same vector space U.

For we can consider the following subspace V' of V [V is the vector
space on which ρ acts, i.e., the set of maps $f\colon G \to U$ such that $f(gh) = \sigma(h^{-1})f(g)$ for $g \in G, h \in H$]:

> V' is the space of maps f of $G \to U$ such that $f(gh') = \sigma(h^{-1})f(g)$
> for $g \in G, h' \in H'$.

Obviously, $\rho(G)(V') \subset V'$; i.e., ρ acting on V is not irreducible.   This
indicates that, in order to *hope* to get irreducible induced representations,
H should be the "maximal" subgroup of G to which the representation σ
can be extended and *remain in the same vector space U*.   In Theorem 9–1,
we have indicated a method for constructing such "maximal" subgroups
in a particular case.   In general, it would seem to be an interesting algebraic problem to determine such "maximal" subgroups.   So far as the
author knows, this sort of problem has not been attacked.

VECTOR BUNDLES ON PROJECTIVE SPACE

As explained in Chapter 1, let $G = SL(n + 1, C)$ and let H be the subgroup such that the quotient G/H is $M = P_n(C)$, the complex projective
space.   Choose indices $1 \leqslant i, j, \ldots, \leqslant n + 1$ and the summation convention.   If $\alpha = (\alpha_{ij}) \in GL(n + 1, C)$, then $\alpha \in H$ is characterized by
the condition

(9–11) $$\alpha_{i1} = 0 \quad \text{for } i > 1.$$

Let us look for one-dimensional homogeneous vector bundles over M,
which are then determined by homomorphisms σ of H into the complex
numbers of absolute value 1.   They are given by

(9–12) $$\sigma(\alpha) = \left(\frac{\alpha_{11}}{|\alpha_{11}|}\right)^r \quad \text{for an integer } r.$$

Suppose $\psi\colon G \to C$ is a map representing a cross section of the vector
bundle on M defined by σ. ψ is then a function $\psi(\alpha_{ij})$ of the matrix
elements of α, and

(9–13) $$\psi((\alpha\beta)_{ij}) = \sigma(\beta^{-1})\psi(\alpha_{ij}) \quad \text{for } \beta \in H.$$

Lemma 9–2

The complex-valued function on $GL(n+1, C)$ satisfies (9–13) if and only if:

(a) ψ does not depend on the α_{ij} for $j > 1$.
(b) $\psi(\lambda \alpha_{i1}) = |\lambda|^r \psi(\alpha_{i1})$ for each scalar $\lambda \neq 0$.

Proof:

If $\beta \in H$, from (9–13) we have

$$\psi((\alpha\beta)_{ij}) = \left(\frac{\beta_{11}}{|\beta_{11}|}\right)^{-r} \psi(\alpha_{ij}) = \psi(\alpha_{ik}\beta_{kj}).$$

Fixing attention on one k and j with $j > 1$, we can choose β_{kj} arbitrarily, with all other entries in the matrix either zero or one. This proves (a) and (b).

We can now relabel the first column of α by

$$z_i = \alpha_{i1}.$$

We see that a cross section ψ of the vector bundle on G/H determined by the unitary representation σ of H is determined by a function ψ of $(n+1)$ complex variables $z_1, \ldots, z_{n+1}$ such that

$$\psi(\lambda z) = \left(\frac{\lambda}{|\lambda|}\right)^{-r} \psi(z) \qquad \text{for each such } \lambda.$$

[In particular, functions on $P_n(C)$, i.e., cross sections of the vector bundle on $G/H = P_n(C)$ determined by the identity representation of H, are determined by functions of z that are homogeneous of degree zero, a result we found in Chapter 1 by a more explicit construction of $P_n(C)$.]

For example, suppose that $r = 0$. Rational functions of z and $\bar{z}$ of the following type are cross sections:

$$\psi(z) = \frac{A^{j_1\cdots j_k}_{i_1\cdots i_k} z_{i_1} \cdots z_{i_k} \bar{z}_{j_1} \cdots \bar{z}_{j_k}}{|z|^{2k}}.$$

Suppose $r = -1$.

$$\psi(z) = \frac{A^{j_1\cdots j_k}_{i_1\cdots i_{k+1}} z_1 \cdots z_{i_{k+1}} \bar{z}_{j_1} \cdots \bar{z}_{j_k}}{|z|^{2k+1}}.$$

Let us now see how $SL(n+1, C)$ acts on these cross sections. Suppose $g = (g_{ij}) \in SL(n+1, C)$: The transform of $\psi(\alpha_{ij}) = \psi(z)$ by g is

$$\psi((g^{-1}\alpha)_{ij}) = \psi(g^{-1}_{ik}\alpha_{k1}).$$

Hence it is just

$$\psi(g^{-1}_{ik}z_k).$$

We see that $SL(n + 1, C)$ acts on cross sections $\psi(z)$ in the obvious way obtained by letting $SL(n + 1, C)$ act on vectors z. This representation of $SL(n + 1, C)$ on cross sections of the vector bundle is not unitary: We have seen that it can be made unitary by adding multipliers, depending on how the volume element for $P_n(C)$ is chosen. The simplest choice is that determined by the condition that the volume element is invariant under the action of $SU(n + 1)$ on $P_n(C)$. [Since $SU(n + 1)$ is compact and acts transitively on $P_n(C)$, there is essentially just one such choice of volume element.] Then, $SU(n + 1)$ acts on functions $\psi(z)$ in the obvious way through its linear action on vectors z. To decompose the action of $SU(n + 1)$ on the cross sections is now a routine algebraic problem, namely to decompose the action of $SU(n + 1)$ on tensors, say of the type

$$A^{j_1 \cdots j_k}_{i_1 \cdots i_{k-r}}$$

where upper and lower indices are symmetric within themselves, and where $SU(n + 1)$ acts on the upper indices through the complex-conjugate representation of $SU(n + 1)$. It is well known that this can be done by imposing vanishing-trace conditions on these tensors. It is also interesting to see how these traceless conditions arise from the geometry. Consider the Laplace differential operator

$$\Delta = \frac{\partial}{\partial z_i} \frac{\partial}{\partial \bar{z}_i}.$$

It commutes with the action of $SU(n + 1)$ on C^{n+1}, and in fact is essentially the only differential operator that does so. It is then natural to impose on the $\psi(z)$ the condition

$$\Delta(|z|^{2k+1}\psi) = 0.$$

For example, if

$$\psi(z) = \frac{A^{j_1}_{i_1 i_2} z_{i_1} z_{i_2} \bar{z}_{j_1}}{|z|^3},$$

then

$$0 = \Delta(A^{j_1}_{i_1 i_2} z_{i_1} z_{i_2} \bar{z}_{j_1}) = \frac{\partial}{\partial \bar{z}_k}(A^{j_1}_{i_1 i_2}(\delta_{i_1 k} z_{i_2} \bar{z}_{j_1} + z_{i_1} \delta_{i_2 k} \bar{z}_{j_1}))$$

$$= A^{j_1}_{j_1 i_2}(\delta_{i_1 k} z_{i_2} \delta_{j_1 k} + z_{i_1} \delta_{i_2 k} \delta_{j_1 k}),$$

or

$$A^{j_1}_{i_1 i_2} \delta_{i_1 j_1} = 0.$$

We can sum up what we have proved in the following way:

Theorem 9–3

For each integer $r \geqslant 0$, there is a homogeneous line bundle[†] on $P_n(C)$ with a $SL(n + 1, C)$-invariant unitary inner product on the fibers. The action of $SU(n + 1)$ on the cross sections of this bundle defines a reducible unitary representation of $SU(n + 1)$. The representations of $SU(n + 1)$ that occur when this representation is decomposed consist of traceless symmetric tensors of the type

$$A^{j_1 \cdots j_k}_{i_1 \cdots i_{k+r}},$$

and each representation occurs only once.

There are certain features of this situation that will reappear in a more general context in Chapter 18. The key fact here is that $SU(n+1)/U(n) = P_n(C)$ is a symmetric space. Note that as the index k runs from 0 to ∞ the representations form a "ladder." The general reason for this is that this symmetric space is of rank 1.[‡] For higher-rank symmetric spaces, the representations that occur form a lattice. We shall also show in Chapter 18 that the unitary representation of $SL(n + 1, C)$ on the cross section obtained by putting in the suitable multipliers is irreducible: The noncompact operators in the Lie algebra of $SL(n + 1, C)$ shift up and down the ladder.

REPRESENTATIONS OF $SL(2, R)$

We shall now sketch Bargmann's method (1947) for constructing the "continuous" family of representations of $SL(2, R)$. In Chapter 1 we saw that $SL(2,R)$ acts on the real projective space of dimension 1,[§] $P_1(R)$. Let us look at this explicitly. Start off with R^2, with coordinates y_1 and y_2. $P_1(R)$ is obtained by identifying (y_1, y_2) and (y_1', y_2'), which differ by a scalar multiple. In the portion of $P_1(R)$ on which $y_2 \neq 0$ (the complement of the "point at infinity") we can introduce the nonhomogeneous coordinate $x = y_1/y_2$. Now, $SL(2, R)$, in its natural linear action on R^2, passes to the quotient to act on $P_1(R)$. Explicitly, if

$$(y_1, y_2) \to (ay_1 + by_2, cy_1 + dy_2),$$

$$x = \frac{y_1}{y_2} \to \frac{ax + b}{cx + d}.$$

† One usually defines a *line bundle* as a vector bundle whose fibers are the complex numbers considered as a real vector space.

‡ Recall that the rank of a symmetric space G/K is the dimension of the maximal Abelian subalgebra of **P**, where **G** = **K** + **P**, with [**K**, **P**] $\subset$ **P**, [**P**, **P**] $\subset$ **K**.

§ This is called the *projective line*.

This, of course, gives the action of matrices

$$\begin{pmatrix} a & b \\ c & d \end{pmatrix}$$

by linear fractional transformations. The isotropy subgroup H of $G = SL(2, R)$ at, say $x = 0$, is determined by the condition $b = 0$. The maximal compact subgroup $K = SO(2, R)$ also acts transitively on $P_1(R)$, with z_2 as isotropy subgroup. This enables one to identify $P_1(R)$ with the unit circle in the complex plane. Bargmann works with this realization of $P_1(R)$.

We shall construct representations of $SL(2, R)$ by letting it act on functions on $P_1(R)$, i.e., functions of x, with multipliers determined by the change of volume element. Now,

$$dx \rightarrow d\left(\frac{ax + b}{cx + d}\right) = \frac{(cx + d)(a\,dx) - (ax + b)(c\,dx)}{(cx + d)^2}$$

$$= \frac{dx}{(cx + d)^2},$$

since $ad - bc = 1$. Hence, the Jacobian with respect to the measure dx is just

$$\frac{1}{(cx + d)^2}.$$

Now,

$$\frac{dx}{1 + x^2} \rightarrow \frac{dx}{(cx + d)^2\{1 + [(ax + b)/(cx + d)]^2\}} = \frac{dx}{1 + x^2}\frac{1 + x^2}{(cx + d)^2 + (ax + b)^2}.$$

Further, $(cx + d)^2 + (ax + b)^2 = x^2(c^2 + a^2) + 2x(cd + ab) + (d^2 + b^2)$. If

$$\begin{pmatrix} a & b \\ c & d \end{pmatrix}$$

is an orthogonal matrix, we see that this is just $1 + x^2$; i.e.,

$dx/(1 + x^2)$ is the measure on $P_1(R)$ that is invariant under $SO(2, R)$.

Thus, we can also define representations parametrized with r and s by means of the formula

$$\psi(x) \rightarrow \psi\left(\frac{ax + b}{cx + d}\right)\left[\frac{1 + x^2}{(cx + d)^2 + (ax + b)^2}\right]^{r+si} = \phi(g)(\psi)(x)$$

where

$$g^{-1} = \begin{pmatrix} a & b \\ c & d \end{pmatrix}.$$

r and s are parameters defining the representation.

The space of functions on $P_1(R)$ is made into a Hilbert space by means of the inner product

$$(\psi_1, \psi_2) = \int_{-\infty}^{\infty} \frac{\psi_1(x)\overline{\psi_2(x)}}{1 + x^2}\, dx.$$

We see from the way the multipliers are defined that the representation is unitary for $r = \frac{1}{2}$. These representations for other values of r thus define an "analytic continuation" of this one-parameter family of the unitary representations of $SL(2, R)$. (This is of interest in connection with Regge-pole theory.)

The point we want to make here is that the finite-dimensional representations of $SL(2, R)$, i.e., the *unitary* representations of $SO(3, R)$ or its covering group $SU(2)$, can be obtained by this process.† In fact, Regge's well-known trick using the Sommerfeld-Watson transform is a method of "continuing" the unitary representations of $SO(3, R)$ to give the unitary representations of $SL(2, R)$.

We can verify this very simply and directly. We know that the finite-dimensional representations of $SL(2, R)$ are obtained from the linear action on (y_1, y_2)-space via the action on homogeneous polynomials of (y_1, y_2) of degree t.

$$f(y_1, y_2) \to f(ay_1 + by_2, cy_1 + dy_2) = \phi(g)(f)/(y_1, y_2),$$

where

$$g^{-1} = \begin{pmatrix} a & b \\ c & d \end{pmatrix}.$$

Now, we can associate with $f(y_1, y_2)$ the function

$$\psi(x) = \frac{f(y_1, y_2)}{(y_1^2 + y_2^2)^{t/2}} = \frac{f(x, 1)}{(1 + x^2)^{t/2}}.$$

ψ is then changed into

$$\psi\left(\frac{ax + b}{cx + d}\right)\left[\frac{1 + x^2}{(cx + d)^2 + (ax + b)^2}\right]^{r+si}$$

---

† In general, we have the following situation: Suppose that G is a noncompact semisimple Lie group, and that ϕ is a linear representation of G by transformations on a finite-dimensional complex vector space V. Suppose K is a maximal compact subgroup, and $\mathbf{G} = \mathbf{K} \oplus \mathbf{P}$ is the Cartan decomposition of $\mathbf{G}$. Then $\mathbf{G}_\mu = \mathbf{K} \oplus i\mathbf{P}$ is the Lie algebra of the dual compact group G_μ. Also, then, $X \to \phi(X)$ for $X \in \mathbf{K}$, $iY \to i\phi(Y)$ for $Y \in \mathbf{P}$ defines a linear representation of G_μ on V. Since V is finite-dimensional, ϕ arises from a representation of G_μ or its simply connected covering group on V. Since the covering group is compact (Weyl's theorem), ϕ defined on G_μ can be made *unitary*.

$$= \frac{f\left(\dfrac{ax+b}{cx+d},\, 1\right)}{\left[1 + \left(\dfrac{ax+b}{cx+d}\right)^2\right]^{t/2}} \left[\frac{1+x^2}{(cx+d)^2 + (ax+b)^2}\right]^{r+si}.$$

Choose $r = -t/2$, $s = 0$. Then we get

$$\frac{f\left(\dfrac{ax+b}{cx+d},\, 1\right)}{(1+x^2)^{t/2}}\, (cx+d)^t.$$

We see that the transform of ψ_2 is obtained from the function

$$(y_1, y_2) \to f(ay_1 + by_2,\, cy_1 + dy_2).$$

Hence, for these values of r and s, the representation reduces to a finite-dimensional representation of $SL(2, R)$, hence to a unitary representation of $SO(3, R)$ [or $SU(2)$].

We have been discussing one continuous family of representations of $SL(2, R)$. One can obtain another in a similar way by means of the following considerations: $P_1(R) = G/H$, where H is the group of matrices of the form

$$\begin{pmatrix} a & 0 \\ c & a^{-1} \end{pmatrix}.$$

There are two finite-dimensional unitary representations of H:

$$\begin{pmatrix} a & 0 \\ c & a^{-1} \end{pmatrix} \to 1 \text{ and } \frac{a}{|a|}.$$

Inducing the first to $G = SL(2, R)$ gives the class of representations discussed above. Inducing the second gives another class. In addition, there are certain "discrete series" and "supplementary series."

CHAPTER 10

REPRESENTATIONS. UNIVERSAL ENVELOPING ALGEBRA AND INVARIANT DIFFERENTIAL EQUATIONS

Let G be a Lie group and let ρ be a representation of G by linear transformations of a real vector space V. We want to allow the possibility that V be infinite-dimensional (indeed, this is the most interesting case for quantum mechanics), but we do not want to get involved at this stage with the details concerning topologies for V, hence we shall proceed in a formal way. By and large, there are general theorems available [particularly the theorem on "analytic vectors" due to Harish-Chandra and Nelson (1959)] enabling one to justify much of what is done in a simpleminded way. However, one can get into real contradictions by assuming without justification that operators have point spectra. (This is one trouble with the Dirac bra-ket notation — it makes it too easy to forget the complications that can occur in infinite dimensions.)

We have seen that every element X in the Lie algebra of **G** induces linear transformation $\rho(X)$ on V as the infinitesimal generator of the one-parameter group $t \to \rho(\exp tX)$. Thus,

$$\rho(X)(v) = \frac{d}{dt} \rho(\exp tX)(v)\Big|_{t=0} \qquad \text{for } v \in V.$$

(Again, there are problems associated with the fact that this derivative does not exist for all $v \in V$, if V is infinite-dimensional.) We have seen that the assignment $X \to \rho(X)$ defines a representation of **G** as a linear Lie algebra of transformations of V; i.e.,

$$\rho([X, Y]) = \rho(X)\rho(Y) - \rho(Y)\rho(X).$$

Now, for $X, Y \in$ **G**, XY makes no sense as an element of **G**, although $\rho(X)\rho(Y)$ does make sense as a linear transformation on V. Let us, however, force XY to make sense by constructing a new object $U(\mathbf{G})$, the *universal associative enveloping* algebra of **G**. In fact, $U(\mathbf{G})$ is the "free

72

algebra" with generators the elements of **G**, with the *only* relations the following laws:

$$X(YZ) = (XY)(Z) \qquad \text{(associativity)},$$
$$XY - YX = [X, Y].$$

The effect of this somewhat abstract construction is to imbed **G** into the *associative* algebra $U(\mathbf{G})$ so that the bracket is given by the commutator. This object is "universal" in the following sense: Suppose that **A** is any associative algebra, which is made into a Lie algebra by defining the bracket as the commutator, and suppose that $\phi : \mathbf{G} \rightarrow \mathbf{A}$ is a map which preserves brackets. Then ϕ can be extended in a unique way to an algebra homomorphism $U(\mathbf{G}) \rightarrow \mathbf{A}$.

There are very close relations between the linear representations of **G** and the algebraic structure of $U(\mathbf{G})$. We shall not emphasize this side of the theory, since it involves more algebraic expertise than it is assumed the reader will have. Jacobson's book (1962) is a good reference for this. However, there are three such important algebraic points that might be mentioned here:

First, suppose that I is a left ideal of $U(\mathbf{G})$; i.e., $U(\mathbf{G})I \subset I$. Then the action of left multiplication of elements of $U(\mathbf{G})$ "passes to the quotient" to act on the vector space $U(\mathbf{G})/I$. In particular, this defines a linear representation of **G** on a vector space. Now, $U(\mathbf{G})$ is infinite-dimensional; hence the same might be true of the $U(\mathbf{G})/I$. Investigating the conditions that $U(\mathbf{G})/I$ be finite-dimensional is an important topic of study, leading to a proof of main facts concerning the description of finite-dimensional representations of semisimple Lie algebras by means of maximal weights. Even in the case where $U(\mathbf{G})/I$ is infinite-dimensional, some important facts concerning the representation can be obtained by this approach.

Second, we shall state, but not prove, the Birkhoff-Witt theorem. Suppose that $X_1, \ldots, X_n$, is a basis of **G**. The theorem then states that the "polynomials" of the form

$$X_1^{k_1} \cdots X_n^{k_n} \qquad k_1, k, \ldots, k_n \geqslant 0$$

form a *basis* for $U(\mathbf{G})$.

Third, we can define the *Casimir operators* of **G** as the center of $U(\mathbf{G})$, i.e., the elements of $D \in U(\mathbf{G})$ such that

$$XD = DX \qquad \text{for all } X \in \mathbf{G}.$$

These are, of course, very important both in the mathematical and physical side of the theory of representations of groups. For example, if ρ is a representation of G by linear transformations on a vector space V, then ρ

can be extended to a homomorphism of $U(\mathbf{G})$ into the associative algebra of linear transformations of V. Now, the concept of "irreducibility" and the circle of ideas centering around Schur's lemma† is a rather involved one for the case of infinite-dimensional V. However, ignoring these technicalities, we see that irreducibility is associated with the fact that $\rho(D)$, for D in the center of $U(\mathbf{G})$, is a multiple of the identity transformation. If ρ is not irreducible, splitting V into its "irreducible parts" may be associated with the process of "diagonalizing" the commuting set of operators $\rho(D)$, for D in the center of $U(\mathbf{G})$. We shall see later the connection this has with differential equations.

Very little is known about the structure of the center of $U(\mathbf{G})$ in the case of a general Lie group $\mathbf{G}$. If $\mathbf{G}$ is a complex semisimple Lie algebra, it is known that the center is finitely generated, with the number of generators equal to the rank of $\mathbf{G}$, i.e., to the dimension of its Cartan subalgebras. This result gives the existence of a certain number of Casimir operators for Lie algebras that can be obtained by "contraction" from semisimple ones. For example, the complex Poincaré group can be obtained by contraction from $SO(4, C)$, which is a rank 2 semisimple group. Its Casimir operators "contract" into the two known Casimir operators of the Poincaré group, i.e., those physicists associate with "mass" and "spin."

Let $U^p(\mathbf{G})$ be the elements of $U(\mathbf{G})$ spanned by elements of the form $X_1 \cdots X_q$, with $X_1, \ldots, X_q \in \mathbf{G}$, and $q \leqslant p$. Thus, $U^p(\mathbf{G})$ consists of operations of degree $\leqslant p$. Note that it makes no sense to talk of an operator as having *precisely* degree p, since reversing the order of elements introduces terms of lower order involving commutators. However, we *can* consider the vector space $U^p(\mathbf{G})/U^{p-1}(\mathbf{G})$ as the space of operators of degree precisely p. It can be considered as spanned by $\tilde{X}_1 \cdots \tilde{X}_p$, where the $\tilde{X}_1, \ldots, \tilde{X}_p$ are regarded as *commuting* operators. Suppose then that $X_1, \ldots, X_n$ is a basis of $\mathbf{G}$, and that D is an element of $U^p(\mathbf{G})$. D admits an expression of the form

$$D = \sum b_{i_1, \ldots, i_p} X_{i_1} \cdots X_{i_p} + \cdots \qquad (1 \leqslant i, \ldots i_p \leqslant n)$$

(The unwritten terms are of lower order.) Now, at the expense of introducing more terms of lower order, we can symmetrize the coefficients $b_{i_1, \ldots, i_p}$. Thus, D goes over, in $U^p(\mathbf{G})/U^{p-1}(\mathbf{G})$, to

† Schur's lemma originally applied to the case where V is a finite-dimensional complex Lie algebra: It then states that if ρ is irreducible, i.e., there is no proper subspace of V left invariant by all operators of $\rho(G)$, then any linear transformation of V commuting with all transformations of $\rho(G)$ must be a multiple of the identity. Its proof for this case is then an almost trivial consequence of the fact that a linear transformation of a finite-dimensional space has an eigenvalue, a fact that breaks down with infinite dimensions.

$$\sum_{1 < i_1, \cdots, i_p \leqslant n} b_{i_1, \cdots, i_p} \tilde{X}_{i_1} \cdots \tilde{X}_{i_p}$$

Let us see how Ad $\mathbf{G}$ acting on $U(\mathbf{G})$ fits into this. For $X \in \mathbf{G}$, Ad $X(D)$ is $XD - DX$. Now,

$$[XX_1 \cdots X_p] = XX_1 \cdots X_p - X_1 \cdots X_p X$$
$$= X_1 X \cdots X_p + [X, X_1] X_2 \cdots X_p - X_1 \cdots X_p X$$

Continuing in this way to move X to the right, we see that eventually the terms containing $(p+1)$ products cancel, and we are left with an element of degree $\leqslant p$. We have then proved that

$$\text{Ad } X(U^p(\mathbf{G})) \subset U^p(\mathbf{G}).$$

Thus, Ad X passes to the quotient to act on $U^p(\mathbf{G})/U^{p-1}(\mathbf{G})$. In fact, if

$$\text{Ad } X(X_i) = \sum_j C_{ij} X_j \qquad \text{for } 1 \leqslant i \leqslant n,$$

then

$$\text{Ad } X(\tilde{X}_{i_1} \ldots, \tilde{X}_{i_p} (= \sum_j (C_{i_1 j} \tilde{X}_j \tilde{X}_{i_2} \cdots \tilde{X}_{i_p} + \cdots + \tilde{X}_{i_1} \cdots \tilde{X}_{i_{p-1}} C_{i_p j} \tilde{X}_j).$$

In other words, Ad X acts on $U^p(\mathbf{G})/U^{p-1}(\mathbf{G})$ just as the linear transformation defined by Ad X acts on *commutative* polynomials with the elements of $\mathbf{G}$ as a vector space considered as generators. In particular, if D is a Casimir operator, its image

$$\tilde{D} = \sum_{1 \leqslant i, \cdots, i_p \leqslant n} b_{i_1, \cdots, i_p} \tilde{X}_i, \ldots, \tilde{X}_{i_p}$$

in $U^p(\mathbf{G})/U^{p-1}(\mathbf{G})$ is invariant under Ad X, for $X \in \mathbf{G}$. Thus

> If a basis for $\mathbf{G}$ is fixed, and Ad G is considered as a group of matrices, then each Casimir operator determines a polynomial in n variables that is invariant under Ad G.

In general, every polynomial in n variables invariant under Ad G does not arise in this way from a Casimir operator. However, if $\mathbf{G}$ is semisimple this is true. To see this, we can invoke the complete reducibility of a linear representation of G. In particular, Ad G acting in $U^p(\mathbf{G})$ leaves $U^{p-1}(\mathbf{G})$ invariant; hence there is a subspace $V^{p-1}(\mathbf{G})$ of $U^p(\mathbf{G})$ with

$$U^p(\mathbf{G}) = U^{p-1}(\mathbf{G}) \oplus V^p(\mathbf{G}) \qquad \text{Ad } G(V^p(\mathbf{G})) \subset V^p(\mathbf{G}).$$

Thus, $V^p(\mathbf{G})$ goes over isomorphically into $U^p(\mathbf{G})/U^{p-1}(\mathbf{G})$; in particular, an element of $U^p(\mathbf{G})/U^{p-1}(\mathbf{G})$ invariant under Ad G corresponds back in

$V^p(\mathbf{G})$ to an element which is invariant under Ad G, i.e., to a Casimir operator.

For example, we have seen that, when $\mathbf{G}$ is semisimple, Ad G acting on $\mathbf{G}$ admits an invariant polynomial of degree 2, namely the Killing form $B(\ ,\ )$. This is the simplest such Casimir operator. Explicitly, if $X_1, \ldots, X_n$ is a basis of $\mathbf{G}$ for which $B(\ ,\ )$ takes its canonical form, namely

$$B(X_i, X_j) = \begin{cases} 0 & \text{if } i \neq j \\ \pm 1 & \text{if } i = j \end{cases},$$

then the corresponding Casimir operator is

$$D = \sum_i \pm X_i X_i.$$

Of course, this operator plays a particularly important role in both representation theory and physics. For example, if $G = SO(3, R)$, this operator has the eigenvalue

$$j(j+1)$$

in an irreducible representation of dimension $(2j + 1)$. In physical terms, for this case D is the "total angular momentum" operator.

There is a general method for constructing polynomials in the variables of $\mathbf{G}$, i.e., elements of $U^p(\mathbf{G})/U^{p-1}(\mathbf{G})$, that are invariant under Ad G. Namely, suppose that ρ is a representation of G by linear transformations on a finite-dimensional vector space V. Then, for $X \in \mathbf{G}$,

$$\lambda \to \det(\rho(X) - \lambda)$$

is a polynomial function of λ of degree n ($n =$ dimension V), and can be written in the form

$$\lambda^n + b_{n-1}(X)\lambda^{n-1} + \cdots + b_0(X).$$

The $b_n(X), \ldots, b_0(X)$ determine polynomial functions of X which are invariant under Ad G.

REPRESENTATIONS AND DIFFERENTIAL EQUATIONS

Let G be a Lie group, H a subgroup, and $\pi: E \to G/H$ a homogeneous vector bundle over G/H. If V is $\Gamma(E)$, the vector space of cross sections of the bundle, we have seen that there is a linear representation of G by linear transformations in V obtained by "translating" cross sections around using the group action. Explicitly, if $\psi \in \Gamma(E)$, $g \in G$, $p \in G/H$, then

$$\rho(g)(\psi)(p) = g\psi(g^{-1}p).$$

Recall that the associated mapping $X \to \rho(X)$ of the Lie algebra of G is defined in the following way:

$$\rho(X)(\psi)(p) = \frac{d}{dt} \rho(\exp Xt)(\psi)(p)\Big|_{t=0}$$
$$= \frac{d}{dt}\left((\exp Xt)/\psi(\exp(-Xt)))\right)\Big|_{t=0}.$$

Making this formula explicit shows that $\rho(X)$ applied to ψ involves applying a first-order partial differential operator to the components of ψ. Now, ρ can be extended to a representation of the universal enveloping algebra $U(\mathbf{G})$ of $\mathbf{G}$. For example,

$$\rho(X_1 \cdots X_r)(\psi) = \rho(X_1)\rho(X_2) \cdots \rho(X_r)(\psi).$$

Thus, we see that the result of applying an rth degree element of $U(\mathbf{G})$ [i.e., an element of $U^r(\mathbf{G})$] to ψ involves applying an rth-order linear differential operator to the components of ψ. Suppose that we would like to reduce the representation ρ of G on $\Gamma(E)$ to its "irreducible components." We shall replace this question with the problem of finding subspaces of U in which the Casimir operators of $U(\mathbf{G})$ act as multiples of the identity. If D is such a Casimir operator, this gives rise to the problem of solving the differential equations

$$\rho(D)(\psi) = \lambda\psi.$$

For example, suppose that G is the Poincaré group and H the Lorentz group, so that G/H is Minkowski space. Suppose that we take the simplest case, namely that where E is the product of G/H with the complex numbers, so that $\Gamma(E)$ just consists of the complex-valued functions on Minkowski space (i.e., we ignore "spin"), so that G acts as the identity map on the fibers of π. It can then be shown (exercise!) that the Casimir operators of $U(\mathbf{G})$ corresponding to spin are identically zero on $\Gamma(E)$. If D is the "mass" Casimir operator, then it can be shown (exercise) that $\rho(D)$ is just the d'Alembertian

$$\rho(D) = \square = \frac{\partial}{\partial x_1^2} - \frac{\partial}{\partial x_2^2} \cdots - \frac{\partial}{\partial x_4^2},$$

so that we are led to the Klein-Gordon equation.

Of course, this is just the reverse of the outlook that is usual in physics. There, one works with a system $(x_1, \ldots, x_n) = x$ of local coordinates for G/H valid in an open set U, and a differential operator, say

$$\Delta(\psi)_a = \sum_{b,i,j} A_{abij}(x) \frac{\partial^2}{\partial x_i \, \partial x_j} (\psi_b) + B_{abi}(x) \frac{\partial \psi_b}{\partial x_i} + C_{ab}(x)\psi_b,$$

acting on an m-vector-valued function $\psi(x) = (\psi_1(x), \ldots, \psi_m(x))$ of the real variables $x_1, \ldots, x_n$. The problem from this point of view can be described as follows: Find a homogeneous vector bundle E over G/H whose fibers have dimension m, and a system of cross sections

$$p \to (\gamma_1(p), \ldots, \gamma_m(p))$$

defined for $p \in U$, such that $\gamma_1(p), \ldots, \gamma_m(p)$ is a basis for $\pi^{-1}(p)$. One can then assign to $(\psi_1(x), \ldots, \psi_m(x))$ the cross section over U:

$$p \to \sum_{\leqslant a \leqslant m} \psi_a(x(p))\gamma_a(p) = \psi(p).$$

Δ corresponds in this way to an operator, denoted also by Δ, which acts on cross sections of $\Gamma(E)$. We can interpret the problem of demonstrating "covariance" of the given system of differential equations in the following way: Find the vector bundle E, and the basis $(\gamma_1, \ldots, \gamma_n)$ of cross sections such that the operators Δ constructed in this way on cross sections of E *commutes* with the action of G on $\Gamma(E)$. Unfortunately, there are no general theorems telling when one can do this or describing the uniqueness of the construction, but in problems that are of interest to physicists it is usually evident how to proceed. Of course, it is more elegant mathematically to start off with the vector bundle. Presumably, nature prefers elegant mathematics; hence one is probably justified in regarding the vector-bundle starting point as the "correct" one.

Let us then sum up these remarks in a more formal way. Let E be a homogeneous vector bundle sitting over a homogeneous space G/H. Let $\Gamma(E)$ be the vector space of cross sections of E, with G acting on $\Gamma(E)$ via the representation ρ constructed as follows:

$$\rho(g)(\psi)(p) = g\psi(g^{-1}p) \qquad \text{for } g \in G, \psi \in \Gamma(E), p \in G/H.$$

A differential operator† Δ mapping $\Gamma(E)$ into itself is called an *invariant differential operator* if it commutes with $\rho(G)$, i.e.,

$$\rho(g)\Delta(\psi) = \Delta\rho(g)(\psi) \qquad \text{for all } \psi \in \Gamma(E), \text{ all } g \in G.$$

Δ is called a Casimir operator if $\Delta = \rho(D)$, where D is a Casimir operator in $U(\mathbf{G})$, i.e., an element in the center of $U(\mathbf{G})$.

So far, we have been working with the "geometric" picture of cross sections of a vector bundle as maps from G/H to a space E sitting over G/H. Let us also look at the analytically more convenient description of $\Gamma(E)$ as the space of all maps $\psi\colon G \to U$, with

$$\psi(gh) = \sigma(h^{-1})\psi(g),$$

---

† We say that a linear mapping $\Gamma(E) \to \Gamma(E)$ is a differential operator if, when written in terms of local coordinates and a basis for cross sections of E, it acts on cross sections by means of a differential operator on the components.

where σ is the linear representation of H (on a vector space U) which characterizes the vector bundle E.   Now, recall that

$$\rho(g_0)(\psi)(g) = \psi(g^{-1}g) \qquad \text{for } g,\, g_0 \in G.$$

This description of how G acts on $\Gamma(E)$ (by "left translation") does not actually involve the transformation law of ψ under right translation by H. This fact makes it convenient to use this description of $\Gamma(E)$ to compare differential operators on cross sections of different vector bundles.

THE DIRAC EQUATION

There are several group-theoretic approaches to the theory of the Dirac equation.   We shall follow the one that seems to be closest to Dirac's original derivation.   Let G be the Lie group that is a semidirect product

$$G = L \cdot T,$$

where L is a subgroup and T is an invariant Abelian subgroup.   We shall consider a homogeneous vector bundle E over G/L, which is determined by a linear representation σ of L on a vector space U.   (Recall that for Wigner's construction we start off with a representation of T.)   We do not expect the induced representation to be irreducible.   Indeed, this is why we can hope to get nontrivial "wave equations" for the cross sections of the vector bundle.   We have seen that an element ψ of $\Gamma(E)$ can be considered to be a mapping $\psi\colon G \to U$ with $\psi(gl) = \sigma(l^{-1})\psi(g)$ for $l \in L$, $g \in G$.   Since $G = T \cdot L$, ψ can be identified with its restriction to T. Definitively then, ψ is a mapping: $T \to U$.   The linear representation ρ of G on $\Gamma(E)$ is then constructed as follows:

(10–1) $\rho(t_0)(\psi)(t) = \psi(t_0^{-1}t) \qquad \text{for } t_0,\, t \in T.$
$\rho(l^{-1})(\psi)(t) = \psi(lt) = \psi(ltl^{-1}l)$
$\qquad\qquad = \sigma(l^{-1})\psi(\operatorname{Ad} l^{-1}(t)) \qquad \text{for } t \in T,\, l \in L.$

For example, suppose that G is the Poincaré group, T the translation subgroup, and L the homogeneous Lorentz group. G/L is then Minkowski space, which can of course be identified with T itself (since the orbit of T at the identity coset covers all of Minkowski space).   Then an element ψ of $\Gamma(E)$ is a mapping of Minkowski space into U.   For example, if σ is the identity representation of L, ψ is a scalar representation; if σ is one of the tensor representations of L, ψ is a tensor field; if σ is a spinor representation of L, ψ is a spinor field; and so on.

Return to the general case.   Let $X_1, \ldots, X_n$ be a basis for $\mathbf{T}$.   We see from (10–1) that (since T is Abelian) a coordinate system $(x_1, \ldots, x_n)$ can be introduced for T so that

$$\rho(X_i)(\psi) = \frac{\partial \psi}{\partial x_i} \qquad \text{for } \psi \in \Gamma(E) \qquad (1 \leqslant i, j, \ldots, \leqslant n).$$

Dirac's idea was to look for a first-order differential operator D mapping $\Gamma(E)$ into itself which commutes with the action of $\rho(G)$ on $\Gamma(E)$. Suppose we introduce a basis $u_1, \ldots, u_m$ for U. ψ can then be written

$$\sum \psi_a u_a \qquad (1 \leqslant a, b, \ldots, \leqslant m),$$

where $(\psi_1, \ldots, \psi_m)$ are real-valued functions on T which are the components of ψ. D would then be of the form

$$\begin{aligned} D(\psi)_a &= \sum_{b,i} A_{ab}^i \frac{\partial \psi_b}{\partial x_i} \\ &= \sum_{b,i} A_{ab}^i \rho(X_i)(\psi_b). \end{aligned}$$

We can rewrite this in a form that is independent of the basis $(u_1, \ldots, u_m)$ that was chosen for U. Let $A^1, \ldots, A^n$ be the linear transformations of U whose matrices with respect to the given basis are $(A_{ab}^1), \ldots, (A_{ab}^n)$. Then

$$D(\psi) = \sum_i A^i \rho(X_i)(\psi).$$

Now we must look for the conditions that D commute with the action of $\rho(G)$, i.e., that

(10–2) $\rho(Y)D(\psi) = D(\rho(Y)(\psi))$ for all $\psi \in \Gamma(E)$, all $Y \in \mathbf{G}$.

First, suppose that $Y \in \mathbf{T}$. Then

$$\rho(Y)D(\psi) = \sum_i \rho(Y)(A^i)\rho(X_i)(\psi) + A^i \rho(Y)\rho(X_i)(\psi).$$

Now

$$\rho(Y)\rho(X_i)(\psi) = \rho([Y, X_i])(\psi) + \rho(X_i)\rho(Y)(\psi).$$

But, $[Y, X_i] = 0$, since T is Abelian. Hence, the condition that (10–2) hold for $Y \in \mathbf{T}$ is that

$$\sum_i \rho(Y)(A^i)\rho(X_i)(\psi) = 0,$$

since this must hold for all $\psi \in \Gamma(E)$, $\rho(Y)(A^i) = 0$ for all $Y \in \mathbf{T}$.

This condition means that

The components of the linear transformations $A^1, \ldots, A^n$ are constant over T.

Now we must look for the conditions of invariance under $\rho(L)$. First note that, for $Y \in \mathbf{L}$, $\psi \in \Gamma(E)$,

$$(10\text{--}3) \qquad \rho(Y)(\psi) = \sum_{i,j} - B_{ij}(Y)x_i\rho(X_j)(\psi) + \sigma(Y)(\psi).$$

The $(B_{ij}(Y))$ are the matrix elements of Ad Y acting on $\mathbf{T}$; i.e.,

$$[Y, X_i] = \sum_j B_{ij}(Y)X_j.$$

The first term expresses the fact that L acts on T in terms of linear homogeneous transformations with respect to the coordinate system $(x_1, \ldots, x_n)$. The coefficients $(B_{ij}(Y))$ are constant, and define the matrix of Ad Y acting on $\mathbf{T}$ with respect to the chosen basis $X_1, \ldots, X_n$ of $\mathbf{T}$. The second term $\sigma(Y)(\psi)$ expresses the fact that $\rho(l)$ acts on ψ not only by "rotating" by Ad l^{-1} (which accounts for the first term) but also by transforming the values of ψ by the given linear representation σ of L. In terms of components, i.e., $\psi = \sum_a \psi_a \mu_a, \sigma(Y)(\psi)_a = (\sigma(Y))_{ab}\psi_b$, with constants $(\sigma(Y))_{ab}$. Then

$$\rho(Y)D(\psi) = \sum_{i,j,k} - B_{ij}(Y)x_i\rho(X_j)A^k\rho(X_k)(\psi) + \sum_k \sigma(Y)A^k\rho(X_k)(\psi),$$

$$D\rho(Y)(\psi) = \sum_{i,j,k} - A^k\rho(X_k)(B_{ij}(Y)x_i\rho(X_j)(\psi)) + \sum_k A^k\rho(X_k)\sigma(Y)(\psi)$$

$$= \sum_{i,j} - A^iB_{ij}(Y)\rho(X)(\psi) + \sum_{i,j,k} - A^kB_{ij}(Y)x_i\rho(X_k)\rho(X_j)(\psi)$$

$$+ \sum_k A^k\sigma(Y)\rho(X_k)(\psi).$$

The condition (10–2) can then be read off as

$$(10\text{--}4) \quad \sum_i - A^iB_{ik}(Y) + A^k\sigma(Y) - \sigma(Y)A^k = 0 \qquad \text{for all } Y \in L.$$

Qualitatively, this condition can be read as follows: Let $E(U)$ be the vector space of linear transformations of U into itself. Since L acts on U, it also acts on $E(U)$. For $l \in L$, $A \in E(U)$ goes into $\sigma(l)A\sigma(l^{-1})$. Then, $A^1, \ldots, A^n$ determine a subspace of $E(U)$ in which L determines a linear transformation which is dual to the linear representation given by Ad L on $\mathbf{T}$. Another more algebraic way of putting this goes as follows.

Let U^* be the dual space of U, and let σ^* be the linear representation of L in U^* dual to σ. Then, the tensor product $\sigma \otimes \sigma^*$ is a representation of L in $U \otimes U^*$. Now, $U \otimes U^*$ can be identified with the space $E(U)$ of linear transformations of U. [In tensor language, elements of $U \otimes U^*$ are tensors of type $(1, 1)$.] In fact, if $u \otimes u^* \in U \otimes U^*$, $u \otimes u^*$ applied to an element $u_0 \in U$ is just $u^*(u_0)u$. Condition (10–4) then requires that there be a linear mapping $\mathbf{T}^* \to U \otimes U^*$ that commutes with the action of L, i.e., the representation $\sigma \otimes \sigma^*$ of L, when reduced into irreducible components, contains a representation of L equivalent to $(\mathrm{Ad}\, L)^*$ acting on L^*.

So far we have not been making any assumption about the properties of $\mathrm{Ad}\, L$ acting on $\mathbf{T}$. Let us look at the condition under hypotheses that hold in the Minkowski case, namely where $\rho(G)$ also commutes with the second-order differential operator

$$\Delta(\psi) = \sum_i \epsilon_i \rho(X_i)^2(\psi) \qquad \text{with each } \epsilon_j \neq 0.$$

Now, for $Y \in \mathbf{L}$,

$$\rho(Y)(\Delta(\psi)) = \sum_i 2\epsilon_i \rho([Y, X_i])\rho(X_i)(\psi)\Delta(\rho(Y)(\psi))$$

$$= \sum_{i,j} 2\epsilon_i B_{ij}\rho(X_i)\rho(X_j)(\psi) + \Delta\rho(Y)(\psi).$$

Hence, the conditions that Δ commute with the action of $\rho(G)$ are

(10–5) $\qquad \epsilon_i B_{ij} + \epsilon_j B_{ji} = 0 \qquad \text{for } 1 \leqslant i, j \leqslant n.$

[For example, in the case where G is the Poincaré group, (10–5) just expresses the fact that $\mathrm{Ad}\, L$ acting on $\mathbf{T}$ preserves the Lorentz metric, if the (ϵ_i) are chosen as the eigenvalues of the Lorentz metric tensor. Δ is just the Klein-Gordon operator, of course.]

If (10–5) is satisfied, conditions (10–4) become

$$\sigma(Y)A^k - A^k\sigma(Y) = \sum_i \frac{\epsilon_k}{\epsilon_i} B_{ki}(Y)A^i,$$

or

$$\sigma(Y)\left(\frac{A^k}{\epsilon_k}\right) - \left(\frac{A^k}{\epsilon_k}\right)\sigma(Y) = \sum_i (B_{kj}(Y))\left(\frac{A^i}{\epsilon_i}\right).$$

This should be compared to the transformation law:

$$[Y, X_k] = \sum_i B_{ki}(Y)X_i,$$

i.e., the A^k/ϵ_k transform in the same way as do the X_i.

Now let us compute

$$D^2(\psi) = \sum_j A^j \rho(X_j) \sum_i A^i \rho(X_i)(\psi)$$
$$= \sum_{i,j} (A^j A^i + A^i A^j) \rho(X_j) \rho(X_i)(\psi).$$

Hence $D^2(\psi) = \Delta(\psi)$ if and only if

(10–6) $$A^i A^i + A^i A^j = \begin{cases} 0 & \text{if } i \neq j \\ \epsilon_i I & \text{if } i = j \end{cases}$$

(I is the identity transformation of U).

Now, σ imbeds **L** in the associative algebra of all linear transformations of U. Suppose in addition we require that the $A^1, \ldots, A^n$ generate the algebra of all linear transformations of U, and that they are linearly independent — we then arrive, as Dirac did, at the fact that the algebra of all linear transformations of U forms the *Clifford algebra* associated with the vector space **T**, and the inner product

$$X_i, X_j = \begin{cases} 0 & \text{if } T \neq j \\ \epsilon_j & \text{if } i = j \end{cases}.$$

If G/L is Minkowski space, the representation σ of L is the *spinor representation*. L is the twofold simply connected covering group of the Lorentz group. [In case dim $T = 4$, L is isomorphic to $SL(2, C)$. In higher dimensions, there is no such identification of the spinor group with a "classical" group.] We can refer to Boerner (1963) for a constructive definition of the Clifford algebra and the spinor group in a form that is most accessible to the physicist. A short but illuminating treatment is given by Chevalley (1946).

We shall now describe how the Dirac equation is defined in a more systematic way, without proof. We start with a real vector space **T** with a Lorentz-type metric. T is defined as the group of all translations on **T**. Let L be the connected component of the group of all homogeneous linear transformations of **T** that preserves the Lorentz metric.

Let L' be the simply connected covering group of L. In terms of the general theory of Lie groups, L' is an abstractly constructed connected Lie group, with a homomorphism α of L' onto L whose kernel is discrete and which is contained in the center of L'. (In case L is the Lorentz group, the kernel is the cyclic group of order 2, whence the fact that L' is a "twofold covering" of L.) The induced Lie algebra homomorphism $\alpha: \mathbf{L}' \to \mathbf{L}$ is then an isomorphism, and enables one to identify the Lie algebras of $\mathbf{L}'$ and $\mathbf{L}$. The characteristic property of L', in general, can be described as follows: Let H be a Lie group, and let ϕ be a Lie algebra homomorphism of **L** into **H**.   In general, ϕ does not arise from a Lie group homomorphism: $L \to H$.   However, there is a group homomorphism: $L' \to H$ whose associated Lie algebra homomorphism: $\mathbf{L}' \to \mathbf{H}$ agrees with ϕ when $\mathbf{L}'$ is identified with $\mathbf{L}$ via α.   In particular, if ϕ is a representation of **L** by linear transformations of a finite-dimensional vector space U, ϕ can be "integrated" to give a linear representation of L' by transformations on U. ϕ can be "integrated" to give a linear representation of L only if the kernel of α is represented by the identity transformation on U.

In case L is the connected Lorentz group, L' as the "spinor group" can be constructed in the following way: **L** is realized as an algebra of linear transformations on **T** that preserve the Lorentz metric.   Using **T** and the Lorentz metric, the Clifford algebra **C** is constructed, first abstractly, as the quotient of the tensor algebra of **T** by a certain ideal.†   Since the Clifford algebra is "naturally" associated with the vector space and the inner product, **L** can be extended to an algebra of derivations of the Clifford algebra.   One proves that all derivations of the Clifford algebra are inner, which enables one to identify **L** with a set of elements of **C** in such a way that the Jacobi bracket in L goes over into commutators in **C**.   [Since the elements also generate **C**, **C** can also be defined as the quotient of the universal enveloping algebra $U(\mathbf{L})$ of **L** by a certain ideal.   However, this way of defining it would be considerably more complicated, and in fact does not seem to be in the literature.]   Now, **C** itself is a real vector space of dimension 2^n, where n is the dimension of **T**.   If n is even, say $n = 2m$, **C** can be represented as the algebra of linear transformation of a vector space U of dimension 2^m.   [Note that the dimension of all linear transformations of a vector space of dimension r is r^2, so that $(2^m)^2 = 2^{2n} = \dim \mathbf{C}$.]   The case n odd is more complicated, but since it does not seem to be needed (yet) in physics, we shall not describe it here.

The representation U has the property that every automorphism of **C** goes over into a linear transformation in U; the Lie algebra of the group of automorphisms of **C** is the set of derivations of **C**.   The connected subgroup corresponding to the subset of derivations defined by **L** is defined as the *spinor group* L'.   Now, if $X_1, \ldots, X_n$ is a Lorentz-orthogonal basis of **T**, they can also be considered as elements of **C**.   The elements of L' subject them to a Lorentz transformation, which defines the homomorphism $\alpha: L' \to L$.   It is proved that L' is simply connected, i.e., every closed curve in L' can be deformed to a point.   Since **L** is realized

† The ideal is that generated by elements of the form $X_1X_2 + X_2X_1 - 2\langle X_1, X_2\rangle$; for $X_1, X_2 \in \mathbf{T}$, where $\langle \ , \ \rangle$ is the Lorentz inner product of vectors.   If $X_1 \ldots, X_n$ is a basis of **T** with $\langle X_i, X_j\rangle = \epsilon_i\delta_{ij}$, then C is the algebra generated by all products $X_{i_1}, \ldots, X_{i_p}$, with the relations: $X_iX_j + X_jX_i = \epsilon_i\delta_{ij}$.

as a set of inner derivations of C, it is also realized as a linear algebra of transformations on U, which can be proved to be irreducible. The corresponding representation ϕ of L' by linear transformations on U is *faithful*, and is the *spinor representation* of L', which is a "twofold" representation of L, the Lorentz group.

We can choose G as the semidirect product of L' and T, where L' acts on translations first via α to L, followed by the usual action of the Lorentz group on translations. (Thus, the action of L' on T is not faithful.) U is taken as the vector space of dimension $2^{(n/2)}$, and σ as the spinor representation of L'. The "wave functions" ψ are mappings $T \rightarrow U$. The action of L' on wave functions is defined by the action of L' on T defining the semidirect product $G = L' \cdot T$, and by transforming the values of ψ by the spinor representation of L'. Since the Clifford algebra is realized as an algebra of linear transformations on U, and since within the Clifford algebra we know that there are elements (namely $X_1, \ldots, X_n$) which transform by a Lorentz transformation under the action of the spinor group (since the spinor group was defined to have this property), we see, in a qualitative way, that everything is set up to define the Dirac equation as a first-order differential operator on cross sections of the vector bundle over T defined by σ which is invariant under $\rho(G)$ and whose square is the image under ρ of the "mass" Casimir operator in the enveloping algebra of G.

If $n = 4$, these considerable algebraic complications are enormously simplified by the lucky accident that L' is isomorphic to $SL(2, C)$. For $2^{(n/2)}$ is now 4, and U can be taken as the two-*complex*-dimension vector space, with the usual action of $SL(2, C)$ on it. The wave functions ψ can then be chosen as having two complex components. However, if one wants to have a parity-conserving theory, wave function with four components must be used. An excellent description of this relation is given by Barut (1964).

CHAPTER 11

LIMITS AND CONTRACTIONS
OF LIE GROUPS

The operation of "contraction" of one Lie group to another is implicit in the group-theoretic approach to physics, particularly in Wigner's work. The first formal definition was given by Segal (1951); Inonu and Wigner (1953) and Saletan (1961) developed the subject from the physicist's point of view, and indicated some fascinating relations to the problems of asymptotic behavior of the "special functions" of mathematical physics. The classical example involving these ideas is in the passage from relativistic to classical mechanics, when the velocity of light is considered to be infinite. Group theoretically, the Lorentz group, the symmetry group of relativistic mechanics, "contracts" to the Galilean group, which is the symmetry group of classical mechanics. A similar, but less precisely known, phenomenon is involved in the passage from quantum to classical mechanics, when Planck's constant is considered to be zero. It is possible that these ideas, exploited systematically, might help in elucidating the current situation in elementary particle–high energy physics. There is also a possibility that some of the ideas of scattering theory may also be viewed in this light. Finally, the subject is also of great mathematical interest, but has barely been developed in the mathematical literature.

We shall begin with Segal's definition, although we shall work with a different one. Let $\mathbf{L}$ be a Lie algebra, and let $(X_1, \ldots, X_n)$ be a basis for $\mathbf{L}$ as a vector space. The numbers (C_{ijk}), such that

$$(11\text{--}1) \qquad [X_i, X_j] = \sum_k C_{ijk} X_k \qquad (1 \leqslant i, j \leqslant n),$$

are called the *structure constants* of the Lie algebra with respect to the given basis. The Jacobi identity imposes certain conditions on these constants; namely

$$(11\text{--}2) \qquad \sum_k (C_{jlk} C_{ikm} - C_{ilk} C_{jkm} - C_{ijk} C_{klm}) = 0.$$

Conversely, if a system (C_{ijk}) of constants satisfies these conditions, the bracket can be defined by (11–1) and makes the vector space into a Lie algebra. Now, suppose that an infinite sequence of bases of **L**, say (X_i^u), for $u = 1, 2, \ldots$, is given, with (C_{ijk}^u) the corresponding structure constants. Suppose that for all (i, j, k), $\lim_{\mu \to \infty} C_{ijk}^u$ exists, and equals, say, C_{ijk}^∞. Since (11–2) is preserved under limits, the C_{ijk}^∞ are the structure constants of a Lie algebra. This Lie algebra, say **L**′, is said to be the *contraction* of **L**.

Now, this is a natural definition, but it is awkward to work with, and it seems to be difficult to prove general theorems about two Lie algebras that are related in this way. In particular, one would like to know all contractions of a given Lie algebra, and conversely in how many ways a given Lie algebra can be exhibited as a contraction. Therefore, we shall work with another definition (it is not yet completely clear how they are related), which is more natural from the geometrical point of view and, as we will show, can serve just as well as Segal's to make precise the mathematical content inherent in the physical ideas.

Definition:

Let L and L' be subgroups of a Lie group G. We will say that L' is a *limit of L within G* if there is a sequence $g_1, g_2, \ldots$ of elements of G such that

Whenever $l_1, l_2, \ldots$ is a sequence of elements of L such that the sequence Ad $g_1(l_1)$, Ad $g_2(l_2)$, $\ldots$ converges, it converges to an element of L'.

It is often more convenient to work with Lie algebras rather than Lie groups, hence we shall actually work with the following "infinitesimal" version of this definition.

Definition:

Let G be a Lie group, and let **L** and **L**′ be subalgebras of **G**. We say that **L**′ is a *limit of* **L** *within* **G** if there exists a sequence $g_1, g_2, \ldots$ of elements of G such that

Whenever $X_1, X_2, \ldots$ is a sequence of elements of **L** such that the sequence Ad $g_1(X_1)$, Ad $g_2(X_2)$, $\ldots$ converges, it converges to an element of **L**.
If **L** and **L**′ are related in this way, we shall write

$$\mathbf{L}' = \lim_{n \to \infty} \text{Ad } g_n(\mathbf{L}).$$

Let us now illustrate these generalities on some examples of interest in physics.

CONTRACTION OF THE LORENTZ GROUP TO THE GALILEAN GROUP

Let Q be the $n \times n$ diagonal matrix

$$\begin{pmatrix} C & & & 0 \\ & -1 & & \\ & & \ddots & \\ 0 & & & -1 \end{pmatrix}.$$

The Lorentz group is the group that preserves the quadratic form defined by this matrix. As we have seen, the Lie algebra of the group is the Lie algebra of $n \times n$ matrices α that satisfy

(11-3) $${}^t\alpha Q + Q\alpha = 0.$$

We want to know what happens as $C \to \infty$. Now, two Q's for two different values of C differ by a change of basis. This means that the Lorentz groups for different values of C are conjugate within $GL(n, R)$. Suppose that $\alpha(C)$ is a matrix-valued function of C that satisfies (11-3) for each C and that converges, as $C \to \infty$, to a matrix $\alpha(\infty)$. Let us work out the conditions that $\alpha(\infty)$ must satisfy. Let $\alpha = (\alpha_{ij})$, with $1 \leqslant i, j \leqslant n$. Then (11-3) is equivalent to the conditions:

(11-4) 　　(a) $\alpha_{ki} + \alpha_{ik} = 0$ 　　for $i, k > 1$,
　　　　　(b) $C^2\alpha_{1i} - \alpha_{1i} = 0$ 　　for $i > 1$,
　　　　　(c) $\alpha_{11} = 0$.

Conditions (a) and (c) hold as $C \to \infty$. (a) obviously implies that the matrix $(\alpha_{ik}(\infty))$ for $1 < i, k \leqslant n$ is in the Lie algebra of $SO(n-1, R)$. (b) implies that $\alpha_{1i}(\infty) = 0$. The resulting relations on $\alpha(\infty)$ are those of the Galilean group, i.e., the Galilean group is a contraction within $GL(n, R)$ of the Lorentz group.

Now we want to consider the variation of the "little" subgroups of the Lorentz group that occur in Wigner's construction of the representations of the Poincaré group. Let us first recall how this goes. We consider the Lorentz group as acting on Minkowski space. The subgroup that leaves invariant a time-like vector is compact, and in fact is isomorphic to $SO(3, R)$. [In fact, the orbit of the Lorentz group at such a vector is a symmetric space, with $SO(3, R)$, the isotropy group, the maximal compact subgroup of the Poincaré group.] However, consider the time-like vector as varying into a light-like vector. The isotropy subgroup of the Lorentz group suddenly changes type, from $SO(3, R)$, and becomes the group of rigid motions of the Euclidean plane.

We shall not pursue these geometric ideas directly here but will develop instead a more group-theoretic approach. Let G be a semisimple, non-compact Lie group with finite center, and let $\mathbf{G} = \mathbf{K} + \mathbf{P}$ be a Cartan decomposition of **G**; i.e., K (the subgroup corresponding to **K**) is a maximal compact subgroup of G, and

$$[\mathbf{K}, \mathbf{P}] \subset \mathbf{P} \qquad [\mathbf{P}, \mathbf{P}] \subset \mathbf{K}.$$

Let $X \in \mathbf{P}$, and let $g(t) = \exp(tX)$ be the one-parameter group generated by X. Our goal is to describe the subgroup H of G which is the limit of K in the following sense:

$$\lim_{t \to \infty} \text{Ad } g(t)(\mathbf{K}) = \mathbf{H}.$$

Now, we know that Ad X acting in **G** has real eigenvalues and can be diagonalized, and its eigenvectors stand in a special relation to **K** and **P**. Let $\mathbf{K}(X)$ be the set of elements of **K** that commute with X. Then these are linearly independent elements $Z_1, \ldots, Z_q \in \mathbf{K}$ and $Y_1, \ldots, Y_q \in \mathbf{P}$ such that

$$[X, Z_i] = \lambda_i Y_i \qquad [X, Y_i] = \lambda_i X_i, \lambda_i > 0 \qquad (1 \leqslant i \leqslant q);$$

hence

$$[X, W_i] = \lambda_i W_i \qquad \text{where } W_i = Y_i + Z_i \text{ for } 1 \leqslant i \leqslant q.$$

Further, $\mathbf{K}(X)$ and the subspace spanned by $Z_1, \ldots, Z_q$ span **K**.

This decomposition of Ad X makes it quite easy to compute Ad $g(t)(\mathbf{K})$. In fact,

$$\text{Ad } g(t)(Z) = Z \qquad \text{for } Z \in \mathbf{K}(X).$$

For $1 \leqslant i \leqslant q$,

$$\text{Ad } g(t)(Z_i) = \text{Ad}(\exp tX)(Z_i)$$

$$= \exp(\text{Ad } tX)(Z_i) = \sum_{j=0}^{\infty} \frac{[\text{Ad}(tX)]^j}{j!} Z_i$$

$$= \sum_{j=0}^{\infty} \frac{(\text{Ad}(tX))^{2j}}{(2j)!} Z_i + \sum_{j=0}^{\infty} \frac{(\text{Ad } tX)^{2j}}{(2j+1)!} [tX, Z_i]$$

$$= \sum_{j=0}^{\infty} \frac{(\text{Ad}(tX))^{2j}}{(2j)!} Z_i + \sum_{j=0}^{\infty} \frac{(\text{Ad } tX)^{2j}}{(2j+1)!} t\lambda_j Y_i.$$

Now,

$$(\text{Ad } tX)^2(Z_i) = t^2 \lambda_i Z_i$$
$$(\text{Ad } tX)^2(Y_i) = t^2 \lambda_j^2 Y_i.$$

Thus,

$$\text{Ad } g(t)(Z_i) = \sum_{j=0}^{\infty} \frac{(t\lambda_i)^{2j}}{(2j)!} Z_i + \sum_{j=0}^{\infty} \frac{(t\lambda_i)^{22+1}}{(2j+1)!} Y_i$$
$$= \cosh(\lambda_i t) Z_i + \sinh(\lambda_i t) Y_i.$$

Hence

$$\frac{\text{Ad } g(t)(Z_i)}{\cosh(\lambda_i t)} = Z_i + \tanh(\lambda_i t) Y_i \to Z_i + Y_i = W_i \qquad \text{as } t \to \infty.$$

We see now that if $Y(t)$ is a one-parameter family of elements of $\mathbf{K}$ such that $\lim_{t \to \infty} \text{Ad } g(t)(Y(t))$ exists, then $\lim_{t \to \infty} \text{Ad } g(t)(Y(t))$ must be in the subalgebra spanned by the centralizer of X in $\mathbf{K}$ and the $Z_i + Y_i$.

We have now proved the following theorem:

Theorem 11–1

Let $t \to g(t)$ be the non-parameter subgroup of G generated by the element $X \in \mathbf{P}$. Let $\mathbf{K}(X)$ be the centralizer of X in $\mathbf{K}$, and let $\mathbf{N}^+(X)$ be the nilpotent subalgebra of $\mathbf{G}$ generated by the eigenvectors of $\text{Ad } X$ for positive eigenvalues. Then $\text{Ad } g(t)(\mathbf{K})$ approaches as $t \to \infty$ the subalgebra $\mathbf{H}(X)$ of $\mathbf{G}$ equal to $\mathbf{K}(X) + \mathbf{N}^+(X)$. Further, $\mathbf{N}^+(X)$ is an ideal in $\mathbf{H}(X)$.

With this general theorem available as a tool, let us look again at Wigner's observation that the group of rigid motions in the plane is a contraction of the rotation group. In fact, if we choose $\mathbf{G}$ so that $\mathbf{K}$ is $\mathbf{SO}(3, R)$, and if we choose $X \in \mathbf{P}$ so that $\mathbf{K}(X)$ is one-dimensional, $\mathbf{N}^+(X)$ must be two-dimensional, hence Abelian, so that $\mathbf{H}(X)$ is in fact the Lie algebra of the group of rigid motions in the plane. Two possibilities for G come immediately to mind:

$$G = SL(3, R) \text{ and } G = \text{the Lorentz group.}$$

It is also possible to refine the argument used in Theorem 11–1 to find all limits of $\mathbf{K}$ within G, in the case where K is the maximal compact subgroup of the semisimple group G. In fact, suppose $g_1, g_2, \ldots$ is a sequence of elements of G such that

$$\lim_{u \to \infty} \text{Ad } g_u(\mathbf{K}) = \mathbf{L}'.$$

Let $\mathbf{A}$ be a maximal Abelian subalgebra of $\mathbf{P}$. We know that g_u can be decomposed as

$$g_u = k_u a_u k_u' \qquad \text{with } k_u, k_u' \in K, a_u \in \exp(\mathbf{A}).$$

Since K is compact, we can suppose without loss in generality that $\lim_{u \to \infty} k_u$ and $\lim_{u \to \infty} k_u'$ exist, equaling, say, k and k'. Then

$$\mathbf{L}' = k \, (\lim_{u \to \infty} \text{Ad } a_u(\mathbf{K})) k'.$$

Now, using the simultaneous diagonalization possible for $\text{Ad } \mathbf{A}$ acting in **G**, it is possible to show (left to the reader) that to every sequence (a_u) in A there is an element $X \in \mathbf{A}$ such that

$$\lim_{u \to \infty} \mathrm{Ad}\ a_u(\mathbf{K}) = \lim_{t \to \infty} \mathrm{Ad}(\exp(t\ X))(\mathbf{K}).$$

These two remarks determine the possibilities for the limits of **K** within G. Note, however, that this sort of argument breaks down if K is not a compact subgroup of G.

CONTRACTION AND ASYMPTOTIC BEHAVIOR OF SPECIAL FUNCTIONS

The contraction idea is important not only for its connection with physics but also because it leads to group-theoretic "explanations" of some of the classical asymptotic formulas for the special function of mathematical physics. For example, Inonu and Wigner (1953) point out how the formula

$$\lim_{i \to \infty} \bar{P}_i^m \left[\cos \left(\frac{t}{i} \right) \right] = J_m(t)$$

is related to the construction of the rotation group into the group of rigid motions in the plane. $[\bar{P}_i^m(\ \ )$ is the appropriately normalized associated Legendre function and $J_m(\ \ )$ is the Bessel function.]

We can see the general reason for this phenomenon quite easily. Let ρ be a representation of a Lie group G by transformations of a vector space V (which may be infinite-dimensional). Suppose that $v_1, v_2, \ldots = (v_i)$ is a basis for V, i.e., that each $v \in V$ can be written

$$\sum_i a_i v_i.$$

(We are leaving open the possibility that i may be a continuous index, and that this sum must be considered as some sort of limit.) Suppose that $X_1, \ldots, X_p$ are elements of **G**. Then, we have an expansion of the form

$$\rho(\exp(X_1 t_i) \cdots \exp(X_p t_p))(v_i) = \sum_j a_{ij}(t_1, \ldots, t_p) v_j.$$

The coefficients $(a_{ij}(t_1, \ldots, t_p))$ as functions of the real variables $t_1, \ldots, t_p$ may be considered as the "special functions" associated with the representation and the basis chosen for V. Most of the classical special functions may be obtained by appropriate choices of the group and the representation.

For example, it is well known that the Legendre functions $P_i^m(\ \ )$ are obtained as matrix elements of representations of $SO(3, R)$, that the

Bessel functions $J_m(\ )$ are matrix elements of representations of the group of rigid motions in the plane, and that this latter group is a contraction of $SO(3, R)$. [See Gel'fand, Minlos, and Shapiro (1963) for the explicit description of the matrix elements.]

Suppose now that L and L' are subgroups of G, and that L' is a contraction of L with G. Let us choose $X_1, \ldots, X_p \in \mathbf{L}$. Let $s \to g(s)$ be a one-parameter family of elements of G such that

$$\lim_{s \to \infty} \text{Ad } g(s)(\mathbf{L}) = \mathbf{L}'.$$

Suppose, in fact, that $(\alpha_{uv}(s))$, $1 \leqslant u, v \leqslant p$, is a matrix function of s such that

$$\text{Ad } g(s)\Big(\sum_v \alpha_{uv}(s)X_v\Big) \qquad \text{for } u = 1, \ldots, p,$$

converges as $s \to \infty$ to elements $X_1', \ldots, X_p' \in \mathbf{L}'$. Then

$$\exp\Big(\sum_v t_u\alpha_{uv}(s)\text{Ad } g(s)(X_v)\Big) \text{ converges as } s \to \infty \text{ to } \exp(t_u X_u')$$

$$\text{for } u = 1, \ldots, p.$$

Suppose that

$$\rho(\exp(X_1't) \cdots \exp(X_p't_p))(v_i) = \sum_j a_{ij}'(t_1, \ldots, t_p)v_j;$$

i.e., the $(a_{ij}'(t_1, \ldots, t_p))$ are the "special functions" associated with this representation of L'. Suppose also that

$$\rho(g(s))(v_j) = \sum_j b_{ij}(s)v_j,$$

$$\rho(g(s)^{-1})(v_i) = \sum_j b_{ij}^{-1}(s)v_j.$$

Thus, we see that there will be limit relations involving the a_{ij}', the b_{ij}, and the α_{uv} as $s \to \infty$. For example, let us write them down explicitly for the case where (α_{uv}) is a diagonal matrix, i.e.,

$$\lim_{s \to \infty} \text{Ad } g(s)\alpha_u(s)X_u = X_u'.$$

Then

$$\rho(g(s)\exp(t_1\alpha_1(s)X_u)\exp(t_2\alpha_2(s)X_2) \cdots \exp(t_p\alpha_p(s)X_p)g(s)^{-1})(v_i)$$
$$= \sum_{j,k,l} b_{ij}^{-1}(s)a_{jk}(t_1\alpha_1(s), \ldots, t_p\alpha_p(s))b_{kl}(s)v_l.$$

Hence

$$\sum_{j,k,l} b_{ij}^{-1}(s)a_{jk}(t_1\alpha_1(s), \ldots, t_p\alpha_p(s))b_{kl}(s)$$

goes, as $s \to \infty$, over into $a_{il}'(t_1, \ldots, t_p)$.

LIMITS OF INDUCED REPRESENTATIONS

We turn to the question of how to put the program outlined in the previous section into effect. Specifically, suppose that L and L' are subgroups of a Lie group G. We know that L' is a limit of L within G, and that ρ is a representation of L by transformations on a vector space V. If we could find a way of embedding V as a subspace of a vector space V' such that ρ extends to a representation of G on V', we would be in a position to apply the remarks of the previous sections. The method of induced representations and vector bundles gives us such a method.

Suppose, for example, that the representation ρ of L on V starts off being an induced representation. Then let H be a subgroup of L and let σ be a representation of H by linear transformations on a vector space U, and suppose that the representation ρ of L on V is obtained by inducing σ to L. Thus, an element ψ of V is either:

1. A mapping $\psi\colon L \to U$ such that $\psi(lh) = \sigma(h^{-1})\psi(l)$ for $h \in H$, $l \in L$.
2. A cross-section mapping $\psi\colon L/H \to E$, where $E \to L/H$ is the homogeneous vector bundle over L/H whose typical fiber is U.

The second, more geometric, definition is better suited to seeing how ρ can be extended to G. In fact, we have an immediate way of extending ρ if the following conditions are satisfied:

(11–5) G has a subgroup H' which contains H such that:

  (a) σ can be extended from H to a representation of H' on the same vector space U.
  (b) The inclusion mapping $L/H \to G/H'$ is one-to-one and onto; i.e., the action of L on the homogeneous space L/H can be extended to an action of G, with isotropy subgroup H'.

Condition (a) guarantees that the vector bundle $E \to L/H$ that is homogeneous under the action of L is also homogeneous under the action of G on $L/H = G/H'$. Thus, an element ψ of $\Gamma(E)$, i.e., a cross-section mapping $L/H \to E$, can also be considered as a cross-section mapping $G/H \to E'$, where E' is the same bundle considered as a G-homogeneous bundle. Thus, the representation ρ of L on $\Gamma(E)$ can be extended to give a representation of G on $\Gamma(E)$: If L' is another subgroup of G that is the limit within G of L, we are in a position to apply the remarks of the previous section and see how the matrix elements associated with the representation ρ of L go over into matrix elements associated with the representation of L'.

Example

Suppose that G is a connected semisimple noncompact Lie group, with finite center, that K is a maximal compact subgroup of G, and that $G = KAN^+$ is an Iwasawa decomposition of G. (Recall that A is an Abelian, N^+ a nilpotent, subgroup of G, N^+ is an invariant subgroup of AN^+, and AN^+ is a solvable group.) K will play the role of L in the above discussion. Let α be a linear representation of AN^+ on a vector space U'. Let $K(\alpha)$ be the subgroup of K constructed in Chapter 9. Recall that $K(\alpha)$ was defined as the set of all $k \in K$ such that

Whenever $gk = k'g'$, for $g, g' \in AN^+$, $k' \in K$,

$$\alpha(k) = \alpha(k').$$

Let $H' = K(\alpha)AN^+$. It is proved in Chapter 9 that $K(\alpha)$ and H' are subgroups of G. Let β be any linear representation of $K(\alpha)$ on a vector space U''. Let $U = U' \otimes U''$, and let σ be the representation of H' such that

$$\sigma(kg) = \beta(k) \otimes \alpha(g) \qquad \text{for } k \in K(\alpha), g \in AN^+.$$

Let $K(\alpha)$ assume the role of H in the above discussion. We see immediately from the Iwasawa decomposition that the inclusion map $K/K(\alpha) \rightarrow G/H'$ is one-to-one and onto, hence G can be made to act as a transformation group on $K/K(\alpha)$ in a way that extends the action of K. We thus obtain a linear representation ρ of G on the vector space $\Gamma(E)$ of cross sections of the vector bundle on G/H' determined by the representation σ. Let X be an element of $\mathbf{A}$, and let $g(t) = \exp(tX)$. We have seen (Theorem 11–1) that

$$\lim_{t \to \infty} \text{Ad } g(t)(\mathbf{K}) = \mathbf{K}(X) + \mathbf{N}^+(X).$$

These facts, in principle, determine† how the representation ρ restricted to K goes over into a representation of $\mathbf{K}(X) + \mathbf{N}^+(X)$.

LIMITS OF NONCOMPACT SYMMETRIC SUBGROUPS

So far, we have a systematic method for computing the limits of the maximal compact subgroups K of the noncompact semisimple Lie group G. Now, the case of a noncompact, symmetric subgroup L of a semisimple Lie group G is more important for physics. For example, the case where

---

† There is one additional complication we have omitted. To get a unitary representation for G on $\Gamma(E)$, it is necessary to present multipliers into the action of G on cross sections, since G acting on G/H' does not admit an invariant measure. Since K is compact, K acting on G/H' does admit an invariant measure; hence the multipliers are the identity on K.

$L =$ the Lorentz group, $G = SL(4, R)$. The theory of those "pseudo-Riemannian" symmetric spaces G/L is quite undeveloped in the mathematical literature (in contrast to the "Riemannian" case, where L is compact). Therefore, we can only present a few remarks about how the theory might go.

Recall that a subgroup L of a Lie group G is a *symmetric subgroup* if its Lie algebra $\mathbf{L}$ is a symmetric subalgebra of $\mathbf{G}$, i.e., if there is a subspace $\mathbf{M}$ of $\mathbf{G}$ such that

$$\mathbf{G} = \mathbf{L} \oplus \mathbf{M} \qquad [\mathbf{L}, \mathbf{M}] \subset \mathbf{P} \qquad [\mathbf{M}, \mathbf{M}] \subset \mathbf{L}.$$

We shall consider one particular class of such subgroups. Namely, we shall suppose that

$$(11\text{--}6) \qquad \begin{aligned} \mathbf{L} &= \mathbf{K} \cap \mathbf{L} \oplus \mathbf{P} \cap \mathbf{L}, \\ \mathbf{M} &= \mathbf{M} \cap \mathbf{K} \oplus \mathbf{M} \cap \mathbf{P}, \end{aligned}$$

where $\mathbf{G} = \mathbf{K} \oplus \mathbf{P}$ is the Cartan decomposition of $\mathbf{G}$, i.e., $K = \exp \mathbf{K}$ is a maximal compact subgroup of G, and $P = \exp \mathbf{P}$ is the space of transvections. There is another way of putting this condition that is more convenient algebraically. Let s and s' be the automorphism of $\mathbf{G}$ such that

$$s^2 = s'^2 = \text{identity}.$$
$$s(X) = X \text{ for } X \in \mathbf{K} \qquad s'(X) = X \text{ for } X \in \mathbf{L}.$$

Then, the conditions (11–6) are equivalent to the condition that s and s' commute.

The following notations will be convenient:

$$\begin{aligned} \mathbf{L} &= \mathbf{L} \cap \mathbf{K} \qquad \mathbf{L}^+ = \mathbf{L} \cap \mathbf{P}, \\ \mathbf{M} &= \mathbf{M} \cap \mathbf{K} \qquad \mathbf{M}^+ = \mathbf{M} \cap \mathbf{P}. \end{aligned}$$

The motivation for this notation is that for $X \in \mathbf{M}^-$ or $\mathbf{M}^+$, Ad X has, respectively, pure imaginary and real eigenvalues.

Let $X \in \mathbf{M}$, and let $g(t) = \exp(tX)$. Our aim is to compute the limiting subalgebras L', i.e., ones satisfying

$$\lim_{t \to \infty} \text{Ad } g(t)(\mathbf{L}) = L'.$$

This is not too interesting if $X \in \mathbf{M}^-$, for then $g(t)$ belongs to a compact subgroup of G; hence $\mathbf{L}'$ will be just a subalgebra of $\mathbf{G}$ that is conjugate to $\mathbf{L}$. Let us first consider the case where

$$(11\text{--}7) \qquad\qquad X \in \mathbf{M}^+.$$

Now, $(\text{Ad } X)^2$, acting on $\mathbf{G}$, leaves $\mathbf{L}$ and $\mathbf{K}$ invariant. Let $\mathbf{C}(X)$ be the centralizer of X in $\mathbf{G}$. Since Ad X acting in $\mathbf{G}$ is completely reducible, $\mathbf{C}(X)$ is also the centralizer of $(\text{Ad } X)^2$. Because of (11–7), $(\text{Ad } X)^2$ has positive eigenvalues. Say that λ^2, with $\lambda > 0$, is such an eigenvalue; i.e.,

$$[X, [X, Y]] = \lambda^2 Y.$$

Then, put $Z = Y + ([X, Y]/\lambda)$,

$$[X, Z] = [X, Y] + \frac{[X, [X, Y]]}{\lambda} = [X, Y] + \lambda Y = Z.$$

$$(\text{Ad } X)^2([X, Y]) = \lambda^2[X, Y].$$

$$\begin{aligned}
\text{Ad } g(t)(Y) &= \text{Ad}(\exp tX)(Y) \\
&= \exp(\text{Ad } tX)(Y) \\
&= \sum_{j=0}^{\infty} \frac{(\text{Ad } tX)^j}{j!}(Y) \\
&= \sum_{j=0}^{\infty} \frac{(\text{Ad } tX)^{2j}}{(2j)!}(Y) + \sum_{j=0}^{\infty} \frac{(\text{Ad } tX)^{2j+1}}{(2j+1)!}(Y) \\
&= \sum_{j=0}^{\infty} \frac{(t\lambda)^{2j}}{(2j)!}Y + \sum_{j=0}^{\infty} \frac{(t\lambda)^{2j}}{(2j+1)!}t[X, Y] \\
&= \cosh(t\lambda)Y + \sinh(t\lambda)\frac{[X, Y]}{\lambda}.
\end{aligned}$$

Hence

$$\lim_{t \to \infty} \frac{\text{Ad } g(t)Y}{\cosh(t\lambda)} = Z.$$

We can conclude, just as in the proof of Theorem 11–1, that $\mathbf{L}'$ has a structure very similar to the one we found in the case where $\mathbf{L}$ was a compact subalgebra of $\mathbf{G}$, namely $\mathbf{L}'$ is a semidirect sum of a nilpotent ideal [namely that spanned by the Z's associated with all nonzero eigenvalues of $(\text{Ad } X)^2$] and a subalgebra $\mathbf{C}(X) \cap \mathbf{L}$.

Now turn to the case

(11–8) $X = X^+ + X^-$ where $X^+ \in \mathbf{M}^+$, $X^- \in \mathbf{M}^-$.

In case $[X^+, X^-] = 0$, we can reduce to the case (11–7), since

$$\begin{aligned}
\text{Ad } g(t) &= \text{Ad}(\exp(tX^+ + tX^+)) = \text{Ad}(\exp(tX^+)\exp(tX^-)) \\
&= \text{Ad}(\exp(tX^-))\text{Ad}(\exp(tX^+)).
\end{aligned}$$

Again, the fact that $(\exp tX^-)$ has in a compact subgroup of G enabled us to say that $\mathbf{L}'$ is obtained as a conjugate subalgebra to one of the limiting subalgebras obtained by first applying case (11–7).

LIMITS WITHIN SEMIDIRECT PRODUCTS

Let a group G be a semidirect product $L \cdot T$ of an Abelian invariant sub-group T and a subgroup L. (Typically, we are thinking of the case where G is the Poincaré group, T the translation, and L the homogeneous Lorentz group.) We have seen that there are two ways of inducing representations from subgroups of G that are of interest for physics. We can start with a representation of L itself, which corresponds geometrically to con-structing a homogeneous vector bundle on G/L, or we can start with a subgroup

$$H = L(X) \cdot T,$$

where $L(X)$ is the centralizer in L of an element X of $\mathbf{T}$.

The first construction does not give irreducible representations of G (but does give rise to "wave equations" on G/L), whereas the second may be expected to be irreducible. How are they related? Traditionally, the relation is via Fourier transforms. However, we also have the follow-ing more geometric relation:

$$L(\mathbf{X}) + \mathbf{T} = \lim_{t \to \infty} \operatorname{Ad} g(t)(\mathbf{L}) \qquad \text{where } g(t) = \exp(tX),\ X \in \mathbf{T}.$$

The proof of this relation is easy:

$$\operatorname{Ad} g(t)(Y) = Y \qquad \text{for } Y \in \mathbf{T},$$
$$[X, [X, Y]] = 0 \qquad \text{for } Y \in \mathbf{L};$$

hence

$$\operatorname{Ad} g(t)(Y) = Y + t[X, Y].$$

Suppose then that

$$\lim_{t \to \infty} \operatorname{Ad} g(t)(Y(t)) = Y \qquad \text{with } Y(t) \in \mathbf{L}.$$

Then

$$Y = \lim_{t \to \infty} \{ Y(t) + [X, tY(t)] \}.$$

This means that $\lim_{t \to \infty} Y(t)$ and $\lim_{t \to \infty} [X, tY(t)]$ exist; hence

$$[X, \lim_{t \to \infty} Y(t)] = 0;$$

i.e.,

$$Y \in \mathbf{L}(X) + \mathbf{T}.$$

EXTENSIONS AND POSSIBLE FURTHER PHYSICAL APPLICATIONS OF THE LIMIT IDEA

Consider the following notion.   Let G be a Lie algebra and let $\lambda \to L(\lambda)$ be a one-parameter family of subalgebras of G.   (The additional generality consists of the fact that we are no longer supposing the subalgebras conjugate within G.   In fact, the interesting applications are in the case where G is infinite-dimensional, so that the "adjoint group of G," i.e., the group of inner automorphisms of G, is a rather vague concept.)   Let us say that a subalgebra L of G is a limit of this sequence [notation: $\lim_{\lambda \to \infty} L(\lambda) = L$] if, whenever $\lambda \to X(\lambda) \in L(\lambda)$ is a one-parameter family such that $\lim_{\lambda \to \infty} X(\lambda) = X$, X must belong to L.

This concept may arise in quantum field theory.   Suppose we have a physical system, described by quantum mechanics.   A general postulate of quantum mechanics then asserts that the family of observables forms a Lie algebra, and that the algebra is represented by a Lie algebra of skew-Hermitian operators on a Hilbert space whose elements define the states of the system (see Chapter 16).   Now, if the system has only a finite number of degrees of freedom, the algebra will essentially have only a finite number of elements.   However, in field theory one expects to encounter observables that are parameterized by points of space-time.   The space integrals of the moments of these observables form a complicated infinite-dimensional Lie algebra whose structure is determined by the interactions among the fields.   The "strength" of the interaction is determined by "coupling constants."   They play the role of λ in the above definition.   One might expect that, as they approach certain limiting values, the Lie algebra of currents approaches as a "limit" certain less complicated Lie algebras.   The irreducible representations of these limiting Lie algebras then serve as an approximation to the true physical situation.   Here we make contact with the well-known ideas of Gell-Mann (1964) on "current algebras."

THE RELATION BETWEEN CONTRACTION AND LIMIT OF LIE ALGEBRAS

Let L be a Lie algebra.   We shall first recast the contraction definition given above in basis-independent form.   Let (X_i) be a fixed basis for L. (Choose indices $1 \leqslant i, j, \ldots, \leqslant n$ and the summation convention.)   Also, let (X_i^α) be a sequence of bases of L, with c_{ijk}^α the corresponding structure constants; i.e.,

$$[X_i^\alpha, X_j^\alpha] = c_{ijk}^\alpha X_k^\alpha.$$

For $\alpha = 1, 2, \ldots$, let ϕ^α be the linear transformation of L such that

$$\phi_\alpha(X_i) = X_i^\alpha.$$

Then

$$[\phi_\alpha(X_i), \phi_\alpha(X_j)] = c_{ijk}^\alpha \phi_\alpha(X_k),$$

or

$$\phi_\alpha^{-1}[\phi_\alpha(X_i), \phi_\alpha(X_j)] = c_{ijk}^\alpha X_k.$$

Thus, we see that the necessary and sufficient condition that $\lim_{\alpha \to \infty} c_{ijk}^\alpha$ exist is that

(11–9) $\lim_{\alpha \to \infty} \phi_\alpha^{-1}[\phi_\alpha(X), \phi_\alpha(Y)]$ exists for all $X, Y \in \mathbf{L}$.

Suppose that this limit does exist. Call it $[X, Y]^\infty$. Then, we see that the mapping

$$(X, Y) \to [X, Y]^\infty$$

defines a new Lie algebra structure having the same underlying vector space structure as $\mathbf{L}$, whose structure constants are $c_{ijk}^\infty = \lim_{\alpha \to \infty} c_{ijk}^\alpha$. This new algebra is then the *contraction* of the given algebra.

Let us look now at several examples of contraction. Suppose first that $\mathbf{K}$ is a subalgebra of $\mathbf{L}$, and that $\mathbf{M}$ is a linear subspace of $\mathbf{L}$ such that

$$\mathbf{L} = \mathbf{K} \oplus \mathbf{M}.$$

Suppose that

$$\phi_\alpha(X) = \left\{ \begin{array}{ll} X & \text{for } X \in \mathbf{K} \\ \dfrac{X}{\alpha} & \text{for } X \in \mathbf{M} \end{array} \right\}.$$

Then, $[X, Y]^\infty = [X, Y]$ for $X, Y \in \mathbf{K}$.

Let $X \in \mathbf{K}$, $Y \in \mathbf{M}$, and let π be the projection of the vector space $\mathbf{L}$ on $\mathbf{M}$. Then

$$\phi_\alpha^{-1}[\phi^\alpha(X), \phi^\alpha(Y)] = \frac{\phi_\alpha^{-1}}{\alpha} [X, Y] = \frac{1}{\alpha}((1 - \pi)([X, Y]) + \alpha\pi[X, Y])$$
$$\to \pi([X, Y]) \quad \text{as } \alpha \to \infty.$$

Finally, for $X, Y \in \mathbf{M}$,

$$\phi_\alpha^{-1}[\phi_\alpha(X), \phi_\alpha(Y)] = \frac{1}{\alpha^2} \phi_\alpha^{-1}[X, Y] \to 0 \quad \text{as } \alpha \to \infty.$$

Hence $[X, Y]^\infty = 0$.

The computations show us the structure of the contracted Lie algebra. It is the semidirect product of an Abelian ideal $\mathbf{M}'$ which is isomorphic *as a vector space* to $\mathbf{M}$, and of the subalgebra $\mathbf{K}$. The adjoint action of $\mathbf{K}$ on $\mathbf{M}'$ is the same as the quotient action of Ad $\mathbf{K}$ in the vector space $\mathbf{L}$ $\mathbf{K}$

Now we shall carry out another computation, which leads to a more complicated structure for the contracted algebra. Suppose that $\mathbf{L}$ is decomposed as a direct sum of subspaces $\mathbf{K} \oplus \mathbf{M} \oplus \mathbf{M}'$, with $\mathbf{K}$ a subalgebra. Let π and π' be the projection of $\mathbf{L}$ on $\mathbf{M}$ and $\mathbf{M}'$, respectively. Suppose that

$$\phi_\alpha(X) = \begin{cases} X & \text{for } X \in \mathbf{K} \\ \dfrac{X}{\alpha} & \text{for } X \in \mathbf{M} \\ \dfrac{X}{\alpha^2} & \text{for } X \in \mathbf{M}' \end{cases}.$$

Then the contracted algebra is readily computed in a similar way:

$[X, Y]^\infty = [X, Y]$ for $X, Y \in \mathbf{K}$.

$[X, Y]^\infty = \pi([X, Y])$ for $X \in \mathbf{K}, Y \in \mathbf{M}$.

$[X, Y]^\infty = \pi'([X, Y])$ for $X \in \mathbf{K}, Y \in \mathbf{M}'$.

$[X, Y]^\infty = 0$ for $X, Y \in \mathbf{M}'$ or $X \in \mathbf{M}, Y \in \mathbf{M}'$.

Now, for $X \in \mathbf{M}, Y \in \mathbf{M}$,

$$\phi_\alpha^{-1}[\phi_\alpha(X), \phi_\alpha(Y)] = \frac{1}{\alpha^2} \phi_\alpha^{-1}[X, Y]$$
$$\to \pi'([X, Y]) \qquad \text{as } \alpha \to \infty.$$

Summing up,

$$[\mathbf{L}, \mathbf{M}]^\infty \subset \mathbf{M} \qquad [\mathbf{L}, \mathbf{M}']^\infty \subset \mathbf{M}' \qquad [\mathbf{M}, \mathbf{M}]^\infty \subset \mathbf{M}',$$
$$0 = [\mathbf{M}, \mathbf{M}']^\infty = [\mathbf{M}', \mathbf{M}']^\infty.$$

Thus $\mathbf{L}^\infty$ is the semidirect sum of the ideal $\mathbf{M} \oplus \mathbf{M}'$ and the subalgebra $\mathbf{K}$. The Lie algebra on $\mathbf{M} \oplus \mathbf{M}'$ is nilpotent, and $\mathbf{M}'$ is in its center. These calculations are typical of the case where the family (ϕ^α) of linear transformations on $\mathbf{L}$ can be simultaneously diagonalized.

It is clear, at least intuitively, that there is some sort of relation between the "contraction" and the "limit" idea. We shall now show one way in which a limit of Lie algebras produces a contraction. Let $\mathbf{G}$ be a Lie algebra and let $\mathbf{L}_\alpha$ be a sequence of isomorphic subalgebras of $\mathbf{G}$, $\alpha = 1, 2, \dots$. Suppose $\mathbf{L}_1 = \mathbf{L}$, and let π be a projection operator of $\mathbf{G}$ on $\mathbf{L}$. Suppose that ϕ_α' is a Lie algebra isomorphism of $\mathbf{L}$ onto $\mathbf{L}_\alpha$. Then $\phi_\alpha = \pi \phi_\alpha'$ is a sequence of linear transformation of $\mathbf{L}$ into itself, which can be used to define contractions of $\mathbf{L}$, as explained above.

Let us see how this goes in simple cases. For example, suppose that $\mathbf{G}$ is a simple Lie algebra, and that $\mathbf{L}$ is a compact, symmetric subalgebra. Let $\mathbf{P}$ be the subspace such that

$$\mathbf{G} = \mathbf{L} \oplus \mathbf{P} \qquad [\mathbf{L}, \mathbf{P}] \subset \mathbf{P} \qquad [\mathbf{P}, \mathbf{P}] \subset \mathbf{L}.$$

Let $X \in \mathbf{P}$, and let

$$\mathbf{L}_\alpha = \mathrm{Ad}(\exp \alpha X)(\mathbf{L}).$$

Suppose that $\mathbf{G}$ is of noncompact type. Let $C(X, \mathbf{L})$ and $C(\mathbf{X}, \mathbf{P})$ be the centralizer of X in $\mathbf{L}$ and $\mathbf{P}$. Let $Y_1, \ldots, Y_m, Z_1, \ldots, Z_m$, be elements in $\mathbf{P}$ and $\mathbf{L}$ respectively such that

$$[X, Y_i] = \lambda_i X_i,$$
$$[X, Z_i] = \lambda_i Y_i \qquad (1 \leqslant i \leqslant m, \lambda_i > 0).$$

Then

$$\pi \, \mathrm{Ad}(\exp \alpha X)(Z_i) = \cosh(\lambda_i \alpha) Z_i.$$

Put $\phi_\alpha = \pi \, \mathrm{Ad}(\exp \alpha X)$, and $W_i = Y_i + Z_i$, $W_{-i} = -Y_i + Z_i$, $1 \leqslant i \leqslant m$. Then $\phi_\alpha(Z) = Z$ for $Z \in C(\mathbf{X}, \mathbf{L})$. For $1 \leqslant i \leqslant m$, $Z \in C(\mathbf{X}, \mathbf{L})$,

$$\phi_\alpha^{-1}[\phi_\alpha(z_i), \phi_\alpha(Z)] = \phi_\alpha^{-1}[\cosh(\lambda_i \alpha) Z_i, Z] = [Z_i, Z].$$

For $1 \leqslant i, j \leqslant m$,

$$
\begin{aligned}
\phi_\alpha^{-1}[\phi_\alpha(Z_i), & \phi_\alpha(Z_j)] \\
&= \cosh(\alpha \lambda_i)\cosh(\alpha \lambda_j)\phi_\alpha^{-1}([Z_i, Z_j]) \\
&= \cosh(\alpha \lambda_i)\cosh(\alpha \lambda_j)\phi_\alpha^{-1}[\tfrac{1}{2}(W_i + W_{-i}), \tfrac{1}{2}(W_j + W_{-j})] \\
&= \frac{\cosh(\alpha \lambda_i)\cosh(\alpha \lambda_j)}{4} \, \pi \, \mathrm{Ad}(\exp(-\alpha X))([W_i + W_{-i}, W_j + W_{-j}]).
\end{aligned}
$$

The limit of this as $\alpha \to \infty$ is now

$$\lim_{\alpha \to \infty} \frac{\cosh(\alpha \lambda_i)\cosh(\alpha \lambda_j)}{4} \, \pi e^{\alpha(\lambda_i + \lambda_j)}[W_{-i}, W_{-j}].$$

Let $\mathbf{L}'$ be the subalgebra of $\mathbf{G}$ spanned by $C(X, \mathbf{L})$ and the W_{-i}. $\mathbf{L}'$ and $\mathbf{L}$ are isomorphic as vector spaces: $Z \in C(X, \mathbf{L})$ goes into $\mathbf{L}$, X_i goes into W_{-i}, $1 \leqslant i \leqslant m$. We see that this linear map is a Lie algebra isomorphism between the contraction of L defined by the sequence ϕ_α and the limiting subalgebra of the sequence $\phi_\alpha'(\mathbf{L}) = \mathbf{L}_\alpha$, namely $\mathbf{L}'$. Thus, in this simple case, the "contraction" and "limit" concept essentially coincide.

CHAPTER 12

DECOMPOSITION OF TENSOR PRODUCTS OF INDUCED REPRESENTATIONS

In this chapter we shall present the general geometric background for the problem of decomposition of tensor products of induced representations.

Suppose that G is a Lie group, that H and H' are subgroups, and that $M = G/H$ and $M' = G/H'$ are the corresponding homogeneous spaces. Let $\sigma\colon H \to A(U)$ and $\sigma'\colon H' \to A(U')$ be linear representations of H and H' on vector spaces U and U'. Let E and E' be the homogeneous vector bundles on M and M' determined by the representations σ and σ', and let $\pi\colon E \to M$, $\pi'\colon E' \to M'$ be their projections. (Then the "fiber" of E is U and the "fiber" of E' is U'.) Let $\Gamma(E)$ and $\Gamma(E')$ be the space of cross sections of the bundles. As we have seen, the action of G on the vector bundles defines linear representations ρ and ρ' of G on both $\Gamma(E)$ and $\Gamma(E')$. We can then construct the tensor product $\rho \otimes \rho'$ representation of G on the tensor product $\Gamma(E) \otimes \Gamma(E')$. However, there is a more geometric picture of how the tensor product is constructed, which will be at the foundation of our treatment.

Let $\psi \in \Gamma(E)$, $\psi' \in \Gamma(E')$. ψ is then a cross-section mapping $M \to E$. Similarly for ψ'. Abstractly, for $g \in G$,

$$(\rho \otimes \rho')(g)(\psi \otimes \psi') = \rho(g)(\psi) \otimes \rho'(g)(\psi').$$

However, $\psi \otimes \psi'$ can be constructed more "geometrically" as a cross section of a vector bundle E'' on the product space $M \times M'$. E'' can be constructed by assigning to each point $(p, p') \in M \times M'$ the fiber $\pi^{-1}(p) \otimes \pi^{-1}(p')$. $\psi \otimes \psi'$ is then the cross section which assigns to $(p, p') \in M \times M'$ the point $\psi(p) \otimes \psi(p')$ in the fiber of E'' over (p, p').

There is an alternative definition of E'': Construct G'' as the product group $G \times G$, and let H'' be the subgroup $H \times H'$. Let σ'' be the tensor product representation $\sigma \otimes \sigma'$ of $H \times H'$ on the vector space $U \otimes U'$. This determines a vector bundle on the homogeneous space G''/H''. Now, G''/H'' can obviously be identified with $G/H \times G/H'$, which is

$M \times M'$. It is left to the reader to show that the vector bundle E'' is precisely the bundle determined by the representation σ''. Similarly, $\Gamma(E) \otimes \Gamma(E')$ can be identified with $\Gamma(E'')$. As notation, let us write $E'' = E \otimes E'$. Then these developments can be summed up in the striking formula

$$\Gamma(E) \otimes \Gamma(E') = \Gamma(E \otimes E').$$

Now, we can consider G as the "diagonal" subgroup of $G \times G$, i.e., as the set of (g, g), with $g \in G$. If ρ'' denotes the representation defined by the action of $G \times G$ on E'', then we see that $\rho \otimes \rho'$, considered as a representation of G, is just the representation ρ'' *restricted* to *the subgroup G of $G \times G$*. G acts on $M \times M'$ in the following way:

$$g(p, p') = (gp, gp').$$

Thus, in general G does not act *transitively* on $M \times M'$. Thus we are faced with the more general problem of the decomposition of the action of a group on cross sections of a vector bundle when the group does not act transitively on the base space of the vector bundle. It will repay our investment to consider the generalities concerning this situation.

Suppose that $\pi : E'' \to M''$ is a vector bundle setting over a space M''. Suppose that a group G acts on M'', and acts linearly on E''. Let us not suppose that G acts transitively on M''. Then we can consider the *orbit space* $G \backslash M''$: A "point" of $G \backslash M''$ is an orbit Gp of G acting on M''. Another way of putting this is to say that $G \backslash M''$ is the quotient of M by an equivalence relation: $p, q \in M''$ are equivalent if and only if there is a $g \in G$ such that $gp = q$. On the other hand, the vector bundle E'', by restriction, defines a vector bundle over each orbit Gp of G. For each point $x \in G \backslash M''$, we can associate the vector space $V(x)$, which consists of the cross sections of E'' restricted to the orbit M_x corresponding to x. This assignment of a vector space $V(x)$ to each orbit x defines a vector bundle over $G \backslash M'$. Each element ψ of $\Gamma(E)$ determines a cross section $x \to \psi_x$ of the vector bundle over $G \backslash M'$; let ψ_x be the restriction of ψ to the orbit determined by x. On the other hand, G acts on each $V(x)$, hence we may say that we have "decomposed" $\Gamma(E)$ under the action of G by exhibiting the family of linear maps $\Gamma(E) \to V(x)$, which are parameterized by the points $x \in G \backslash M''$. Of course, G acting in each $V(x)$ is not necessarily irreducible, but its decomposition is a question that can be dealt with separately (say that we "know" how to decompose the action of groups on cross sections of vector bundles when the group acts transitively on the base space of the bundle).

This does not end the problem, of course. We can consider another sort of complication. Suppose that $\Gamma(E'')$ is a Hilbert space. How then do we make each $V(x)$, for $x \in G\backslash M$, into a Hilbert space so that $\Gamma(E'')$ is exhibited as the "direct integral" of the $V(x)$'s as x ranges over $G\backslash M$? Let us look at this in a simplest case, namely where each fiber of E'' has a Hilbert-space structure which is invariant under the action of G and M'' has a measure dp'' which is invariant under the action of G. $\Gamma(E)$ can then be made into a Hilbert space by defining the inner product (,) in the following way:

For $\psi_1, \psi_2 \in \Gamma(E)$,

$$(\psi_1, \psi_2) = \int_M (\psi_1(p''), \psi_2(p'')) \, dp''.$$

$((\psi_1(p''), \psi_2(p''))$ is the Hilbert space inner product in the fiber over p''.) Now suppose that each orbit x carries a measure dp''_x and $G\backslash M$ carries a measure dx such that the "generalized Fubini theorem" holds, namely

$$\int_M f(p'') \, dp'' = \int_{G\backslash M} dx \left\{ \int_{M_x} f(p) \, dp''_x \right\}.$$

Then we can define the Hilbert space structure in $V(x)$ by defining

$$(\psi_1, \psi_2) = \int_{M_x} (\psi_1(p''), \psi_2(p'')) \, dp''_x.$$

We then see that $\Gamma(E)$ is a Hilbert space as decomposed as the "direct integral"

$$\int V(x) \, dx$$ of the family $x \to V(x)$ of Hilbert spaces.

Let us now return to the case where $E'' = E \otimes E'$, $M'' = M \times M'$, $M = G/H$, and $M' = G/H'$. Let $(\rho, \rho') \in M''$. g acts on (p, p') by sending it into (gp, gp'). Let p'_0 be the identity coset in G/H'. Then the orbit of G contains a point of the form (p, p'_0). Two such points, of the form (p, p'_0) and (gp, p'_0), can be on the same orbit of G if and only if $g \in H'$. Thus, we have proved that

> The orbits of G on $G/H \times G/H'$ are in one-to-one correspondence with the orbits of H' on G/H, i.e., with the double cosets of the form $H'gH$.

In general, the problem of computing the orbits of an intransitive group is difficult and unsolved. We shall look at one general situation which, when appropriately specialized, applies to the case of interest in physics, i.e., where G is the Poincaré group.

Suppose that G is a connected, noncompact semisimple group (with no center) and that K is a maximal compact subgroup, so that G/K is a symmetric space. Let $\mathbf{G} = \mathbf{K} \oplus \mathbf{P}$ be the Cartan decomposition of its Lie algebra. We ask how the orbits of K on G/K are computed. Let

$P = \exp(\mathbf{P})$. We have seen that the map $X \to \exp(X)$ is one-to-one and onto from $\mathbf{P}$ to P, and that G acts on P in such a way that it is identified with G/K. For $k \in K$, $X \in P$, $\exp(\mathrm{Ad}\, k(X)) = \mathrm{Ad}\, k(\exp(X)) = k \exp X k^{-1}$. Let $\mathbf{A}$ be a maximal Abelian (i.e., Cartan) subalgebra of $\mathbf{P}$. Since $\mathrm{Ad}\, K(\mathbf{A}) = \mathbf{P}$, we see that each orbit of K on G/K contains a point from $\exp(\mathbf{A})$.

Definition:

Let $N(\mathbf{A}, K)$ be the normalizer of $\mathbf{A}$ in K, i.e., the set of $k \in K$ such that $\mathrm{Ad}\, k(\mathbf{A}) = \mathbf{A}$. Let $C(\mathbf{A}, K)$ be the centralizer of $\mathbf{A}$ in K, i.e., the set of $k \in K$ such that $\mathrm{Ad}\, k(X) = X$ for all $X \in \mathbf{A}$. It can be proved that $C(\mathbf{A}, K)$ is a connected, invariant subgroup of $N(\mathbf{A}, K)$, and that the quotient group $W = N/C$ is a finite group. W is called the Weyl group of the symmetric space. W is, in fact, just a group of linear transformations on the vector space $\mathbf{A}$, since each $k \in N(\mathbf{A}, K)$ induces the linear transformation $\mathrm{Ad}\, K$ on $\mathbf{A}$, and the elements corresponding to $C(\mathbf{A}, K)$ act as the identity on $\mathbf{A}$. Now, one can prove the following theorem:

The orbits of K acting on G/K (i.e., the double cosets KgK) are in one-to-one correspondence with the orbits of W on A.

This does not end the story. There is also a very beautiful general fact (due, as is everything else in the theory of symmetric spaces, to E. Cartan) describing the orbits of W on $\mathbf{A}$. This involves the concept of the *Weyl chamber*. To define it, choose an arbitrary regular element X_0 of $\mathbf{A}$. [Recall that X_0 is regular if the centralizer of X_0 in K is of minimal dimension, i.e., if the centralizer is precisely $C(\mathbf{A}, K)$.] Let $\sum$ be the nonzero real-valued linear forms on $\mathbf{A}$ describing the roots of the symmetric space, i.e., the forms describing the eigenvalues of $\mathrm{Ad}(\mathbf{A})$. Recall that $\sum_+$, the "positive" roots, are defined as those which are positive on X_0. Now, the Weyl chamber of $\mathbf{A}$ (relative to X_0) is defined as the set of $X \in \mathbf{A}$ such that

$$\lambda(X) \geqslant 0 \qquad \text{for all } \lambda \in \textstyle\sum_+.$$

Let $\mathbf{A}^+$ be this subset of $\mathbf{A}$. (It is a convex subset.) The theorem we have in mind states that:

Each orbit of the Weyl group W on $\mathbf{A}$ contains precisely one point in $\mathbf{A}^+$. Hence, the orbits of K on G/K are in one-to-one correspondence with the points of the Weyl chamber $\mathbf{A}^+$.

The Weyl chamber is evidently dependent on the choice of X_0. However, it can also be proved that another Weyl chamber, obtained by choosing another regular element of **A**, can be transformed into the one defined by X_0 by a transformation of the Weyl group. In fact, the elements of the Weyl group are in one-to-one correspondence with the Weyl chambers. Explicitly, if X_0' is another element in the "inside" of the Weyl chamber, i.e.,

$$\lambda(X_0') > 0 \qquad \text{for all } \lambda \in \Sigma_+,$$

then the Weyl chambers defined by X_0 and X_0' coincide.

We say that an element X is a "singular" element if it lies on the "wall" of the Weyl chamber, i.e., if $\lambda(X) = 0$ for at least one $\lambda \in \Sigma_+$. The *number* of such λ's measures the degree of singularity of X. Another way of putting this is to say that the singular elements are those whose centralizers in K are larger than $C(\mathbf{A}, K)$.

In decomposing tensor products, we meet the following problem of integral geometry. If $(p, p') \rightarrow f(p, p')$ is a function on $G/K \times G/K = M \times M'$, decompose $\int_{M \times M'} f(p, p') \, dp \, dp'$ into an integration over the orbits of G, followed by an integration over the orbit space. We have seen that the orbit space for the action of G on $M \times M'$ can be identified with A^+, a Weyl chamber in a Cartan subalgebra. Then we have the problem of finding the measure on $\mathbf{A}^+$ so that $\int_{M \times M'} f(p, p') \, dp \, dp'$ can be written as the average of f over the orbits of G, followed by an integration of the resulting function over $\mathbf{A}^+$ with respect to the measure. This measure has been already computed, in a slightly different context, by Helgason [(1962), pp. 379–382]. We shall not go into detail here, but merely quote the results.

Let $X \rightarrow g(X)$ be the following function on **A**:

$$g(X) = \prod_{\lambda \in \Sigma_+} \sinh \lambda(X) \times \text{volume } (K/C(A, K)).$$

Then the measure is just g times the Euclidean measure dx on **A** given by its vector-space structure.

Turn now to the "rank-1" case, where all this becomes ridiculously simple.

Definition:

G/K is a *rank-1* symmetric space if dim $\mathbf{A} = 1$, i.e., if K acting on **P** acts transitively on the one-dimensional subspaces of **P**.

As one might expect, the theory of rank-one symmetric spaces is much simpler than the general theory of symmetric spaces. Putting aside the exceptional Lie groups, their dual compact symmetric spaces are the spheres and projective spaces. Luckily, the example of main interest in physics, the case where G is the Lorentz group and K is Wigner's little group, is of this type. (Its dual symmetric space is the sphere; it is itself just the Lobachewsky space of constant negative curvature.) Note that in the rank-1 case the Weyl group has just one element, reflection through the origin, and the Weyl chamber is just a half-line; there are no singular elements except for the origin. (In the general theory of symmetric spaces the singular elements cause most of the trouble.)

Finally, let us look in a qualitative way at what is involved in decomposing the tensor product of two representations of the Poincaré group. Changing notation, let G be the Poincaré group, i.e., $G = L \cdot T$, with L the Lorentz group and T the translation. Let α and α': $T \to C$ be characters of T, i.e., homomorphisms into the complex numbers, and let K be $L(\alpha)$, $K' = L(\alpha')$. For example, K is the set of $l \in L$ such that $\alpha(\text{Ad } k(t)) = \alpha(t)$ for all $t \in T$. We deal with the case where K and K' are a maximal compact subgroup of L, i.e., the case of real mass. Let β and β' be representations of K and K' on vector spaces U and U'.

Let $M = L/K$ and $M' = L/K'$. Let E and E' be the homogeneous vector bundles over M and M' (respectively) determined by the representations β and β'. The corresponding induced representations ρ and ρ' of G on $\Gamma(E)$ and $\Gamma(E')$ are constructed as follows:

> Let ψ: $M \to E$ be a cross section of E. For $l \in L$, $\rho(l)(\psi)$ is the transform of ψ by l, i.e., $p \to l^{-1}\psi(lp)$. For $t \in T$,
>
> $$\rho(t)(\psi)(p) = \alpha(t)\psi(p).$$

(The formulas are similar for E'.)

The tensor product is constructed as follows: An element of the vector space is a cross section ψ: $M \times M' \to E \otimes E'$. Then, for $l \in L$, $t \in T$, $p \in L/K$, and $p' \in L/K'$,

$$(\rho \otimes \rho')(l)(\psi)(p, p') = l^{-1}\psi(lp, lp'),$$
$$(\rho \otimes \rho')(t)(\psi)(p) = \alpha(t)\alpha'(t)\psi(p).$$

The orbits of G acting on $M \times M'$ are all (except for the "singular" orbits, which are a set of measure zero) of the form $G/(K \cdot T)$. We can sum up in the following way:

> The irreducible representations of the Poincaré group are determined by a character α of T (the "momentum" of the particle described by the representation) and an irreducible representa-

tion β (which is "spin") of $L(\alpha)$, the "little subgroup" corresponding to α. In case the momentum vector determined by α has real mass, $L(\alpha)$ is conjugate to $K = SO(3, R)$, the maximal compact subgroup of the Lorentz group L. The tensor product of two representations of real mass decomposes into a one-parameter direct sum of irreducible representations whose momentum vectors are the sum of the momenta and whose "spin" is contained among the representations of K obtained by decomposing the tensor-product representation $\beta \otimes \beta'$ of K.

[For the most complete treatment in the physics literature that is known to the author, refer to the paper by Moussa and Stora (1965).]

CHAPTER 13

THE GROUP–THEORETIC VERSION OF THE FOURIER TRANSFORM

One of our main goals in these notes is to indicate how the representation of semidirect products (e.g., the Poincaré group) and semisimple groups can be treated on a unified basis by means of the theory of induced representations. However, in the traditional treatment of the Poincaré group the Fourier transform plays a central role, relating the representations as cross sections of vector bundles on Minkowski space and as cross sections of vector bundles on the quotient of the Lorentz group by the little subgroups. At first sight, it would seem that this is a special feature that would have no analogue for semisimple groups, since they cannot act transitively on Euclidean spaces, as can the Poincaré group. (One physical motivation for wanting to treat representations of the Poincaré and semisimple groups in a unified way might be described as follows. Minkowski space can be described geometrically as a manifold with a pseudo-Riemannian metric of Lorentz type of zero curvature, with the Poincaré group as the group of its isometries. This group is important in physics because, of course, relativistic physics is closely tied to the geometry of this space. Suppose, however, that we want to consider "physics" on a space of the same type with small constant curvature, i.e., the deSitter space. Its group of isometries is semisimple; hence its linear representations should be determined and compared with those of the Poincaré group. In fact, in terms of the notations of Chapter 11, the limit of these groups as the curvature goes to zero is the Poincaré group.)

However, there is a group-theoretical construction which in certain situations reduces to the Fourier transform. To describe it, we need the following data: a Lie group G, two subgroups L and H of G, and linear representations σ and σ' of L and H, respectively, on a vector space U, which determines vector bundles E and E' over G/L and G/H. Thus, elements ψ and ψ' of $\Gamma(E)$ and $\Gamma(E')$ can be considered as maps $G \to U$ and $G \to U'$ such that

$$\psi'(gh) = \sigma'(h^{-1})\psi(g) \quad \text{for } g \in G, h \in H,$$
$$\psi(gl) = \sigma(l^{-1})\psi(g) \quad \text{for } g \in G, l \in L.$$

Now, there is a transform $\psi \to \hat{\psi}$ associating, at least in a formal way, an element $\hat{\psi} \in \Gamma(E)$ with each map $\psi: G \to U$:

(13–1)
$$\hat{\psi}(g) = \int_L \sigma(l)\psi(gl)\,dl.$$

Here, "dl" means the left-invariant volume element on the Lie group L. (Of course, since L is not necessarily compact, this integral might not necessarily converge, but we shall not worry about that here.) Then, for $l_0 \in L$,

$$\psi(gl_0) = \int_L \sigma(l)\psi(gl_0l)\,dl,$$

using the left invariance of dl,

$$\int_L \sigma(l_0^{-1}l)\psi(gl)\,dl = \sigma(l_0^{-1})\int_L \sigma(l)\psi(gl)\,dl = \sigma(l_0^{-1})\psi(g).$$

Hence, $\hat{\psi}$ is really an element of $\Gamma(E)$. If we apply this to an element $\psi \in \Gamma(E')$, we obtain a map $\Gamma(E') \to \Gamma(E)$. This commutes with the action of G on $\Gamma(E')$ and $\Gamma(E)$. In fact,

$$\widehat{\rho(g_0)(\psi)}(g) = \int_L \sigma(l)\psi[\rho(g_0)(\psi)](gl)\,dl$$
$$= \int_L \sigma(l)\psi(g_0gl)\,dl$$
$$= \rho(g_0)(\hat{\psi})(g),$$

which shows explicitly that the map $\Gamma(E') \to \Gamma(E)$ commutes with the action of g.

To show the relation to the classical Fourier transform, suppose now that G is a semidirect product $L \cdot T$ of an Abelian invariant subgroup T and a semisimple Lie group L. Suppose H is of the form $K \cdot T$, where K is a maximal compact subgroup of L. $\hat{\psi}$ is determined by its restriction to T:

(13–2)
$$\hat{\psi}(\tau) = \int_L \sigma(l)\psi(\tau l)\,dl = \int_L \sigma(l)\psi(l \cdot l^{-1}\tau l)\,dl$$
$$= \int_L \sigma(l)\sigma'(\mathrm{Ad}\ l^{-1}(\tau))\psi(l)\,dl.$$

Suppose that K is the "little" subgroup of L corresponding to the representation σ'; i.e.,

$$\sigma'(\mathrm{Ad}\ k(\tau)) = \sigma'(\tau) \qquad \text{for } k \in K,\ \tau \in T.$$

Suppose also that

$$\sigma'(k) = \sigma(k) \qquad \text{for } k \in K.$$

Now, if $l \to f(l)$ is a function on L, we have a decomposition of the form

$$\int_L f(l) \, dl = \int_{L/K} dp \left\{ \int_K f(lk) \, dk \right\}.$$

[Since $l \to \int f(lk) \, dk$ is invariant under right multiplication by K, it can be considered as a function on L/K. dp denotes the volume element on L/K invariant under the action of L.] Continuing with (13–2), we have

$$(13\text{–}3) \quad \hat{\psi}(\tau) = \int_{L/K} dp \left\{ \int_K \sigma(lk)\sigma'(\mathrm{Ad}(lk)^{-1}(\tau))\psi(lk) \, dk \right\}$$

$$= \int_{L/K} dp \left\{ \int_K \sigma(l)\sigma(k)\sigma'(\mathrm{Ad}\ l^{-1}(\tau))\psi(l)\sigma(k^{-1}) \, dk \right\}$$

$$= \int_{L/K} dp \{\sigma(l)\sigma'(\mathrm{Ad}\ l^{-1}(\tau))\psi(l)\},$$

since $\sigma(k) = \sigma'(k)$. [Note that $l \to \sigma(l)\sigma'(\mathrm{Ad}\ l^{-1}(\tau))\psi(l)$ is invariant under right multiplication by K, which shows that it is a function on L/K, as the formula indicates.]

If, for example, U and U' are both one-dimensional [so that $\sigma(l) =$ identity for $l \in L$, i.e., the spin-zero case], $\psi(\tau)$ reduces to the usual Fourier transform formulas for solutions of the Klein-Gordon equation:

$$\hat{\psi}(x) = \int_{p^2 = m^2} e^{ip \cdot x} \frac{d^3 p}{|p_4|}.$$

For then L/K is identified with the quadric $p^2 = m^2$ in **Minkowski** space. $[p = (p_1, \ldots, p_4);\ p \cdot x$ is the Lorentz inner product; $d^3 p / |p_4|$ is the volume element on the quadratic which is invariant under the action of the Lorentz group.]

We leave to the reader the program of carrying out the sort of calculations that are usually made in physics with the Fourier transform in this group-theoretic setting. For example, one such problem might be to find the inner product on the $\hat{\psi}$-representation corresponding to the inner product in the ψ-representation defined by the L-invariant measure on L/K. The reader might also want to consider the mass-zero and mass-negative representations, where the little groups are no longer compact.

Now we turn to exhibiting the analogous "Fourier transform" in case G is a semisimple group. (We shall only consider a simple illustrative situation.) Changing notation, let K be its maximal compact subgroup, and $G = KAN^+$ on Iwasawa decomposition. Let $C(A, K)$ be the centralizer of A in K, and let $H = C(A, K)AN^+$. Suppose representation σ of K is the identity; the representation σ' of H is one-dimensional, so that σ' is the identity on $C(A, K)N^+$, and is just a character of A. (The corresponding vector bundle on G/H is thus a line bundle.)   Then, for $\psi \in \Gamma(E')$,

$$(13\text{–}4) \qquad\qquad \hat{\psi}(g) = \int_K \psi(gk)\, dk.$$

Note that there are no problems with the convergence of the integral, since K is compact.

Theorem 13–1

A cross section ψ of the line bundle E' over G/H is an eigenvector of each Casimir operator of $U(\mathbf{G})$.   Hence, its transform $\hat{\psi}$, considered as a function on G/K, is also an eigenfunction of each Casimir operator of $U(\mathbf{G})$.   If σ' is the identity, ψ, hence also $\hat{\psi}$, is annihilated by each Casimir operator of $U(\mathbf{G})$.

Proof:

Introduce a coordinate system $(x_1, \ldots, x_n) = x$ for a neighborhood of the identity coset of G/H, equal to zero at the identity coset.   In this coordinate system, a cross section ψ of $\Gamma(E')$ is represented by a function $\psi(x)$.   Introduce indices $i_1, i_2, \ldots$ running between 1 and n.   Suppose Δ is a differential operator of order p acting on $\Gamma(E')$ which commutes with G.   [For example, Δ may be a Casimir operator of $U(\mathbf{G})$.]   We shall prove that p is zero, i.e., Δ just acts on ψ by multiplying by a function.

Say that Δ takes the form

$$\Delta(\psi) = A_{i_1 \cdots i_p} \frac{\partial \psi}{\partial x_{i_1} \cdots \partial x_{i_p}} + \cdots.$$

(The unwritten terms involve derivatives of order lower than p.)   For $X \in \mathbf{G}$, $\rho'(X)(\psi)$ will be of the form

$$\rho'(X)(\psi) = B_i \frac{\partial \psi}{\partial x_i} + C\psi.$$

[B_i are functions determined by the action of the one-parameter group $t \to \exp(tX)$ on G/H.   The coefficient C depends on X and the vector bundle, hence is zero if σ' is the identity.]

$$0 = [\Delta, \rho'(X)](\psi) = \Delta\rho'(X)(\psi) - \rho'(X)\Delta(\psi),$$

which expresses the fact that Δ is invariant under the action of G on $\Gamma(E')$.

Choose X as a regular element of $\mathbf{A}$.   In fact, we can choose X so that $\mathbf{H}$ is spanned by the eigenvectors of $\mathrm{Ad}\, X$ for nonnegative eigenvalues;

hence Ad X acting on G/H has only negative eigenvalues. With this choice of X, $B_i(0) = 0$, reflecting the fact that the one-parameter group $t \to \exp(tX)$ leaves invariant the point of G/H whose coordinates are $x = 0$. Then

$$\left(\frac{\partial B_i}{\partial x_j}(0) \right)$$

is essentially the matrix of Ad X acting in G/H.

In computing $[\phi(X), \Delta]$, let us suppose, for notational convenience, that $p = 2$: This case is sufficiently representative of the general case. Then

$$[\Delta, \phi(X)](\psi)(0) = A_{i_1 i_2} \left[\frac{\partial B_i}{\partial x_{i_2}} \frac{\partial^2 \psi}{\partial x_{i_1} \partial x_i} + \frac{\partial B_i}{\partial x_{i_1}} \frac{\partial^2}{\partial x_i \partial x_{i_2}} \psi \right] + \cdots .$$

(The unwritten terms involve either lower-order partial derivatives or terms that are zero at $x = 0$.)

Suppose, for example, that

$$\frac{\partial B_i}{\partial x_j}(0) = \begin{cases} 0 & \text{if } i \neq j \\ \lambda_i & \text{if } i = j \end{cases} .$$

Then, the condition $[\Delta, \phi'(X)](\psi) = 0$ requires that

$$A_{i,i}(0)\lambda_i \frac{\partial^2 \psi}{\partial x_{i_1} \partial x_i} + A_{i i_2}(0)\lambda_i \frac{\partial^2 \psi}{\partial x_i \partial x_{i_2}} = 0,$$

or

$$A_{i_1 i}(0) = 0 \qquad \text{for } 1 \leqslant i, i_1 \leqslant n$$

(since λ_i is $\neq 0$). Then, the pth-order terms for $p \geqslant 1$ of Δ are zero at $x = 0$, i.e., at the identity coset of G/H. However, the argument can be repeated at every point of G/H. The result is that $\Delta(x)$ must be of the form

$$\psi \to A\psi.$$

Then

$$[\rho'(X), \Delta(\psi)] = \left(B_i \frac{\partial A}{\partial x_i} \right) \psi,$$

forcing: $B_i(\partial A/\partial x_i) = 0$. Since this is true for each $X \in \mathbf{G}$, A must be a constant, i.e., Δ is a constant multiple of the identity. If σ' is the identity, and if Δ is the differential operator induced by a Casimir operator, then Δ has no zeroth-order term, forcing Δ to be identically zero. Q.E.D.

This sort of "Fourier transform" can be specialized to give both the "Poisson integral formula" for harmonic functions on symmetric spaces and the "Harish-Chandra formula" for spherical functions. [See the papers by Furstenberg (1963) and the author (1961, 1962) for the Poisson formula and Helgason's book (1962) for the Harish-Chandra formula.]

The Poisson formula is obtained by taking σ as the identity, so that $\psi \in \Gamma(E')$ satisfies

$$\psi(gh) = \psi(g),$$

i.e., is a function on G/H.   Now, $g \to \hat{\psi}(g)$, given by

$$\hat{\psi}(g) = \int_K \psi(gk) \, dk,$$

is, as a function G/K, annihilated by all the Casimir operators of $U(G)$, when the operators are considered as differential operators on G/K via the action of G on G/K.   (This follows from Theorem 13–1.)   Now, the function $k \to \psi(gk)$ is invariant under right multiplication by $C(\mathbf{A}, K)$, hence defines a function on $K/C(\mathbf{A}, K)$.   We have seen that $K/C(A, K)$ can be identified with G/H also, from the Iwasawa decomposition of G. Let b denote a typical point of $K/C(A, K) = B$, and let db be a volume element on B invariant under the action of K on G.   (This invariant volume element exists, since K is compact.) G also acts on B, but the volume element is not invariant under the action of G.   Let $J_g(b)$ be the Jacobian of this action; i.e.,

$$\int_B f(gb) \, db = \int_B J_g(b)f(b) \, db$$

for each function $b \to f(b)$ on B.   Then

$$\hat{\psi}(g) = \int_B J_g(b)\psi(b) \, db,$$

[when we regard the function $k \to \psi(k)$ as a function $b \to \psi(b)$ on B]. This is the Poisson formula.

On the other hand, the Harish-Chandra formula starts with a nontrivial one-dimensional representation ρ' of H, and a $\psi \in \Gamma(E')$ that is invariant under the action of K on G/K; i.e.,

$$\psi(kg) = \psi(g).$$

The Iwasawa decomposition writes g as kan, with $k \in K$, $a \in A$, and $n \in N^+$; hence

$$\begin{aligned} \psi(g) = \psi(an) &= \sigma'(an)\psi(e) \\ &= \sigma'(a)\psi(e). \end{aligned}$$

If we normalize ψ to be one at the identity element e of G, we see that ψ is uniquely determined by σ'.   On the other hand, $\hat{\psi}$ given by (13–5) is, as a function on G/K, invariant under the action of K, and an eigenfunction for the Casimir operators of $U(G)$, i.e., is what Helgason calls a spherical function on the symmetric space G/K.† Since Helgason gives an extensive and excellent survey of their properties in Chapter 10 of his book, we shall not pursue it further here, beyond pointing out to the reader that the theory gives in a systematic way many of the properties of the "special functions" of mathematical physics.

For example, the integral representation of the Legendre function $P_a(\theta)$,

$$P_a(\cosh r) = \frac{1}{2\pi} \int_0^{2\pi} (\cosh r + \sinh r \cos \mu)^a \, d\mu,$$

is a special case of the Harish-Chandra formula [associated with the symmetric space $SL(2, R)/SO(2, R)$].

Note the relation of Theorem 13–1 to the question of irreducibility of representations of G on $\Gamma(E')$. It has been conjectured that this representation is always irreducible, which would imply the result of Theorem 13–1. (However, note that the proof of Theorem 13–1 is considerably simpler than proofs of irreducibility.) This is not yet proved in complete generality, although substantial results in this direction have been proved by Gel'fand and Neumark (1957) and Bruhat (1956). [Strictly speaking, they are interested in the case where the representation ρ of G on $\Gamma(E)$ has multipliers inserted to make it unitary. However, the proof of Theorem 13–1 goes over to this case also.]

Finally, a transform closely related to the one we have been considering was introduced by Gel'fand and Graev (1964), and it plays an important role in the analysis of representations of noncompact semisimple Lie groups. Let G be a connected noncompact semisimple Lie group with finite center. Consider an Iwasawa decomposition:

$$G = AN^+K.$$

Let M be the symmetric space G/K, and let p_0 be the point of M representing the identity coset. Let N be the *orbit* N^+p_0 of N at M, considered as a submanifold of M. Consider the collection $\{gN\}$ of translates by elements of G of this one submanifold. A submanifold of M occurring among this collection is called a *horocycle* of M. (The motivation for this name comes from geometry, and will not concern us here.) Now, the subgroup of G consisting of the elements that transform N into itself is readily seen to be $N^+C(A, K)$ [recall that $C(A, K)$ consists of those $k \in K$ that commute with every element of A]; hence the "space" of horocycles is just

---

† The definition varies from author to author. Some call these "zonal spherical functions."

the coset space $G/N^+C(A, K)$. Take a function $p \to \psi(p)$ on M. Now, each horocycle inherits from M a volume element that is invariant under the subgroup of G that maps the horocycle into itself. Hence we can form the "transform" $\hat{\psi}$ of ψ by assigning to each horocycle [which is just then an element of $G/N^+C(A, K)$] the integral of ψ over this horocycle. $\hat{\psi}$, obtained in this way, is a function on $G/N^+C(A, K)$. We leave it to the reader to verify that this transform $\psi \to \hat{\psi}$ is the same as our basic "Fourier transform" of functions on G/L to functions on G/H, with K playing the role of L and $N^+C(A, K)$ playing the role of H. This transform is, in a sense, the "reverse" of the Harish-Chandra transform, but we cannot go into that here. Further work on the integration-over-horocycle theory has been done by Helgason (1963).

CHAPTER 14

COMPACTIFICATIONS OF HOMOGENEOUS SPACES

Problems of asymptotic behavior of functions defined by differential and integral equations are very important for physics. However, these are usually not random equations but those possessing a high degree of symmetry. Despite this basic fact, the methods that are usually developed mask the special group-theoretic nature of the problem. Those asymptotic problems are not of immediate, direct concern, since an adequate survey cannot be made here, but may be regarded as part of the underlying motivation for the geometric work to follow.

We might also pose a more speculative reason for studying compactifications. We would like to make mathematical sense out of the vague ideas concerning "high-energy limit" and "approximate symmetry" that are now floating around in the physics literature. For example, "energy" is a function on Minkowski momentum space. "High-energy limit" might mean, geometrically, passing to the boundary of a compactification of Minkowski space (for example, the conformal compactification to be described below). A geometric picture of "high-energy limit" might go as follows: One might have two groups G_1 and G_2 acting on a space M, leaving invariant a subset D of M, hence also leaving invariant the boundary ∂D of D in M. One might picture the groups not commuting on D, but actually commuting on ∂D. At points of D "near" to the boundary, one group would be an approximate symmetry of the other.

However, the grand goal of understanding the geometric foundation of these important questions will remain in the background, since we shall only develop a specific set of ideas here. Despite its fundamental importance, relevant compactification ideas have not been studied very much by mathematicians. The most intensive work has been in connection with the "ideal boundary" of Riemann surfaces, i.e., the two-dimensional situation. The higher dimensional problems of importance in physics have quite a different, more difficult nature, and require much more emphasis on group-theoretic ideas. Recent important work has been done by Satake (1960), Furstenberg (1963), and Moore (1964). The topics treated here are based on the author's work (1962, 1964, 1965a, 1965b).

117

Definition:

Let G, H, G', H' be Lie groups, with H a subgroup of G, H' and G subgroups of G'. Suppose that $H' \cap G = H$. Then, the coset space G/H may be considered as a subspace of G'/H' by assigning the coset gH' to the coset gH, for $g \in G$. If, in addition, G'/H' is compact, we will say that it is a *homogeneous space compactification* of G/H.

An alternative, more geometric picture might be useful. Suppose that a Lie group G acts on a compact space M, and that the isotropy subgroup of G at the point $p_0 \in M$ is the subgroup H of G. Then the coset space G/H is imbedded in M as the orbit Gp_0 of G at the point p_0. If, in addition, G is contained in a transformation group G' on M that acts transitively on M, we have the situation described above, with H' the isotropy subgroup of G at p_0.

Adopting this transformation-group viewpoint, we can see several important general problems. Since G leaves the orbit Gp_0 invariant, it also leaves invariant the closure $\overline{Gp_0}$ of the orbit and the boundary of the orbit. What is the structure of the orbits of G on the boundary? Given two sequences of elements $g_1, g_2, \ldots$ and $g_1', g_2', \ldots$ of G, what is the condition that the sequences $g_1 p_0, g_2 p_0, \ldots$ and $g_1' p_0, g_2' p_0, \ldots$ of elements of Gp_0 approach the same point of the boundary of Gp_0? A beginning toward answering some of these questions in case G is a semisimple group and H is a maximal compact subgroup of G has been made in a paper by the author (1965a). We will not attempt such generality, but will present some of the more concrete results from this paper.

GRASSMANIAN COMPACTIFICATIONS OF HOMOGENEOUS SPACES

We shall first describe Grassman manifolds. Let V be a finite-dimensional real vector space. If r is an integer less than the dimension of V, let $G^r(V)$ be the "space" of r-dimensional real subspaces of V, which is called the *Grassman manifold of r-dimensional subspaces of V*. A typical element of $G^r(V)$ will be denoted by U. $G^r(V)$ itself can be exhibited as a coset space, which will provide a topology and manifold structure for it. To see this, let $GL(V)$ be the linear transformations of V whose determinant is nonzero. $GL(V)$ acts on $G^r(V)$ in the obvious way as a transformation group. If $g: V \to V$ is an invertible linear transformation and $U \subset V$ is an r-dimensional linear subspace, so is its transform $g(U)$. Regarding U as a "point" of $G^r(V)$, this defines the action of $GL(V)$ on $G^r(V)$. Since any two p-dimensional subspaces can be transformed onto each other by a linear transformation (proof: choose bases for both), $GL(V)$ acts transitively on $G^r(V)$. Now, $GL(V)$ is a Lie group. [Proof: Choosing a basis for V, $GL(V)$ becomes isomorphic to $GL(n, R)$, where $n = \dim V$.] If U is a fixed r-dimensional subspace, the isotropy subgroup of $GL(V)$ is the space of transformations mapping U into itself. If the basis of V is chosen so that the first r elements lie in U, then H becomes the set of matrices with zeros in the upper-right-hand block.

A maximal compact subgroup of $GL(V)$, namely one isomorphic to $SO(n, R)$, acts transitively on $G^r(V)$. With proper choice of basis, the isotropy subgroup of $SO(n, R)$ becomes $SO(r, R) \times SO(n - r, R)$. In particular, $G^r(V)$ is itself compact.

For the proof, one has only to choose a positive-definite inner product for V, and consider only positively oriented orthonormal bases of V. $GL(n, R)$ reduces to the subgroup $SO(n, R)$.

Turn now to a Lie group G which has a faithful representation by linear transformations on V. For the sake of simplicity of notation, g will denote both a typical element of G and the linear transformation it induces on V. Then, G, as a subgroup of $GL(V)$, acts on $G^r(V)$. If U is an r-dimensional subspace of V, and if $H \subset G$ is the isotropy subgroup of G at U, we evidently have exhibited G/H as the orbit of G on $G^r(V)$ at U, and have "compactified" G/H by plunging it into $G^r(V)$. In terms of our basic definition, $G' = GL(V)$ and $H' =$ isotropy subgroup of $GL(V)$ at U.

Let us look a little more closely at what "convergence" means in $G^r(V)$, in order to see its "geometric" meaning. Let $(v_1, \ldots, v_n)$ be a basis of V such that $(v_1, \ldots, v_r)$ is a basis of U.

Theorem 14–1

Let $g_1, g_2, \ldots$ be a sequence of elements of G, and let U' be another r-dimensional subspace of V. Then if $\lim_{\alpha \to \infty} g_\alpha(U) = U'$, the following condition is satisfied:

(14–1) Whenever $u_1, u_2, \ldots$ is a sequence of elements of U such that $\lim_{\alpha \to \infty} g_\alpha(u_\alpha)$ converges, the limit belongs to U'.

Conversely, if (14–1) is satisfied, there is a subsequence of the (g_α) such that $g_\alpha(U) \to U'$ as $\alpha \to \infty$ through the subsequence.

Proof:

Let $U_\alpha = g_\alpha(U)$, $\alpha = 1, 2, \ldots$. Our basic definition of "convergence" in $G^r(V)$ in terms of the coset space G'/H' requires that there exist a sequence $g_1', g_2', \ldots$ of elements of $GL(V)$ such that $\lim_{\alpha \to \infty} g_\alpha' = g'$, $g_\alpha'(U) = U_\alpha$, and $g'(U) = U'$. Then $g_\alpha^{-1} g_\alpha' \in H'$; i.e.,

$$(g_\alpha^{-1} g_\alpha')(U) = U \qquad \text{for } \alpha = 1, 2, \ldots.$$

Put $h_\alpha = g_\alpha^{-1} g_\alpha'$; i.e., $g_\alpha = g_\alpha' h_\alpha^{-1}$. Suppose $u_1, u_2 \ldots$ is a sequence of elements of U such that

$$\lim_{\alpha \to \infty} g_\alpha(u_\alpha) = u'.$$

Then, $g_\alpha(u_\alpha) = g_\alpha' h_\alpha^{-1}(u_\alpha)$. Since $\lim g'$ exists, $\lim_{\alpha \to \infty} h_\alpha^{-1}(u_\alpha)$ must exist. Since $u_\alpha \in U$, $h_\alpha^{-1}(u_\alpha)$ must converge, as $\alpha \to \infty$, to an element $u_0 \in U$. Then $u' = g'(u_0) \in U'$, which shows that (14-1) is satisfied.

Conversely, suppose that (14-1) is satisfied. Now, for each α, the elements $g_\alpha(v_1), \ldots, g_\alpha(v_r)$ are linearly independent. At most, taking subsequences, we can find a sequence of elements $(g_\alpha') \in GL(V)$ such that

$\lim_{\alpha \to \infty} g_\alpha' g_\alpha(v_i)$ converges for $1 \leqslant i \leqslant n$, hence $\lim_{\alpha \to \infty} g_\alpha' g_\alpha = g \in GL(V)$, but also $g_\alpha' g_\alpha(v_1), \ldots, g_\alpha' g_\alpha(v_r)$ is a linear combination of $g_\alpha(v_1), \ldots, g_\alpha(v_r)$.†

Thus, for each α, $g_\alpha^{-1} g_\alpha' g_\alpha = h_\alpha \in H'$, i.e., maps U into itself.

Now $g_\alpha' g_\alpha = g_\alpha h_\alpha$; hence

$$g(U) = \lim_{\alpha \to \infty} g_\alpha(U).$$

Now $\lim_{\alpha \to \infty} g_\alpha h_\alpha(v_i)$ converges for $1 \leqslant i \leqslant r$.

By 14-1, it converges to an element of U', since $h_\alpha(v_i) \in U$ for $1 \leqslant i \leqslant r$. But again $g_\alpha h_\alpha = g_\alpha' g_\alpha \to g$ as $\alpha \to \infty$. Hence, $g(U) = U'$, which shows that $\lim_{\alpha \to \infty} g_\alpha(U) = U'$, as required.   Q.E.D.

---

† For example, this construction might proceed as follows. Provide V with a positive-definite inner product. One applies the Gram-Schmidt orthogonalization process to each basis $g_\alpha(v_1), \ldots, g_\alpha(v_n)$. The result is a sequence of orthonormal bases $g_\alpha' g_\alpha(v_1), \ldots, g_\alpha' g_\alpha(v_n)$ which will have the required properties, since given a sequence of orthonormal bases one can always find a subsequence that converges. Recall how the Gram-Schmidt process proceeds. Let $<\ ,\ >$ be the inner product: $g_\alpha(v_1)$ is replaced by

$$g_\alpha' g_\alpha(v_1) = \frac{g_\alpha(v_1)}{<g_\alpha(v_1), g_\alpha(v_1)>^{1/2}};$$

$g_\alpha(v_2)$ is replaced by

$$\frac{g_\alpha(v_2) - <g_\alpha(v_2), g_\alpha' g_\alpha(v_1)> g_\alpha' g_\alpha(v_1)}{\text{length of the numerator}},$$

and so forth.

Remark:

This pattern of argument fits into a much more general context that may be useful in further investigations. Suppose that instead of being a finite-dimensional vector space, V is a general topological space. Suppose that G' is a topological group that acts as a transformation group on V. Now, G' permutes the closed subsets of V: Suppose that E [replacing $G^r(V)$] is a family of closed subsets of V that is acted on transitively by G', with subgroup H' as an isotropy subgroup, so that E can be given a topological structure by identification with the coset space G'/H'. Suppose now that G is a subgroup of G', with $H = G \cap H'$, so that the coset space G/H is imbedded in G'/H'. Then, condition (14–1) relates the closure of the orbit of G/H in G'/H' to what one intuitively thinks of as "convergence" of subsets of a space. However, the converse of condition (14–1) will not be true in general, since we have used a rather special property of the specific situation, namely that expressed by the footnote. However, the argument will go through if G' has a compact subgroup which also acts transitively on G'/H'.

To the best of the author's knowledge, there is no general characterization of the homogeneous spaces G/H which admits such a compactification. However, for the homogeneous spaces that are of the most immediate mathematical or physical interest, there are fairly obvious methods for choosing the representation.

The first case of interest is that where the adjoint representation of G is faithful, and where **H** is its own normalizer in **G**; i.e., $X \in \mathbf{G}$ and

$$[X, \mathbf{H}] \subset \mathbf{H} \text{ implies } X \in \mathbf{H}.$$

Then we can take V as **G** itself, the representation of G on **V** as the adjoint representation, and the subspace U as **H**. Theorem 14–1 shows us the relation to the idea of "limits" of Lie groups introduced in Chapter 11. For example, if U' is a subspace of V given by a subalgebra **H'** of **G** and U' is on the closure of the orbit of G at the point U of $G^r(V)$, then **H'** is the limit of **H** written **G**. Then the computations of limits of certain subalgebras presented in Chapter 11 translate over to computations about the closure of the orbit G/H in $G^r(V)$.

For example, suppose that G is a semisimple, noncompact group without center and that H is a maximal compact subgroup. Let $G = HAN^+$ be an Iwasawa decomposition of G, and let X be a regular element of **A** in the Weyl chamber of **A** used to define this specific Iwasawa decomposition. We see that the limit of $t \to \exp(tX)(\mathbf{H})$ is the subalgebra $\mathbf{C(A, H)} + \mathbf{N^+}$.

The isotropy subgroup of G at this point of $G^r(V)$ is then the subgroup $C(A, H)AN^+ = L$. In previous chapters we have seen the importance of these homogeneous spaces G/L for the problem of exhibiting the representations of G. Presumably the fact that G/L lies in the "boundary" of the symmetric space G/H plays an important role in the study of the analytical properties of these representations. This has been made explicit for the special case of harmonic functions on G/H by works of Furstenberg (1963), Moore (1964), and the author (1961, 1962) (although even here much of the finer structure of the theory is yet to be done), but the general situation is not at all clear.

One special computation is instructive. Suppose that $G = SL(2, R)$, $H = SO(2, R)$. Instead of this general sort of compactification, we can use a more familiar one, where G/H is embedded as the unit circle in the complex z-plane. In fact, $SL(2, C)$ acts on the complex z-plane via linear fractional transformations:

$$\begin{pmatrix} a & b \\ c & d \end{pmatrix} \text{ acting on } z \text{ is just } \frac{az + b}{cz + d}.$$

(The point at infinity must also be added to the complex z-plane, of course.) Now, $SL(2, R)$ preserves the real axis, $z - \bar{z} = 0$, hence maps the upper half-plane into itself. One can see easily that it acts transitively on the upper half-plane. Let us look at the isotropy subgroup at $z = i$:

$$\frac{ai + b}{ci + d} = i$$

implies

$$ai + b = -c + di,$$

forcing

$$a = d; \ b = -c;$$

$ad - bc = 1$ forces

$$a^2 + b^2 = 1.$$

Thus,

$$\begin{pmatrix} a, & b \\ c, & d \end{pmatrix}$$

is an orthogonal matrix; i.e., the isotropy subgroup is $SO(2, R)$. On the other hand, the upper half-plane is conformal to the interior of the unit circle by a linear fractional transformation; hence $SL(2, R)$ is conjugate within $SL(2, C)$ to a subgroup which acts transitively on the interior of the unit circle. In this sense we can say that the interior is just $SL(2, R)/SO(2, R)$.

Suppose now that $\phi(z)$ is a complex-valued function on G/H that is invariant under H, and that it is an eigenfunction for the Casimir operators of $U(\mathbf{G})$, i.e., is a spherical function on G/H. Helgason shows that the Harish-Chandra formula amounts to the following. An Iwasawa decomposition $G = HAN^+$ can be chosen such that, for $X \in \mathbf{A}$,

$$\phi(\exp tX \cdot 0) = P_a(\cosh t) = \frac{1}{2\pi} \int_0^{2\pi} (\cosh t + \sinh t \cos \theta)^a \, d\theta.$$

Now, it can be calculated that

$$z(\exp tX \cdot 0) = \frac{e^t - 1}{e^t + 1}.$$

This formula makes the asymptotic behavior of $\phi(\exp tX \cdot 0)$ as $t \to \infty$ transparent. In fact,

$$e^t = \frac{1 - z(\exp tX \cdot 0)}{1 + z(\exp tX \cdot 0)};$$

hence

$$\cosh t = \frac{1 + z^2}{1 - z^2} \qquad \sinh t = \frac{2z}{1 - z^2},$$

$$\phi(\exp tX \cdot 0) = \frac{1}{2\pi(1 - z(\exp tX \cdot 0)^2)^a} \int_0^{2\pi} [(1 + z^2) + 2z \cos \theta]^a \, d\theta.$$

Now, the integrand has no singularity as $t \to \infty$. The point of this simple calculation is that the geometric picture of how G/H is compactified (i.e., as the interior of the unit circle) immediately guides one to the asymptotic behavior. This is esthetically satisfying, since, as we saw in the previous chapter, the Harish-Chandra formula involved a "Fourier transform" of a function on the homogeneous space G/AN^+, which is just the unit circle, i.e., the "boundary" of G/H in the compactification. We shall leave the problem of asymptotic behavior of the spherical functions at this point, since carrying it further would involve us in the technicalities of symmetric spaces. We refer the reader to work by Harish-Chandra (1958) and Gindikin and Karpelevitch (1962).

CHAPTER 15

ON THE CLASSIFICATION
OF SUBGROUPS

It is obviously a problem of great interest for both mathematics and physics to classify the subalgebras of a given Lie algebra. (For example, one might want to know in how many ways the Poincaré group can be a subgroup of a larger group.) However, approached directly, this is a formless problem of considerable complexity, and it is more fruitful to divide it into subproblems that individually have a more precise algebraic or geometric content. In this chapter we shall survey some of these diverse results. The basic references are Dynkin (1957a, 1957b) and Borel and deSiebenthal (1949).

First, we shall describe how a general Lie algebra is put together from the semisimple and the solvable Lie algebras. Let $\mathbf{G}$ be a Lie algebra. If it is not semisimple, it has solvable ideals. The sum of all solvable ideals is a "maximal" solvable ideal of $\mathbf{G}$, called the *radical*, and denoted by $\mathbf{R(G)}$. Then, the quotient Lie algebra $\mathbf{G}/\mathbf{R(G)} = \mathbf{S}$ is semisimple. *Levi's theorem* then asserts that this extension of $\mathbf{S}$ by $\mathbf{G}$ splits into a semidirect product; i.e., there is a subalgebra $\mathbf{S}'$ of $\mathbf{G}$ such that

$$\mathbf{G} = \mathbf{S}' \oplus \mathbf{R(G)}.$$

$\mathbf{S}'$ may be called the "semisimple part" of $\mathbf{G}$. However, it is not uniquely defined. *Malcev's theorem* extends Levi's, and asserts that any semisimple subalgebra of $\mathbf{G}$ is conjugate by an inner automorphism to a subalgebra of $\mathbf{S}'$.

Malcev's theorem is typical of one sort of classification theorem for subalgebras. One tries to restrict attention to subalgebras having a certain algebraic property, and prove that there is one "maximal" one, so that all other subalgebras with this property are conjugate to a subalgebra of the maximal one. The conjugacy theorem for compact subalgebras of a noncompact semisimple Lie algebra or maximal Abelian subalgebras of compact Lie algebras are other examples. Another is the *Morosov theorem:* There is a maximal solvable subalgebra of a complex semisimple Lie algebra such that any other solvable subalgebra is conjugate to a subalgebra of it.

MAXIMAL SUBALGEBRAS OF MAXIMAL RANK OF COMPACT LIE ALGEBRAS

Let **G** be a compact semisimple Lie algebra (i.e., its Killing form is negative definite). A subalgebra **H** is a *maximal rank subalgebra* of **G** if it contains a maximal Abelian subalgebra of **G**. We now describe the classification of the maximal rank subalgebras of **G** as done by Borel and deSiebenthal (1949). Again, the true problem is to describe the *maximal* subalgebras of maximal rank, for then the classification of all such subalgebras can be made recursively. We begin by stating without proof three very powerful general theorems concerning compact semisimple groups.

Theorem 15–1

Let G be a connected compact semisimple Lie group, and let H be a connected subgroup whose Lie algebra **H** is a maximal rank subalgebra of **G**. Then, the center of H is not contained in the center of **G**. In particular, if **H** is a maximal subalgebra of **G**, H is the connected component of the centralizer of a single element of G.

To illustrate this theorem, we can compare the even-dimensional spheres $S_{2n} = SO(2n + 1)/SO(2n)$ with the odd-dimensional ones $S_{2n-1} = SO(2n)/SO(2n - 1)$. In the former case, the isotropy subgroup is of maximal rank (rank $= n$), in the latter case, not (rank of group $= n$, rank of subgroup $= n - 1$).

To illustrate the even-dimensional case, suppose $n = 1$. The matrix

$$\begin{pmatrix} 1 & 0 & 0 \\ 0 & -1 & 0 \\ 0 & 0 & -1 \end{pmatrix}$$

is in the center of $SO(2n)$, but not in the center of $SO(2n + 1)$.

Conversely, suppose H is the centralizer of an element $g_0 \in G$. Let **C** be a maximal Abelian subalgebra of **G**. Let C be the connected subgroup of G generated by **C**. One can prove that C is a closed subgroup of G. Hence C is a compact, connected Abelian Lie group, i.e., a group that is called a *torus* in Lie theory, since it can be shown to be isomorphic as a Lie group to a product of circle groups. (The ordinary torus is the product of two circles.) Since **C** is maximal Abelian, C is a *maximal torus* in G. (In fact, one can prove that C is a maximal Abelian subgroup of G.) Another property of compact Lie groups is that every element lies on a one-parameter subgroup, i.e., there is an element $X \in$ **G** with

$$g_0 = \exp(X).$$

By Theorem 6–3, there is an element $g \in G$ such that

$$\text{Ad } g(X) \in \mathbf{G};$$

hence

$$g g_0 g^{-1} \in C.$$

Thus, the centralizers of elements of G are maximal rank subgroups, and to classify the maximal subgroups of maximal rank up to conjugacy by inner automorphism it suffices to consider centralizers of elements of C.

Let X_0 be a fixed regular element of C, and let $\sum_+$ be the system of roots of $\mathbf{G}$ with respect to C that are positive on X_0. (See Chapter 8 for the notation used here.) Let $\lambda_1, \ldots, \lambda_r$ be a system of simple roots. Then every positive root can be written as the sum $n_1 \lambda_1 + \cdots + n_r \lambda_r$ with non-negative integers $n_1, \ldots, n_r$. Let λ_m be the root for which these coefficients are as large as possible (i.e., the maximal weight for the adjoint representation of $\mathbf{G}$). The next major theorem we use was proved by Cartan (1953b):

Theorem 15–2

Suppose that G is also simply connected. Let $\mathbf{F}$ be the set of all elements X of C such that

$$\lambda_i(X) \geqslant 0 \qquad \text{for } 1 \leqslant i \leqslant r,$$
$$\lambda_m(X) \leqslant 2\pi.$$

Then every element of G is conjugate to precisely one element of the set $\exp(\mathbf{F})$ in G. ($\mathbf{F}$ is called the *fundamental polyhedron* of the group G.)

Finally, we shall state the third general theorem, which, in this definitive form, is due to Bott (1958).

Theorem 15–3

Suppose G is a semisimple, simply connected compact Lie group. Then the centralizer in G of an element of G is connected.

To illustrate the power of these generalities, we might remark that the described properties of the fundamental polyhedron make the problem of finding the center of the simply connected G, hence also the nonsimply connected realizations of G, very easy. For, suppose $g_0 \in G$ commutes with all elements of G. Then it must be in $\exp(\mathbf{F})$, i.e.,

$$g_0 = \exp(X), \ X \in \mathbf{F}.$$

Such a g_0 can be in the center of G if and only if

(15–1) $\lambda_j(X)$ is an integer multiple of 2π for $j = 1, \ldots, r$.

Suppose

$$\lambda_m = m_1\lambda_1 + \cdots + m_r\lambda_r.$$

One can prove that all the integers $m_1, \ldots, m_r$ are positive. Hence the condition $\lambda_m(X) \leqslant 2\pi$ is compatible with (15–1) only if

(15–2) $\lambda_j(X) = 0$ for all j but one, say j_0 $m_{j_0} = 1$ and $\lambda_{j_0}(X) = 2\pi$.

Hence the number of nonidentity elements in the center of G is equal to the number of m's that are equal to 1. For example, $SU(n + 1)$ is of rank n and all m's are equal to 1; hence there are n nonidentity elements in its center. (In fact, its center is Z_{n+1}, the cyclic group of order $n + 1$.) One can readily read off the order of the centers of the other simply connected compact simple groups from Table 1 on page 128.

Let us now return to the question of classifying maximal subalgebras **H** of maximal rank of a compact simple† Lie algebra **G**. Let G be the simply connected group whose Lie algebra is **G**.

Theorem 15–4

Let $g = \exp(X)$ be an element of $\exp E$ whose centralizer **H** in **G** is maximal, but not all of **G**. Then, all $\lambda_1, \ldots, \lambda_r$, except one, must be zero on X.

Say that $\lambda_1(X) \neq 0$. Let $m_1, \ldots, m_r$ be the integers such that

$$\lambda_m = m_1\lambda_1 + \cdots + m_r\lambda_r.$$

If $m_1 > 1$, then $\lambda_1(X) = 2\pi/m_1$ and **H** is semisimple. If $m_1 = 1$, $\lambda_1(X)$ can have any value, and **H** is not semisimple.

Conversely, if $g = \exp(X)$, with $X \in \mathbf{F}$, $\lambda_1(X) = 2\pi/m_1$ if $m_1 > 1$, or $\lambda_1(X) < 2\pi$ if $m_1 = 1$, then H, the centralizer of g in G, is a maximal subgroup of G which is semisimple if $m_1 > 1$, and which is the sum of a semisimple ideal of rank $r - 1$ and center X if $m_1 = 1$. **H** is a symmetric subalgebra of **G** if and only if

$$m_1 = 1 \text{ or } 2.$$

† It can be shown [see Borel and deSiebenthal (1949)] that the classification for semisimple **G** can be reduced to that for simple **G**.

TABLE 1 Maximal Subgroups of Maximal Rank

Structure of group	"Classical" representation	Dynkin diagram $(X_1, \ldots, X_r)$ are dual vectors in C to simple root system $\lambda_1, \ldots, \lambda_r$	Maximal root $\lambda_m = m_1\lambda_1 + \cdots + m_r\lambda_r$	Structure of maximal subgroups of maximal rank
A_r	$SU(r+1)$	$X_1\ X_2\ \cdots\ X_{r-1}\ X_r$	$\lambda_1 + \cdots + \lambda_r$	$U(i) \times SU(r+1-i)$ $i = 1, 2, 3, \ldots$
B_r	$SO(2r+1)$	$X_1\ X_2\ \cdots\ X_{r-1}\ X_r$	$2\lambda_1 + 2\lambda_2 + \cdots + 2\lambda_{r-1} + \lambda_r$	$SO(i) \times SO(r-i)$ $i = 1, 2, \ldots$
C_r	$Sp(r)$	$X_1\ X_2\ \cdots\ X_r$	$\lambda_1 + 2\lambda_2 + \cdots + 2\lambda_r$	$U(r)$; $Sp(i) \times Sp(r-i)$ $i = 1, 2, \ldots$
D_r	$SO(2r)$	$X_1\ X_2\ X_3\ \cdots\ X_r$	$\lambda_1 + \lambda_2 + 2\lambda_3 + \cdots + 2\lambda_{r-1} + \lambda_r$	$U(r)$; $SO(i) \times SO(r-i)$ $i = 1, 2, \ldots$
E_6		$X_1\ X_2\ X_3\ X_4\ X_5\ X_6$	$3\lambda_1 + 2\lambda_2 + 2\lambda_3 + 2\lambda_4 + \lambda_5 + \lambda_6$	$A_1 \times A_5$; $A_2 \times A_2 \times A_2$ $D_5 \times SO(2)$
E_7		$X_1\ X_2\ X_3\ X_4\ X_5\ X_6\ X_7$	$4\lambda_1 + 3\lambda_2 + 3\lambda_3 + 2\lambda_4 + 2\lambda_5 + 2\lambda_6 + \lambda_4$	$A_1 \times D_6, A_1, A_2 \times A_5$ $E_6 \times SO(2)$
E_8		$X_1\ X_2\ X_3\ X_4\ X_5\ X_6\ X_7\ X_8$	$6\lambda_1 + 5\lambda_2 + 4\lambda_3 + 4\lambda_4 + 3\lambda_5 + 3\lambda_6 + 2\lambda_4 + 2\lambda_8$	$D_8, A_1 \times E_1, A_8, A_2 \times E_6$ $A_4 \times A_4$
F_4		$X_1\ X_2\ X_3\ X_4$	$4\lambda_1 + 3\lambda_2 + 2\lambda_3 + 2\lambda_4$	$A_1 \times C_3, B_4, A_2 \times A_2$
G_2		$X_1\ X_2$	$3\lambda_1 + 2\lambda_2$	$A_1 \times A_1, A_2$

128

Proof:

Let λ be an element of $\sum_+$, with $\lambda = n_1\lambda_1 + \cdots + n_r\lambda_r$. Then, as in Chapter 8, there are two root vectors W_λ and $W_{-\lambda} \in \mathbf{G}_c$, with

(a) $[X, W_\lambda] = i\lambda(X)W_\lambda$ $[X, W_{-\lambda}] = -i\lambda(X)W_\lambda,$

(b) $W_\lambda + W_{-\lambda}$ and $\dfrac{1}{i}(W_\lambda - W_{-\lambda})$ belong to $\mathbf{G}$.

Then $\operatorname{Ad} g(W_\lambda) = e^{i\lambda(X)}W_\lambda$; $\operatorname{Ad} g(W_{-\lambda}) = e^{-i\lambda(X)}W_{-\lambda}$.

Suppose that $\lambda_j(X) \neq 0$ for two j's; e.g., $j = 1, 2$. Now $\mathbf{H}$ is spanned by $\mathbf{C}$ and the elements $W_\lambda + W_{-\lambda}$ and $(1/i)(W_\lambda - W_{-\lambda})$ for roots $\lambda \in \sum_+$ for which either $\lambda(X) = 0$ or $\lambda(X) = 2\pi$. For either $\lambda = \lambda_1$ or $\lambda = \lambda_2$, these elements cannot be in $\mathbf{H}$ [For, by assumption, $\lambda_1(X) \neq 0 \neq \lambda_2(X)$. Suppose $2\pi = \lambda_1(X) = \lambda_2(X)$. Then, $\lambda_m = m_1\lambda_1 + \cdots + m_r\lambda_r$, with all m's positive, hence $\lambda_m(X) > 2\pi$]. Suppose, say, that for $\lambda = \lambda_2$ these elements do not lie in $\mathbf{H}$. Then, $W_{\lambda_2} + W_{-\lambda_2}$ and $(1/i)(W_{\lambda_2} - W_{-\lambda_2})$, together with $\mathbf{H}$, must generate $\mathbf{G}$, since $\mathbf{H}$ is a maximal subalgebra of $\mathbf{G}$. This forces $W_{\lambda_1} + W_{-\lambda_1}$ and $(1/i)(W_{\lambda_1} - W_{-\lambda_1})$ to belong to $\mathbf{H}$, since otherwise all roots could not be obtained by putting together $\mathbf{H}$ and $W_{\lambda_1}, W_{-\lambda_1}$. This forces

$$\lambda_1(X) = 2\pi.$$

Then also

$$\lambda_m(X) = 2\pi = \sum_{j=1}^{r} m_j\lambda_j(X),$$

forcing $\lambda_j(X) = 0$ for $j \geqslant 1$, a contradiction.

This proves the first part of the theorem. Suppose then that $\lambda_j(X) = 0$ for $j \geqslant 2$. If $m_1 > 1$, note that only for X satisfying $\lambda_1(X) = 2\pi/m_1$, and only this X, does $\mathbf{H}$ contain $W_{\lambda_m} + W_{-\lambda_m}$ and $(1/i)(W_{\lambda_m} - W_{-\lambda_m})$; hence $\lambda_1(X)$ must have this value if $\mathbf{H}$ is to be maximal. If $m_1 = 1$, $\lambda_1(X)$ must be less than 2π, for we have seen otherwise that g is in the center of G; i.e., $\mathbf{H}$ would equal $\mathbf{G}$. On the other hand, any value of $\lambda_1(X)$ less than 2π leads to the same $\mathbf{H}$, and X is in the center of $\mathbf{H}$; hence $\mathbf{H}$ is not semisimple.

We leave the proof of the last statement of Theorem 15–4 to the reader.

To close the classification of the maximal subalgebras of maximal rank of the compact simple Lie algebras, we list in Table 1 the structure of these subalgebras, which is very useful in all sorts of classification problems. (For example, it, together with the classification of the outer automorphisms of the compact simple Lie algebras, which we shall not go into here, but which is not too hard, leads very easily to a classification of the symmetric subalgebras.)

In Table 1 A_r, B_r, C_r, and D_r refer to the main classes of simple Lie algebras. The corresponding "classical" linear group is added for the reader's convenience. G_2, F_4, E_6, E_7, and E_8 refer, of course, to the exceptional Lie algebras.

We shall also explain how the Dynkin diagram is formed. In Chapter 8 we showed that

$$a_{ij} = \frac{2B(X_i, X_j)}{B(X_j, X_j)} \text{ is an integer} \qquad \text{for } 1 \leqslant i, j \leqslant r.$$

[X_i is the element of **C** such that

$$B(X_i, X) = \lambda_i(X) \text{ for all } X \in \mathbf{C}. \quad B \text{ is the Killing form.}]$$

The Killing form also defines a Euclidean metric on **C**, since it is negative definite. Let θ_{ij} be the angle between the vectors X_i and X_j. Then

$$\cos^2 \theta_{ij} = \frac{B(X_i, X_j)^2}{B(X_i, X_i)B(X_j, X_j)}.$$

But,

$$B(X_i, X_j) = \tfrac{1}{2}a_{ij}B(X_j, X_j) = \tfrac{1}{2}a_{ji}B(X_i, X_i).$$

Then

$$\cos^2 \theta_{ij} = \frac{\tfrac{1}{4}a_{jj}^2 B(X_j, X_j)^2}{(a_{ij}/a_{ji})B(X_j, X_j)^2} = \tfrac{1}{4}a_{ij}a_{ji}.$$

Since $\cos^2 \theta_{ij} < 1$, $a_{ij}a_{ji}$ is < 4. Thus, there are four cases: $a_{ij}a_{ji} = 3, 2, 1$, or zero. To form the Dynkin diagram, we represent each X_i as a point in the plane, joining X_i and X_j by $a_{ij}a_{ji}$ lines. The classification process then proceeds to show that the Dynkin diagrams of the simple compact Lie algebras are precisely the ones shown in Table 1.

MAXIMAL COMPLEX SUBALGEBRAS OF MAXIMAL RANK OF THE COMPLEX SIMPLE LIE ALGEBRA

Let **G** be a compact simple Lie algebra, and let $\mathbf{G}_c = \mathbf{G} + i\mathbf{G}$ be its complexification. $\mathbf{G}_c$ is a complex simple Lie algebra. It can be proved that every complex simple Lie algebra arises in this way from a compact one. If **C** is a maximal Abelian subalgebra of **H**, then $\mathbf{C}_c = \mathbf{C} + i\mathbf{C}$ is also a maximal Abelian (Cartan) subalgebra of $\mathbf{G}_c$. Let **H** be a maximal subalgebra of $\mathbf{G}_c$ that contains $\mathbf{C}_c$. It arises from a maximal subalgebra **H**′ of maximal rank of **G**, so this classification can be reduced to Theorem 15–1. (However, **H** is not necessarily **H**′ + i**H**′, although it contains it. We will have **H**′ = **H** ∩ **G**.)

Case 1. **H** *is semisimple*

Let $\sum_+(H)$ be the positive roots of the Lie algebra **G** such that W_λ and $W_{-\lambda}$ belong to **H**. By the structure theory of complex semisimple Lie algebras, it can be proved that **H** is spanned by C_c and the W_λ and $W_{-\lambda}$ for $\lambda \in \sum_+(H)$. Let **H**$'$ be the subalgebra of **G** spanned by **C** and the $W_\lambda + W_{-\lambda}$, $(1/i)(W_\lambda - W_{-\lambda})$, for $\lambda \in \sum_+(H)$. We leave it to the reader to show that **H**$'$ is a maximal subalgebra of **G** if **H** is a maximal subalgebra of **G**$_c$. Hence, Theorem 18–1 applies to **H**$'$. In this case, of course, **H** $=$ **H**$'$ $+$ i**H**$'$.

Case 2. **H** *is not semisimple*

We shall only state the result without proof here. Let **H** $=$ **R** $\oplus$ **S** be the Levi decomposition of **H**; i.e., **R** is a maximal solvable ideal of **H** and **S** is a maximal semisimple subalgebra of **H**. Then one proves that **R** is spanned by all root vectors W_λ, for $\lambda \in \sum_+$, and $C_c \cap$ **R**, which is one-dimensional. $C_c \cap$ **S** is a Cartan subalgebra of **S**, and is equal to

$$\textbf{L} + i\textbf{L}, \text{ where } \textbf{L} \text{ is a semisimple subalgebra of rank } r - 1 \text{ of } \textbf{G}.$$
$$[\textbf{L}, \textbf{C} \cap \textbf{R}] = 0,$$

and

$$\textbf{H}' = \textbf{L} \oplus (\textbf{C} \cap \textbf{R}) \text{ is a maximal subalgebra of maximal rank of } \textbf{G}.$$

The next step on the program of classifying subalgebras of semisimple algebras would be to classify those maximal subalgebras that do not contain a Cartan subalgebra. For example, suppose that **G** is a semisimple compact Lie algebra and that **H** is a maximal subalgebra that does not contain a maximal Abelian subalgebra of **G**. As a first remark, we see that **H** is semisimple. For, if not, there would be an element X in the center of **H**; hence its centralizer would be a subalgebra of **G** which would contain a maximal Abelian subalgebra of **G** and would contain **H**; hence **H** could not be maximal. This trivial remark then enables Dynkin to apply the enormously powerful structure theory of semisimple Lie algebras and their representations. We shall leave this topic at this point, since his papers are quite clear and detailed and can be read by anyone who is familiar with the structure theory. One interesting remark for physics is that the imbedding of $SU(2) \times SU(3)$ into $SU(6)$ used by Gursey, Radacati, and Sakita is one special case of Dynkin's classes of maximal subalgebras.

CHAPTER 16

GROUP–THEORETIC PROBLEMS IN PARTICLE QUANTUM MECHANICS

We shall concentrate now on applications of group-theoretic ideas to quantum mechanics. Of course, it will not be possible to give a proper exposition of the mathematical foundations of quantum mechanics: For this we refer to Von Neumann (1955) and Mackey (1963). However, the approach used here is much closer to Dirac's.

Let us adopt the quickest jumping-off position to go from classical to quantum mechanics. Consider a classical mechanical system whose configuration and momentum space variables are $(q_1, \ldots, q_n) = q$ and $(p_1, \ldots, p_n) = p$. The space whose variables are p and q is *phase space*, denoted by Π. A classical observable is a real-valued function $(p, q) \to f(p, q)$ of these variables. Such an observable generates a one-parameter group† of transformations of Π. The orbits of this group are the solutions of the Hamilton equations:

$$(16\text{–}1) \qquad \frac{dq}{dt} = \frac{\partial f}{\partial p} (q(t), p(t))$$
$$\frac{dp}{dt} = - \frac{\partial f}{\partial q} (q(t), p(t)).$$

This group is composed of canonical transformations of phase space, i.e., it leaves invariant the two-differential form

$$\omega = dp_1 \wedge dq_1 + \cdots + dp_n \wedge dq_n$$

(hence also the volume element form $dp_1 \wedge \cdots \wedge dp_n \wedge dq_1 \wedge \cdots \wedge dq_n$ on phase space, since it is the result of exterior multiplication of n copies of ω. This is just Liouville's theorem in statistical mechanics.) Conversely, any one-parameter group of canonical transformations arises in

† This is not quite accurate, since the solutions of (16–1) may not exist for all t, for an arbitrary choice of f. However, if the first derivatives do not grow too fast at infinity, this will not happen. We refer to van Hove (1951) for a fuller discussion.

this way from an observable. The group of canonical transformations may be regarded as the most general "symmetry group" of classical mechanics. This mapping of observables to one-parameter subgroups is the basic feature of an abstract "dynamic system," in either classical or quantum mechanics.

This mapping of observables to generators of one-parameter subgroups of canonical transformations is not one-to-one: If f is a constant, clearly it generates the identity transformation. However, the set of observables can be given a Lie algebra structure also. To see how this is done, let us see how another observable $g(p, q)$ changes along the group generated by $f(p, q)$:

$$\frac{d}{dt} g(p(t), q(t)) = \frac{\partial g}{\partial p}\frac{dp}{dt} + \frac{\partial g}{\partial q}\frac{dq}{dt}$$

$$= \text{[using (16–1)]} \frac{\partial g}{\partial p}\frac{\partial f}{\partial q} - \frac{\partial g}{\partial q}\frac{\partial f}{\partial p} (p(t), q(t))$$

$$= \{g, f\}(p(t), q(t)),$$

where we define the *Poisson bracket* $\{g, f\}$ of two observables as

(16–2) $$\{g, f\} = \frac{\partial g}{\partial p}\frac{\partial f}{\partial q} - \frac{\partial g}{\partial q}\frac{\partial f}{\partial p}.$$

(Of course, we are using a somewhat symbolic vector notation here. Written out in full it should be

$$\{q, f\} = \sum_i \frac{\partial g}{\partial p_i}\frac{\partial f}{\partial q_i} - \frac{\partial g}{\partial q_i}\frac{\partial f}{\partial p_i}.\Big)$$

It is readily verified by a direct, if tedious, calculation that this bracket operation makes the set of observables **O** into a Lie algebra; i.e., the Poisson bracket satisfies the Jacobi identity. Note also that the constant functions constitute the center of this Lie algebra. Now, the quotient Lie algebra of **O** by its center is the Lie algebra of the group of canonical transformations. (There are certain technical complications in the way of making this precise. Note, for example, that the group of canonical transformations is not really a Lie group, since it is "infinite-dimensional." In fact, it constitutes one of the "infinite Lie pseudo groups" first investigated by Lie and Cartan. Of course, this is reflected also in the fact that **O** is infinite-dimensional as a real Lie algebra.)

The group of canonical transformations is, so to speak, the "symmetry group" of classical mechanics as a whole, before any one explicit system is considered. To tie up with what is usually meant by "classical mechanics" in physics, one must focus attention on a subalgebra of **O**. For example, in Newtonian mechanics, one is usually given one observable $H(p, q)$

(the "energy" or "Hamiltonian") in a distinguished role, and several other observables which have relatively simple commutation relations with H, playing the role of the linear and angular momenta. Note that the observables that are at most quadratic in p's and q's together form a Lie algebra, i.e., those of the form

$$(16\text{–}3) \qquad f(p, q) = \sum_{i,j} a_{ij}p_ip_j + b_{ij}p_iq_j + c_{ij}q_iq_j + d_ip_i + e_iq_i.$$

Those with $d_i = 0 = e_i$ form a real simple Lie algebra of type C_n (i.e., they generate the real linear symplectic group). One usually, in Newtonian mechanics, considers Hamiltonians $H(p, q)$ of the form

$$(16\text{–}4) \qquad\qquad H(p, q) = \tfrac{1}{2}p^2 + V(q),$$

where $V(q)$ is the "potential."

In general, if H is a Hamiltonian of a specific system, one may consider the "symmetries" of H in the broad sense as the set of f's such that

$$(16\text{–}5) \qquad\qquad \{f, H\} = 0.$$

Then, the one-parameter groups generated by f and H commute; hence the group generated by f can be put to work to find the group generated by H. Of course, much attention is given in the classical literature on mechanics [e.g., Whittaker (1944)] to the use of such symmetries to explicitly "solve" the Hamilton equations with Hamiltonian H. Also, there is a classical theorem which asserts that there are always n functionally independent functions $f_1, \ldots, f_n$ satisfying (16–5) which are "in involution"; i.e., $\{f_i, f_j\} = 0$ for $1 \leqslant i, j \leqslant n$. This result, however, is local and is merely an existence theorem. In general, finding them is of the same order of difficulty as actually solving the Hamilton equations. There are fascinating relations to global problems (e.g., concerning stability of the solar system), which have only recently been successfully attacked in generality [for example, see Arnold (1962)]. For Hamiltonians of type (16–4), one can ask for the set of f's of type (16–3) which do commute with H and V. The set of these constitute the "obvious" symmetries of the system. It seems to be traditional in the physics literature to refer to the others as "hidden."

Now we turn to quantum mechanics. In general, quantum mechanics has a formal structure parallel to that of classical mechanics, but, in principle, having nothing to do with it. For the purposes of group theory, it is convenient to think of two objects as given to define a quantummechanical "dynamic system": a Lie algebra $\mathbf{O}^q$ of "observables" and a linear representation of $\mathbf{O}^q$ by operators on a Hilbert space V, each of which generates a one-parameter group of unitary transformations of V.

Let us briefly recall what these terms mean. V is a *Hilbert space* if it is a vector space over the complex numbers and has a (Hermitian) inner product which to $\psi_1, \psi_2 \in V$ assigns a complex number (ψ_1, ψ_2), satisfying (in addition to bilinearity) the following rules:

$$(\psi_1, \psi_2) = \overline{(\psi_2, \psi_1)},$$
$$(c\psi_1, \psi_2) = c(\psi_1, \psi_2); \quad (\psi_1, c\psi_2) = \bar{c}(\psi_1, \psi_2),$$

for each complex number c.   (The bar denotes a complex conjugate.)

$$(\psi, \psi) \geqslant 0, \text{ and is zero only if } \psi = 0.$$

In addition we require completeness.   To define it, let $\|\psi\| = \sqrt{(\psi, \psi)}$ be the associated inner product on V. A sequence $\psi_1, \psi_2, \ldots$ of elements of V is a Cauchy sequence if $\lim_{m,n \to \infty} \|\psi_m - \psi_n\| = 0$.   We require then that every Cauchy sequence have a limit.

If one does not have this completeness (such an object is sometimes called a "pre-Hilbert space"), it is possible to "complete" the space to a Hilbert space by adding the Cauchy sequences as ideal elements, following the pattern by which the real numbers are defined starting from the rational numbers.

The typical example of a Hilbert space is obtained by taking a space M, a measure dp on M, and letting V be the square-integrable complex functions on M, with

$$(\psi_1, \psi_2) = \int_M \psi_1(p)\overline{\psi_2(p)} \, dp.$$

A linear transformation A on V is *unitary* if

$$(A(\psi_1), A(\psi_2)) = (\psi_1, \psi_2) \qquad \text{for } \psi_1, \psi_2 \in V.$$

The set of all unitary transformations on V forms a group, denoted by $U(V)$.   Even though $U(V)$ is far too big to have any of the really nice properties of a Lie group, we can define its Lie algebra in a similar way as the set of one-parameter subgroups.   Let $t \to A(t)$ and $t \to B(t)$ be one-parameter subgroups.   We can define the "sum" as the one-parameter group

$$t \to \lim_{n \to \infty} \left(A\left(\frac{t}{n}\right) B\left(\frac{t}{n}\right) \right)^n,$$

and the "bracket" as the group

$$t \to \lim_{n \to \infty} \left(A\left(\frac{t}{n}\right) B\left(\frac{t}{n}\right) A\left(-\frac{t}{n}\right) B\left(-\frac{t}{n}\right) \right)^{n^2}.$$

Of course, we can also exhibit the Lie algebra by means of linear operators on V that are the infinitesimal generators: X, the generator of the group $t \to A(t)$, is defined by

$$X(\psi) = \lim_{t \to 0} \frac{A(t)(\psi) - \psi}{t}.$$

Typically, this limit will not exist for all $\psi \in V$ and we consider X as only defined on a dense subset of V, which is its "domain." The characteristic algebraic property of X is the following "skew-Hermitian" property:

$$(X(\psi_1), \psi_2) + (\psi_1, X(\psi_2)) = 0 \qquad \text{for } \psi_1, \psi_2 \text{ in the domain of } X.$$

Note that this can be transformed into a more familiar form on replacing X by iX:

$$(iX(\psi_1), \psi_2) = i(X(\psi_1), \psi_2) = -i(\psi_1, X(\psi_2)) = (\psi_1, iX(\psi_2)),$$

i.e., iX is a "symmetric" or "Hermitian" operator. Of course, the commutation relations then take the form

$$[iX, iY] = -[X, Y] = i(i[X, Y]).$$

Thus, the usual custom of defining observables as symmetric operators puts i into the commutation relations in a rather mysterious way, and often obscures the group-theoretic content. An additional analytic property ("self-adjointness") characterizes such operators, which are the generators of one-parameter groups. Of course, all of this is treated in detail in treatises on functional analysis [e.g., Riesz and Nagy (1955)], and we can do no more here than make these brief comments. In addition, a paper by Trotter (1958) is useful in showing the relation of the standard facts to the group theory.

Now, the "bracket" of two one-parameter groups can usually be defined in more familiar form as the commutator of their generators, $\psi \to [X, Y](\psi) = XY(\psi) - YX(\psi)$, if one is sufficiently careful about the discussion of the domain of definitions of X and Y. Again, we cannot go into these technicalities, taking the physicists' optimistic attitude that this is the best of all possible worlds and everything will work out in the end. Of course, the technicalities concerning the possible pathology of unbounded operators *are* very important and of great current physical interest in connection with questions about the meaning of quantum field theory.

Now, let us return to a quantum mechanical dynamical system, in its very general form; namely a given Lie algebra $\mathbf{O}^q$ of "observables" and a representation of it by a Lie algebra of skew-Hermitian operators on a Hilbert space V. For notational simplicity, we shall let such letters as $X, Y, \ldots$ represent both elements of $\mathbf{O}^q$ and the corresponding operators on ψ. The vectors $\psi \in \psi$ with $\|\psi\| = 1$ are the "states" of the system. For an observable X and a state ψ, the inner product $(iX(\psi), \psi)$ is a real number (because iX is a symmetric operator) and is to be thought of as the "expectation value" of the observable X in the state ψ. This is to be compared with classical mechanics. A "state" is then a point (p, q) of phase space, an observable is a real-valued function on phase space, and its value at the point (p, q) plays the same role as does the expectation value $(iX(\psi), \psi)$.

Although in principle quantum mechanics is independent of classical mechanics, certainly it has had its most convincing successes in the problems of nonrelativistic particle mechanics, where the connection with classical mechanics is in the foreground. We can explain what is involved here in the following terms: We are given a classical mechanical system whose phase space is (p, q)-space, and the observables are a set of real-valued functions on phase space closed under Poisson bracket. To "quantize" this system involves defining the quantum observables as the *same* Lie algebras as the classical ones, and looking for a unitary representation of this algebra to define the states.

There is a remarkable mathematical fact underlying the success of this program, namely the *Stone–von Neumann* theorem. Suppose we consider the simplest case of a one-dimensional configuration space, so that q and p and 1 are observables. Suppose that the given classical observables contain p, q, and 1. Now

$$\{p, q\} = 1 \qquad \{q, 1\} = 0 = \{p, 1\}.$$

Thus, p, q, and 1 generate a three-dimensional (nilpotent) Lie algebra that is called the *Heisenberg algebra*. Suppose that $p \to X$, $q \to Y$, $1 \to Z$ is an irreducible representation of this algebra by skew-Hermitian operators on a Hilbert space V. Notice that 1 is in the center of the algebra; hence Z is just a constant multiple of the identity. Since Z is skew-Hermitian, this constant must be purely imaginary, say of the form ih, with h real. Hence

$$Z(\psi) = ih\psi \qquad \text{for } \psi \in V.$$

The Stone–von Neumann theorem now asserts that an irreducible unitary representation of the Heisenberg group† is uniquely determined by this constant h. Further, the representation can be obtained by representing the algebra by skew-Hermitian operators on the square-integrable functions of the real variable q:

q applied to a function $\psi(q)$ is $iq\psi(q)$,

p applied to $\psi(q)$ is $-h\dfrac{d\psi}{dq}$,

1 applied to $\psi(q)$ is $ih\psi(q)$.

We refer to von Neumann's paper for the proof (1931). Another very elegant proof can be found in a paper by Kirilov (1964). [In this paper

---

† The Heisenberg group is the (simply connected) Lie group whose Lie algebra is the Heisenberg algebra.

Kirilov surveys the whole theory of unitary representations of nilpotent Lie groups. It is remarkable that the classification of representations of the Heisenberg group (which is a nilpotent Lie group) plays a key role in the theory for general nilpotent groups, in much the same manner as the role played by representations of $SO(3)$ in the representation theory of general semisimple groups.]

Another point of interest is the "probability" interpretation enforced by the Stone–von Neumann theorem. We have already pointed out that $-(iY\psi, \psi)$ is, from basic postulates, interpreted as the "expected value" of the observable q in the state ψ. But, in terms of the representation given for these operators, this is just

$$\int_{-\infty}^{\infty} q\psi(q)\overline{\psi(q)}\, dq.$$

We see that $q \to |\psi(q)|^2\, dq$ is to be regarded as a probability measure on configuration space, i.e., a state of the system is not located precisely at a point in configuration space, as in classical mechanics, but is only located with a certain probability.

Now, the Heisenberg algebra only forms part of the Lie algebra of observables for a classical mechanical system with which we are familiar in Newtonian mechanics. To get "dynamics" we will have to add functions that are quadratic in p and q. Now

$$\begin{aligned} \{p^2, q\} &= 2p & \{q^2, p\} &= 2q, \\ \{pq, q\} &= p & \{q;\ p\} &= -q. \end{aligned}$$

These relations tell us that the Heisenberg algebra is an ideal in the Lie algebra of all observables that are of degree at most 2 in p and q.

The unitary representation of the Heisenberg algebra can be extended to the function of the form

$$H = \tfrac{1}{2}p^2 + V(q)$$

(i.e., the Hamiltonians of Newtonian systems) by following the Schrödinger rules:

$$p^2 \to i\,\frac{d^2}{dq^2},$$

$$V(q) \to \text{multiplication by } iV(q).$$

(Let us normalize h to be 1.)

This enables us to "quantize" classical Newtonian particle dynamical systems. Finding the one-parameter unitary group generated by the operator corresponding to H amounts to solving the Schrödinger equation:

$$\frac{\partial \psi}{\partial t} = i\,\frac{\partial^2 \psi}{\partial q^2} + V(q).$$

Now, we can describe more accurately the problem of "hidden" symmetries in ordinary quantum mechanics: We have already described the observables of such that $\{f, H\} = 0$ as the classical symmetries, "obvious" if also $\{f, V\} = 0$, "hidden" if $\{f, V\} \neq 0$. Given a Lie algebra of such classical symmetries, we must construct the algebra of observables generated by them, the Heisenberg algebra and H, and ask whether the given unitary representation of the Heisenberg algebra and H can be extended to this bigger algebra. If so, the algebra operators generated by the additional symmetries will commute with the operator corresponding to H, i.e., the energy, and can be used to obtain information about the energy spectrum and degeneracy, which is usually the most important problem in elementary quantum mechanics.

We shall first discuss the "obvious" symmetries. Suppose $\{f, V\} = 0$, and f is a linear function of p, of the form

$$f = a(q)p + b(q).$$

The one-parameter group of canonical transformations generated by f is then what is called an "extended point transformation." In fact, the Hamilton equations take the form

$$\frac{dq}{dt} = a(q) \qquad \frac{dp}{dt} = \frac{\partial a}{\partial q} p(t) + \frac{\partial b}{\partial q}.$$

We see that the curves $t \to q(t)$ are the orbits of a one-parameter group of transformations of configuration space that leave the potential function $V(q)$ invariant. Following the Schrödinger rules, one might suspect that the way to "quantize" f could be to replace it by the differential operator acting on function $\psi(q)$.

$$\Delta_f = a \frac{d}{dq} + ib.$$

Now, this is not quite satisfactory, since it is not skew-Hermitian (unless $a = $ constant). However, we can add a function $c(q)$ to make it so. Let $A_f = \Delta_f + c$ and let us see whether the condition that Δ_f^* be skew-Hermitian determines c. We can then consider only the case $b = 0$, since multiplication by ib is skew-Hermitian.

$$(A_f(\psi), \psi') = \int_{-\infty}^{\infty} \left(a(q) \frac{d\psi}{dq} + c\psi \right) \overline{\psi}' \, dq$$

$$= \text{(after integrating by parts and assuming that } (q) \text{ vanishes}$$

$$\text{at infinity)} \int_{-\infty}^{\infty} \left[-\frac{da}{dq} \psi \overline{\psi}' + \psi \overline{(c\psi')} - a\psi \frac{\overline{d\psi'}}{dq} \right] dq.$$

We see that $(A_f(\psi), \psi') = -(\psi, A_f(\psi'))$ if

$$-c = c - \frac{da}{dq} \quad \text{or} \quad c = \frac{1}{2}\frac{da}{dq}.$$

Hence, the proper assignment of an operator to an observable of the form $a(q)p$ is $a(q)(d/dq) + \frac{1}{2}(da/dq)$.

Let us now check that the assignment

$$a(q)p \to a\frac{d}{dq} + \frac{1}{2}\frac{da}{dq}$$

is compatible with the representation of the Heisenberg algebra and the Hamiltonian:

$$\{a(q)p, a_1(q)p\} = \left(a\frac{da_1}{dq} - \frac{da_1}{dq}a_1\right)p$$
$$\left[a(q)\frac{d}{dq} + \frac{1}{2}\frac{da}{dq}, a_1(q)\frac{d}{dq} + \frac{1}{2}\frac{da_1}{dq}\right](\psi)$$
$$= a(q)\frac{d}{dq}\left(a_1\frac{d}{dq} + \frac{1}{2}\frac{da_1}{dq}\psi\right) + \frac{1}{2}\frac{da}{dq}\left(a_1\frac{d\psi}{dq} + \frac{1}{2}\frac{da_1}{dq}\psi\right)$$
$$- a_1(q)\frac{d}{dq}\left(a\frac{d\psi}{dq} + \frac{1}{2}\frac{da}{dq}\psi\right) - \frac{1}{2}\frac{da_1}{dq}\left(a\frac{d\psi}{dq} + \frac{1}{2}\frac{da}{dq}\psi\right)$$
$$= a\left(\frac{da_1}{dq}\frac{d\psi}{dq} + a_1\frac{d^2\psi}{dq} + \frac{1}{2}\frac{d^2a_1}{dq}\psi + \frac{1}{2}\frac{da_1}{dq}\frac{d\psi}{dq}\right)$$
$$+ \frac{1}{2}\frac{da}{dq}\left(a_1\frac{d\psi}{dq} + \frac{1}{2}\frac{da_1}{dq}\psi\right)$$
$$- a_1\left(\frac{da}{dq}\frac{d\psi}{dq} + a\frac{d^2\psi}{dq} + \frac{1}{2}\frac{d^2a}{dq}\psi + \frac{1}{2}\frac{da}{dq}\frac{d\psi}{dq}\right)$$
$$- \frac{1}{2}\frac{da_1}{dq}\left(a\frac{d\psi}{dq} + \frac{1}{2}\frac{da}{dq}\psi\right)$$
$$= \left(a\frac{da_1}{dq} - a_1\frac{da}{dq}\right)\frac{d\psi}{dq}$$
$$+ \frac{1}{2}\left(a\frac{d^2a_1}{dq^2} - a_1\frac{d^2a}{dq^2} + \frac{da}{dq}\frac{da_1}{dq} - \frac{da_1}{dq}\frac{da}{dq}\right)\psi.$$

We see from this computation that the assignment (16–5) of skew-Hermitian operators to observables that are linear in q does in fact have the property that Poisson brackets go into operator commutators.

We can also check the case of an observable $q \to V(q)$ and another of the form $a(q)p$.

$$\{a(q)p, V\} = a(q)\frac{dV}{dt} \times \left[a\frac{d}{dq} + \frac{1}{2}\frac{da}{dq}, iV\right](\psi)$$
$$= i\left(a\frac{d}{dq}(V\psi) = Va\frac{d}{dq}\psi\right) = i\left(a\frac{dV}{dq}\right)\psi.$$

Summing up, we have proved:

Theorem 16–1

The set of observables of the form $a(q)p + b(q)$ forms a Lie algebra under Poisson bracket. The assignment

$$a(q)p + b(q) \rightarrow a\frac{d}{dq} + \frac{1}{2}\frac{da}{dq} + ib$$

defines a representation of this Lie algebra by a Lie algebra (with respect to commutator bracket) of skew-Hermitian operators.

Remark:

The result generalizes to the case of n-dimensional configuration space. $\sum_i a_i(q)p_i$ is replaced by

$$\sum_i \left(a_i \frac{\partial}{\partial q_i} + \frac{1}{2}\frac{\partial a_i}{\partial q_i} \right).$$

When we try to similarly "quantize" (i.e., assign operators to) other classical observables, we see that inevitably difficulties arise. For example, we might imagine trying to quantize all polynomials in p and q by setting up a suitable ordering for the products, assigning operators by following the Schrödinger prescription, and then making the differential operators obtained in this way skew-Hermitian. The practical difficulties that are encountered in this approach are mirrored in a general theorem by van Hove (1951), asserting that it is impossible to quantize sufficiently large systems of classical observables in such a way that Poisson brackets go over to operator brackets. However, this does not preclude the possibility of finding representations of Lie algebras of classical symmetries for special classes of classical dynamical systems. For example, we shall see later that this is possible for the hydrogen atom. In general, it seems to be an open topic of research to analyze the structure of classical systems for which this is possible. Physicists seem convinced that there is no problem here — they have faith in the correspondence principle, which asserts in part that every essential ingredient of a classical problem carries over to quantum mechanics.

It is instructive to look at some examples.

HARMONIC OSCILLATORS

The Hamiltonian for the most general system of linear oscillations has the form

$$H = \sum_{i,j} a_{ij}q_iq_j + b_{ij}q_ip_j + c_{ij}p_ip_j.$$

Now, the set of all observables that are at most quadratic in p and q forms a Lie algebra in p and q. Those that are precisely quadratic form a subalgebra. In fact it is the Lie algebra of the real symplectic group. (It is a real form of the simple Lie algebra of type C_n.) The observables that are of degree 0 or 1 in p and q (the Heisenberg algebra) form an ideal in this algebra. Theorem 16–4 enables us then to construct a unitary representation of this Lie algebra which extends the representation of the Heisenberg algebra; thus H when quantized admits the same symmetries as it does classically, i.e., the centralizer of H in this Lie algebra. It has been suggested recently that this simple example of a mechanical system admitting a symmetry group through its dynamics might serve as a model for an explanation of the internal symmetry schemes appearing now in elementary-particle physics. For example, one very suggestive fact is that the centralizer of the element

$$H = \sum_i \tfrac{1}{2}(p_i p_i + q_i q_i)$$

in the symplectic group is just $SU(n)$. In fact, $SU(n)$ has already appeared in nuclear physics for basically this reason.

We can also look at the Heisenberg-Dirac derivation of the energy spectrum of the harmonic oscillator in this light. Suppose then that configuration space is one-dimensional:

$$H = \tfrac{1}{2}(p^2 + q^2),$$
$$f = (p + q); \; g = (p - q),$$
$$\{H, f\} = p - q = g,$$
$$\{H, g\} = p - q = -f.$$

Then

$$\{H, f + ig\} = g - if = -i(f + ig),$$
$$\{H, f - ig\} = g + if = i(f - ig),$$
$$\{f, g\} = -2,$$
$$\{f + ig, g - ig\} = 4i.$$

Consider now a unitary representation of the Lie algebra spanned by f, g, and H. Let X and Y be the operators on the Hilbert space V corresponding to the elements $\tfrac{1}{2}(f + ig)$ and $\tfrac{1}{2}(f + ig)$. (X and Y are not skew-Hermitian then.) 1 goes over into a similar operator, say ih. Then, X and Y satisfy the following commutation relations:

$$[Y, X] = h.$$

Suppose that H, as an operator on V, has at least one discrete eigenvalue; i.e., there is a $v_0 \in V$ with

$$H(v_0) = iE_0 v_0.$$

Then

$$H(X(v_0)) = [H, X](v_0) + X(H(v_0))$$
$$= iX(v_0) + iE_0X(v_0)$$
$$= (i + iE_0)(X(v_0)),$$

$$H(Y(v_0)) = [H, Y](v_0) + Y(H(v_0))$$
$$= -iY(v_0) + IE_0Y(v_0)$$
$$= i(E_0 - 1)v_0.$$

Thus, X shifts the energy up one notch, Y shifts it down. They are just the familiar creation and annihilation operators. What is very important about this group-theoretic picture of well-known facts is that the energy spectrum appears as a *single* irreducible representation of a noncompact group containing the energy operator.

Return now to an n-dimensional configuration space. Theorem 6–1 tells us that we may extend the representation of the Heisenberg algebra to a representation of the whole algebra of polynomials of degree at most 2 in the variables p and q. We obtain in this way a skew-Hermitian representation of the Lie algebra of the real symplectic group. The explicit formula for the one-parameter group generated by the Hamiltonian may be found in every quantum mechanics text. (They involve Hermite polynomials.) Motivated by a group-theoretic spirit, it is interesting to inquire if there is a representation of the *whole* real symplectic group whose infinitesimal generators are the given operators. Curiously, this does not seem to have been investigated until recently, in a paper by Shale (1962). (One may remark that there remain many problems in elementary quantum mechanics to be investigated from a serious mathematical point of view.) We shall not go into the details here — it turns out that there is *no* such representation of the symplectic group itself, but that there is one of a twofold covering group of the real symplectic group. [The real symplectic group is *not* simply connected. Its fundamental group is infinitely cyclic; in fact, it is just the fundamental group of its maximal compact subgroup $U(n)$. Hence, its universal covering group is an infinite-sheeted covering.]

There is an interesting analogy here with the spinor representation of the orthogonal groups. It was first discovered by Cartan as a representation of its Lie algebra (before the global connection between Lie groups and Lie algebras was completely clarified), and later was shown to arise from genuine representation of a twofold covering group of the orthogonal group, a group that was then called the spinor group. Then, of course, the spinor group was constructed explicitly as a subgroup of the group of automorphisms of the Clifford algebra. There have been many examples in Lie group theory of groups that were first discovered by means of an abstract property, and that were later explicitly constructed (for example, the simple exceptional Lie algebra, G_2, F_4, E_5, E_6, and E_8). As a final remark, it seems that the other representations of the symplectic group alone (i.e., the representations that do *not* extend to the Heisenberg algebra) may be important in certain problems of nuclear physics.

THE HYDROGEN ATOM†

The nonrelativistic, nonspin hydrogen atom (one particle moving under the inverse-square law) presents another problem where the "dynamics" determines a "hidden" symmetry group, whose representation "solves" the physical problem. Here, however, the symmetry enters in a much more subtle, interesting fashion. We shall sketch the facts here. There are many papers about this in the physics literature. The most relevant for our purposes are by Pauli (1926), Fock (1935), Bargmann (1936), and a survey article by McIntosh (1959).

Here configuration space is three-dimensional. Choose indices

$$1 \leqslant i, j, \ldots \leqslant 3,$$

and the summation convention. The Hamiltonian has the form

$$H = \frac{1}{2} p_i p_i - \frac{1}{r} \qquad \text{with } r^2 = q_i q_i.$$

The functions

$$f_{ij} = q_i p_j - p_i q_j$$

represent the Lie algebra of the group of rotations about the origin in q-space; i.e., $SO(3, R)$. One readily verifies that

$$\{H, f_{ij}\} = 0.$$

These symmetries carry over when the system is quantized, and account for the rotational degeneracies of the energy levels. Of course, these are the obvious symmetries of the problem, and are present for any spherically symmetric potential. However, a special feature of the Coulomb potential is that the following functions on phase space also generate symmetries of H:

$$f_k = \frac{q_k}{r} - q_k(p_j p_j) + (p_j q_j)p_k;$$

i.e., we have

$$\{H, f_i\} = 0.$$

† I am grateful to Y. Dothan for many helpful comments about this material.

These functions taken together as a 3-vector function on phase-space define the *Lenz vector*. The commutation relation (at the classical level) between them and the f_{ij} can be calculated by a straightforward, but tedious, calculation as

(16–6) $$\{f_i, f_j\} = 2Hf_{ij},$$

(16–7) $$\{f_{ki}, f_j\} = (\delta_{ji}\delta_{kl} - \delta_{jk}\delta_{il})f_l.$$

Note that these commutation relations do not define a Lie algebra. However, let us divide phase space into three parts, I, II, and III, namely those parts where H is $< 0, > 0$, and $= 0$. Since H commutes with f_i, we can divide (16–1) by H to obtain

(16–8) $$\left\{ \frac{f_i}{\sqrt{-H}}, \frac{f_i}{\sqrt{-H}} \right\} = -2f_{ij} \text{ in region I,}$$

(16–9) $$\left\{ \frac{f_i}{\sqrt{H}}, \frac{f_i}{\sqrt{H}} \right\} = 2f_{ij} \text{ in region II,}$$

(16–10) $$\{f_i, f_j\} = 0 \text{ in region III.}$$

These relations tell us that, in region I, $f_i/\sqrt{-H}$ and the f_{ij} satisfy the commutation relations of $SO(4)$. In region II, the $f_i/\sqrt{H}$ and the f_{ij} satisfy the commutation relations of the Lorentz group, a noncompact real form of $SO(4)$. In the transitional region III, the f_{ij} and f_i satisfy the commutation relations of the group of rigid motions in Euclidean 3-space, which is the semidirect product of $SO(3)$ and an Abelian group.

This has all been at the level of classical mechanics. When one tries to quantize, i.e., represent these functions by skew-Hermitian operators in such a way that the commutation relations with the Heisenberg algebra are maintained, one has, a priori, no guarantee of success. However, this can be done (for example, by following the "Schrödinger" prescription for replacing functions of p and q by differential operators on q-space).

Now, when we quantize a system of classical observables by finding a representation by skew-Hermitian operators in which the Poisson bracket goes over to the commutator bracket, we have not at all used the fact that the classical observables, as functions of p and q, form a *ring*, and that the Poisson bracket by an element h is a derivation; i.e.,

$$\{h, fg\} = \{h, f\}g + f\{h, g\}.$$

One might inquire then whether, when quantizing, it is possible to have ordinary products go over into operator products. Let us look at this for the hydrogen atom.

Note that

$$(16\text{--}11) \qquad \epsilon_{ijk} f_{jk} f_i = \epsilon_{ijk} (q_j p_k - p_j q_k) \left(\frac{q_i}{r} - q_i (p_j p_j) + (p_j q_j) p_i \right)$$
$$= 0,$$

$$f_k f_k = \left(\frac{q_k}{r} - q_k p^2 + p \cdot q p_k \right) \left(\frac{q_k}{r} - q_k p^2 + p \cdot q p_k \right)$$
$$= 1 - r p^2 + \frac{(p \cdot q)^2}{r} - r p^2 + q^2 p^4 - (p \cdot q)^2 p^2$$
$$+ \frac{(p \cdot q)^2}{r} - (p \cdot q)^2 p^2 + (p \cdot q)^2 p^2$$
$$= 1 - 2(p \cdot q)^2 H + 2 p^2 r^2 H,$$

$$f_{ij} f_{ij} = (q_i p_j - p_i q_j)(q_i p_j - p_i q_j)$$
$$= 2 r^2 p^2 - 2(p \cdot q)^2.$$

Hence

$$(16\text{--}12) \qquad\qquad f_i f_i - 1 = H f_{ij} f_{ij}.$$

Now, one can verify by a direct calculation that relations (16–11) and (16–12) are maintained when the f_i and f_{ij} are replaced by operators according to the Schrödinger prescription:

$$f_{ij} \to \Delta_{ij} = q_i \frac{\partial}{\partial q_j} - q_j \frac{\partial}{\partial q_i},$$

$$f_k \to \Delta_k = \frac{i}{r} \frac{\partial}{\partial q_k} - i q_k \frac{\partial}{\partial q_j} \frac{\partial}{\partial q_j} + i q_j \frac{\partial}{\partial q_j} \frac{\partial}{\partial q_k}.$$

We can read off from these relations the most important qualitative facts about the energy spectrum of the hydrogen atom. For example, in region I, where $H < 0$ (the bound-state region),

$$(16\text{--}13) \qquad\qquad \frac{f_i}{\sqrt{-H}} \frac{f_i}{\sqrt{-H}} + f_{ij} f_{ij} = \frac{1}{H}.$$

This tells us that, after quantization, $1/H$ is the Casimir operator of $SO(4)$. Relation (16–11) also carries over to the following group-theoretic fact: The Lie algebra of $SO(4)$ is the direct sum of two ideals, each isomorphic to the Lie algebra of $SO(3)$. Relation (16–11) tells us that the representations of $SO(4)$ on the eigenstates for a given value of H are the tensor products of the *same* representation of $SO(3)$, i.e., of the type (l, l), where l is the maximal weight labeling representations of $SO(3)$.

These remarks (which are essentially due to Pauli) do not completely exhaust the facts about the energy spectrum of the hydrogen atom which one obtains from a direct analysis of the Schrödinger equation using traditional differential-equation techniques. For example, the representations of $SO(4)$ on the negative-energy stationary states is *irreducible*, and each representation of type (l, l), with integer l, occurs once. Fock's remarks complete this picture. He shows by an explicit calculation, involving a Fourier transform from q- to p-space, then a change of variable to the 3-sphere, that the representation of $SO(4)$ and H on the negative-energy states is unitarily equivalent to the unitary representation of $SO(4)$ on functions on the 3-sphere. As we shall show in Chapter 17, there is a noncompact group acting on the 3-sphere [a real form of $SO(5)$, the deSitter group] which acts *irreducibly* on functions on the 3-sphere. (There are similar remarks for positive-energy states, with the hyperboloid in 4-space replacing the 3-sphere.) Summing up, we get a qualitative picture of the structure of the bound states of the hydrogen atom which may be very important as a source of insight into elementary-particle physics:

> The bound states of the hydrogen atom belong to a simple irreducible unitary representation of a noncompact semisimple Lie group, with the energy a function of the Casimir operator of the maximal compact subgroup.

To close this chapter, we shall present a series of general theorems concerning quantization of an algebra of classical observables (i.e., functions of p's and q's) that are useful in verifying that the classical relations described above for the hydrogen atom can be successfully quantized. These general facts may be useful in other situations.

Theorem 16–2

The set of observables which are series of functions of the type $f = qp^j$ and p^j, $j = 0, 1, \ldots$, is a Lie algebra under a Poisson bracket. Making the following operator assignments:

$$qp^j \to qd^j$$
$$p^j = d^j$$

defines a representation of this algebra by differential operators. (d^j denotes the differential operator $\partial^j / \partial q^j$.) The theorem also carries over to the case of an n-dimensional configuration space. For example, $q_1 p_1^{k_1} \cdots p_n^{k_n}$ goes over into the operator

$$q_1 \frac{\partial^{k_1}}{\partial q_1^{k_1}} \cdots \frac{\partial^{k_n}}{\partial q_n^{k_n}}.$$

Proof:

$$\{qp^i, qp^k\} = jqp^{i-1}p^k - p^i kqp^{k-1} = (j-k)qp^{i+k-1},$$
$$[qd^i, qd^k](\psi) = qd^i(qd^k\psi) - qd^k(qd^i\psi)$$
$$= q(jd^{k+i-1}\psi + qd^{i+k}\psi - kd^{k+i-1}\psi - qd^{i+k})$$
$$= q(j-k)d^{i+k-1}\psi,$$

shows that the Poisson bracket goes over to an operator bracket. Similarly,

$$\{p^i, qp^k\} = jp^{i+k-1},$$
$$[d^i, qd^k](\psi) = d^i(qd^k\psi) - qd^{i+k}\psi = jd^{i+k-1}\psi,$$

which finishes the proof.

Now, there is a unique differential operator of lower degree than j such that

$$(i)^{i-1}qd^i + \theta_j$$

is skew-Hermitian. (Exercise: Find θ_j explicitly.) Further, the commutator of two skew-Hermitian operators is skew-Hermitian. Hence

$$[(i)^{i-1}qd^i + \theta_j, (i)^{k-1}qd^k + \theta_k]$$

is skew-Hermitian. But, the term of highest degree in this commutator is

$$[(i)^{i-1}qd^i, (i)^{k-1}qd^k] = (i)^{i+k-2}(j-k)qd^{i+k-1}.$$

Hence, by the uniqueness of θ_j,

$$\theta_{j+k-1} = \frac{1}{(j-k)} \left([(i)^{i-1}qd^i, \theta_k] + [(i)^{k-1}qd^k, \theta_j] + [\theta_j, \theta_k] \right).$$

This proves that the assignment

$$qp^i \rightarrow (i)^{i-1}qd^i + \theta_j$$

sends the Poisson bracket into a commutator bracket. For similar reasons we see that the assignment $p^k \rightarrow (i)^{k-1}d^k$ sends the Poisson bracket into a commutator bracket. In fact, we can formalize this argument:

Theorem 16–3

Suppose that L is a Lie algebra (under a commutator bracket) of differential operators acting on complex-valued functions $\psi(q_1, \ldots, q_n)$. For $\Delta \in L$, let $\theta(\Delta)$ be the differential operator such that $\Delta + \theta(\Delta)$ is skew-Hermitian. Then, if $\Delta + \theta(\Delta)$ has the same terms of highest degree as Δ, for each $\Delta \in \mathbf{L}$, the mapping $\Delta \rightarrow \Delta + \theta(\Delta)$ sends commutators into commutators.

We leave the proof in the general case as an exercise.

Now we can state the definitive theorem concerning quantization of observables that are linear in $q_1, \ldots, q_n$.

Theorem 16–4

Consider a configuration space of n dimensions, with variables $q_1, \ldots, q_n$, and consider the Lie algebra L of classical observables of the form

$$f(p, q) = \sum (\alpha_{k_1 \cdots k_n} + \beta_{jk_1 \cdots k_n} q_j) p_1^{k_1} \cdots p_n^{k_n}.$$

(α's and β's are constants.)

Assign to each such f a differential operator Δ_f in the following way:

$$f = p_1^{k_1} \cdots p_n^{k_n} \to (i)^{(k_1 + \cdots + k_n - 1)} \frac{\partial^{k_1}}{\partial q_1^{k_1}} \cdots \frac{\partial^{k_n}}{\partial q_n^{k_n}} = \Delta_f,$$

$$f = q_j p_1^{k_1} \cdots p_n^{k_n} \to q_j(i)^{(k_1 + \cdots + k_n - 1)} \frac{\partial^{k_1}}{\partial q_1^{k_1}} \cdots \frac{\partial^{k_n}}{\partial q_n^{k_n}} = \Delta_f.$$

Then Poisson brackets go over to commutator brackets. If, for each $f \in \mathbf{L}$, θ_f is the differential operator such that $\Delta_f + \theta_f$ is skew-Hermitian, then θ_f has lower degree than Δ_f; hence the assignment $f \to \Delta_f + \theta_f$ sends Poisson brackets into commutator brackets.

STRONG–COUPLING THEORY FOR THE HYDROGEN ATOM

Suppose we introduce a parameter λ on the Coulomb potential:

$$H_\lambda = \tfrac{1}{2} p_i p_j - \frac{\lambda}{r}.$$

If the f_{ij} are defined as above, and the f_k^λ are defined as

$$f_k^\lambda = \frac{\lambda q_k}{r} - q_k(p_j p_j) + (p_j q_j) p_k,$$

one verifies readily that the same structure relations are satisfied as for $\lambda = 1$. Thus, we have a typical situation considered in Chapter 11, namely a sequence of Lie subalgebras. The limit as $\lambda \to \infty$ may be considered physically as the "strong-coupling theory." Suppose we concentrate attention on the negative-energy states. Then

$$\frac{1}{\sqrt{\lambda}} \frac{f_k^\lambda}{\sqrt{-H_f}} \to \frac{q_k/r}{\sqrt{1/r}} = \frac{q_k}{\sqrt{r}} \qquad \text{as } \lambda \to \infty.$$

Then, the limiting algebra is the semidirect sum of the $SO(3)$-algebra generated by the f_{ij} and the Abelian ideal generated by $q_k/\sqrt{r}$.

CHAPTER 17

GROUPS IN ELEMENTARY–
PARTICLE PHYSICS

Until recently, group theory played only a subsidiary role in quantum mechanics. Only simple ideas and groups appeared [e.g., $SO(3, R)$, $U(2)$], and many physicists were convinced that an amateur knowledge of group theory sufficed, since it was used only as a tool to analyze complicated phenomena that could, in principle at least, be understood directly.

At any rate, group theory seems to have moved to a more central place in the work of those physicists who are trying to understand elementary particle–high energy physics, although there is not yet a unifying intellectual structure in which one can place these phenomena. However, one can see two attractive features to this program: First, one feels confident that, whatever the final unified theory that will emerge, the symmetry ideas will remain. Second, the study of symmetry can be used in conjunction with experiments to grope toward the right answers, a sort of "phenomenological group theory."

In this chapter we shall attempt to explain some of these insights from a mathematician's point of view, to provide a feeling for the sort of applications one might expect of the group-theoretic ideas. We shall not be so concerned with details as with the underlying ideas, and apologize in advance for only mentioning the names of a few ideas and workers in this vast and very active field.

As explained in the last chapter, the basic principles of quantum mechanics seem to require the postulation of a Lie algebra of observables and a representation of this algebra by skew-Hermitian operators on a Hilbert space V. One also expects some correlation of these observables and the representation to space-time and the symmetry group of space-time, the Poincaré group. A convenient mathematical way of specifying this correlation is to require that the Poincaré group act as a group of automorphisms on the observables and as a group of unitary transformations on the Hilbert space, so that the transform of the observable by an element g of the Poincaré group goes over to the transform of the corresponding operator by the unitary operator on V corresponding to g. Precisely, if X is an observable,

$$(gX)(\psi) = g(X(g^{-1}(\psi))) \qquad \text{for } \psi \in V.$$

This general insight motivates the importance of the classification of the irreducible unitary representations of the Poincaré group, first done by Wigner precisely for this reason. Now, the representation of the Poincaré group on V is not irreducible: By the general theory of representations of locally compact groups, V can be split up into a direct integral of subspaces on which the Poincaré group acts irreducibly, so that the problem for the physicist is to decide how the Wigner representations can be put together to give *the* Hilbert space which reflects the physical situation. However, the subspaces in which the Poincaré group acts irreducibly are the "single particle states." This argument also motivates the feeling that "elementary particles" are associated with the irreducible representations of the Poincaré group, or of some larger group that contains or is an extension† of the Poincaré group.

It is also important, at least for the mathematician, to realize that the association of particles with representation of the Poincaré group gives a precisely defined meaning to "momentum," "energy," "mass," and "spin." To see how this goes, let us choose indices $1 \leqslant i, j, k, \ldots, \leqslant 4$, together with the summation convention. The Lie algebra of the Poincaré group is generated by elements X_i, Y_{jk} satisfying relations of the form

$$[X_i, X_j] = 0,$$
$$[X_i, Y_{jk}] = g_{ki}X_j - g_{ji}X_k,$$
$$[Y_{ij}Y_{kl}] = g_{li}Y_{kj} - g_{ki}Y_{lj} + g_{kj}Y_{li} - g_{lj}Y_{ki},$$
$$Y_{ij} + Y_{ji} = 0.$$

(g_{ij} is the Lorentz metric tensor: $g_{ij} = 0$ if $i \neq j$, $g_{11} = 1 = -g_{22} = -g_{33} = -g_{44}$.)

Construct the following elements of the enveloping algebra of the Poincaré group:

$$M = g_{ij}X_iX_j,$$
$$W_i = \tfrac{1}{2}\epsilon_{ijkl}X_jY_{kl}.$$

(ϵ_{ijk} is the symbol that is antisymmetric in all its indices with $\epsilon_{1234} = 1$.)

$$W = -g_{ij}W_iW_j.$$

One verifies that M and W are Casimir operators, and that W_i transforms under the adjoint representation like the X_i, i.e., like a 4-vector. Now, in an irreducible representation, M and W are diagonal. Their eigenvalues are m^2 and $m^2s(s + 1)$, where m and s are identified with the spin of the particle described by that representation. This can be checked by direct calculation on what we called earlier the Wigner construction of representations of the Poincaré group. Of course, it must be proved

---

† A group G' is an extension of a group G if there is a homomorphism of G' on G.

that every irreducible unitary representation of the Poincaré group is of Wigner type, but this has been done in the mathematical literature.

The operators corresponding to the S_i form the *energy-momentum vector:* X_0 is the energy operator and X_1, X_2, and X_3 the three components of space momentum. Thus, a vector ψ for which $X_i(\psi) = 0$ for $1 \leqslant i \leqslant 3$ is "at rest." Its "energy" is then m^2. (c, the velocity of light, is taken to be 1.)

The W_i are associated with "polarization." Note that

$$X_m W_i = \tfrac{1}{2}\epsilon_{ijkl}X_m X_j Y_{kl},$$
$$W_i X_m = \tfrac{1}{2}\epsilon_{ijkl}X_j Y_{kl}X_m$$
$$= -\tfrac{1}{2}\epsilon_{ijkl}X_j[X_m, Y_{kl}] + \tfrac{1}{2}\epsilon_{ijkl}X_m X_j Y_{kl}$$
$$= -\tfrac{1}{2}\epsilon_{ijkl}X_j(g_{lm}X_k - g_{km}X_l) + \tfrac{1}{2}\epsilon_{ijkl}X_m X_j Y_{kl}.$$

Hence $[X_m, W_i] = 0$: The W_i then act on the "eigenvectors"† of the X_i, i.e., on the states of given momentum.

We see then that many of the "kinematic" ideas associated with physics can be associated with algebraic properties of the Poincaré group. It is very tempting for a mathematician, at least, to suspect that the newer physical ideas such as isospin and hypercharge ("strangeness") can be similarly associated with a bigger group. Of course, this is an idea that is undergoing very active development by physicists right now.

So far, when talking about the Poincaré group, we have meant the connected group. It is important to consider the nonconnected group also, for example by considering the full group of automorphisms of the connected Poincaré group. Instead of considering only unitary representation, one can allow the discrete automorphisms to go over into antiunitary transformations; i.e., one satisfying

$$(g\psi, g\psi) = \overline{(\psi, \psi)}.$$

One can then analyze the irreducible representations of the connected Poincaré group for their behavior with respect to these automorphisms.

We shall not pursue the program of showing how the "kinematic" ideas of elementary-particle physics can be analyzed with the Poincaré group. Wightman's article (1960) can be read for more details. Lurcat's article (1964) is also interesting as an indication of how quantum field theory can be freed from its reliance on space-time and made wholly group-theoretic. The next step in a discussion of the foundations of group-theoretic elementary-particle physics should be the extension of these ideas to those groups associated with isospin and hypercharge. These ideas are, at least on the surface, very simple, indeed even simpler than those associated with the Poincaré group. Here, one considers a compact connected Lie

† Strictly speaking, the eigenvectors of the X_i are generalized functions.

group K. Let $\mathbf{C}$ be a maximal Abelian subalgebra of $\mathbf{K}$, i.e., a Cartan subalgebra of $\mathbf{K}$. Say that $X_1, \ldots, X_r$ form a basis of $\mathbf{C}$. The "new" group of physics is now

$$P \times K = G$$

where P is the Poincaré group.

The single-particle states are now given by unitary representations of G, which are, of course, just tensor products of unitary representations of P and K. The representations of P we know, the Wigner representations. Suppose that ρ is an irreducible representation of K on a vector space $V(K)$. We know that the operators $\rho(\mathbf{C})$ can be diagonalized; say that $v_1, \ldots, v_n$ are the eigenvectors. Let $i\lambda_1, \ldots, i\lambda_n$ be the weights of the representation; i.e.,

$$[X, v_j] = i\lambda_j(X)v_j \qquad \text{for } 1 \leqslant j \leqslant n, X \in \mathbf{C}.$$

What is done is to associate strongly interacting particles with each of the basis vectors, "quantum numbers" (e.g., charge, hypercharge), with the elements $X_1, \ldots, X_r$. Then $\lambda_j(X_k)$ is the kth quantum number of the jth particle. (So far, of course, $r = 2$, since there seem to be two such quantum numbers.)

Thus the single-particle states are elements of

$$V(P) \otimes V(K),$$

where $V(P)$ is a Hilbert space with an irreducible representation of the Poincaré group P. The many-particle states are now basically tensor products of these single-particle Hilbert spaces. One way of looking at "interactions" is that they should amount to some operations on the many-particle states, picking out certain subspaces among the *possible* irreducible components among the tensor product of two many-particle states. One usually asks for invariance of this "interaction" under the action of P. However, if one also requires invariance under H, clearly the group K begins to play a nontrivial role.

These "internal" symmetry groups first arose in nuclear physics in the following context. One associates the proton and neutron with weight vectors of a two-dimensional vector space, and K with $SU(2)$, leading to the isospin scheme. The invariance of interaction under $SU(2)$ is associated with "charge independence" of the nuclear forces. In fact, the proton and neutron do not behave precisely alike in interactions. For example, their masses are close, but not exactly the same. One tries to associate this with some sort of "approximate symmetry" of the interaction under K. (For example, the "weakly interacting" particles do not have this sort of symmetry at all.)

The next jump, made by Gell-Mann and Ne'eman (1964) after much groping during the 1950s for the correct group, was to associate eight baryons and eight mesons with the eight-dimensional representation of $SU(3)$. The most important achievement from the mathematical point of view in this theory is the *Gell-Mann–Okubo mass formula*.

For free particles, "mass" is just the eigenvalue of the Casimir operator of the Poincaré group that we labeled as the mass operator. This would predict *equal* masses for all particles in one irreducible representation of $G \times K$. In fact, the masses of, say, the eight baryons are close to each other but not zero. Presumably *either* the fact that $SU(3)$ is only an approximate symmetry, or the effect of the physical forces other than the strong interaction, accounts for this difference. Gell-Mann now essentially guesses (with motivation from perturbation theory) that the real mass operator on the vector space $V(K)$ should be a tensor of type $(1, 1)$, which transforms as the eighth component of the eight-dimensional representation of $SU(3)$ under the action of $SU(3)$ on these tensors. Certain free constants are obtained in the formula for the operator. These constants can be fitted with part of the data, and the formula then used to predict the rest of the data. The great victory for this scheme was the discovery last year of the Ω^- particle with predicted mass.

The next step, taken by Gursey and Radicati (1964) and, independently, by Sakita (1964), was, in analogy with Wigner's (1937) supermultiplet theory, to try to put together particles of different spin (the baryons have spin $\frac{1}{2}$, $\frac{3}{2}$, . . . , the mesons spin 0, 1, . . .) by choosing a group containing $SU(3)$. Now, for fixed momentum, "spin" can be associated with an irreducible representation of the simply connected covering group of $SO(3)$, namely $SU(2)$. Thus, a particle with a certain spin and certain $SU(3)$ content may be regarded, when "static," as a representation of $SU(3) \times SU(2)$. A natural way of constructing a larger group is to take the tensor product, and take the smallest associative algebra of 6×6 matrices containing the tensor product; one obtains $SU(6)$. They found that representation of $SU(6)$, when reduced out with respect to $SU(3) \times SU(2)$, accounts remarkably well for sets of particles of different spin. Having thrown away the Poincaré group, except $SU(2)$, and gotten such remarkable results, many physicists proceeded to try to put the Poincaré group back in. This is, of course, now the most active and confused field, and many workers have recently reported essentially equivalent approaches.

For example, one general way of looking at this has recently been pointed out by Michel and Sakita. Take a *finite-dimensional* representation of the Poincaré group, take the tensor product with $SU(3)$, and take the smallest group of matrices containing this tensor product. One obtains in this way a group containing both the Poincaré group and $SU(3)$.

Now, look for an irreducible unitary representation, and reduce it out with respect to P and $SU(3)$.

Of course, following Gell-Mann's idea in the mass formula, one common feature of all these schemes is the attempt to link physical objects like magnetic moments and mass to operators that transform in an appropriate way under the enlarged group. This gives one some control other than mathematical elegance over the possible choices of the bigger group. This assumption about these objects is ad hoc, justified by its success. It has been thought that combining the two groups in a more natural group-theoretic or geometric way might point the way toward better understanding. For example, one might postulate that "mass" is *always* associated with precisely the relevant Casimir operator of the Poincaré group, not as in the Gell-Mann theory.† One might hope to do this by putting together the Poincaré and internal symmetry group in a more interesting way than merely the product. There has been a deluge of work along these lines in the physics literature in the last year. We will only briefly report on some of it. First, the initial work of McGlinn (1964), which was put into definitive form by Michel (1964), then the very recent work of O'Raifeartaigh concerning the possibilities of obtaining discrete masses by imbedding the Poincaré group in a larger group.

Let $P = L \cdot T$ be the Poincaré group, a semidirect product of the Lorentz group L and the translation group T. Let G be a group containing P as a subgroup and another group S (the "internal" symmetric group). Suppose that every element of G can be written in at least one way as a product P of an element of S times an element of G, i.e., $G = S \cdot P$. Suppose also that there is at least one Lorentz transformation $l \in L$ that commutes with S. (For physical reasons, the internal symmetry group should commute with the Lorentz group.) Consider the homogeneous space G/P. The elements of G that act trivially on this space form an invariant subgroup I of G. The element l of the Lorentz group that is postulated to commute with S must be in I.

A coset of G/P is of the form sP, for $s \in S$. Then $l \cdot sP = (ls)P = (sl)P = slP = sP$. But, the only invariant subgroups of the Poincaré group that contain even one element of the Lorentz rotations is the whole group. We conclude (following McGlinn and Michel) that P is an invariant subgroup of G, and that G is a semidirect product of P and S. Thus, Ad S must map T into itself. If we assume further that S commutes with L, since Ad L acts irreducibly in $\mathbf{T}$, the only possibility is that Ad S acts on $\mathbf{T}$ complexified by diagonal matrices. For example, if S is semisimple, this forces S to commute with T.

† There it may be thought of as a linear combination of the Casimir operator of the Poincaré group and the "eighth" element of the Lie algebra of $SU(3)$.

We turn now to consideration of the work of O'Raifeartaigh (1965), who poses the problem of "prolonging" the Poincaré group in the following way.   Is it possible to imbed the Poincaré group P as a subgroup of another Lie group G so that G has an irreducible unitary representation in which the "mass" Casimir operator of P has a discrete eigenvalue?   O'Raifeartaigh shows that if this can be done, there is only one such eigenvalue; i.e., *no mass splittings with discrete masses are possible with finite-dimensional group G*.   We shall sketch his arguments.

An element X of a finite-dimensional Lie algebra $\mathbf{G}$ is said to be *nilpotent* if all eigenvalues of Ad X are zero, i.e., if Ad X raised to a sufficiently high power is zero.   One can prove that the following condition is necessary and sufficient that X be nilpotent.

The trace of the transformation (Ad $X)^n$ *is zero, for* $n = 1, 2, \ldots$.

[(Ad $X)^n$ means the linear transformation Ad X on $\mathbf{G}$ repeated n times. The trace is defined by exhibiting this transformation as a matrix after choosing a basis for G.]   Another useful fact:

> If A and B are linear transformations of a finite-dimensional vector space, the trace of the commutator $[A, B] = AB - BA$ is zero.

One proves, using these two facts, that each element $X \in \mathbf{T}$ is a nilpotent element of $\mathbf{G}$, where T is the translation subgroup of the Poincaré group P, which is considered to be a subgroup of G.   [The key fact is that (Ad $X)^n$ can be written as a commutator already within $\mathbf{P}$.]   Let $M = g_{ij}X_iX_j$ be the Casimir operator of $\mathbf{P}$.   Suppose $\mathbf{G}$ is realized as an irreducible algebra of skew-Hermitian operators on a Hilbert space V.   Suppose v_0 is an eigenvector of M, i.e.,

$$(M - m)(v_0) = 0.$$

Let Y be any element of $\mathbf{G}$.   Let n be sufficiently large.   Then

$$(M - m)^n Y(v_0) = [(M - m)^n, Y](v_0).$$

Now,

$$[(M - m)^n, Y] = (M - m)^{n-1}[M, Y] + (M - m)^{n-2}[M, Y](M - m) + \cdots;$$

hence

$$[(M - m)^n, Y](v_0) = (M - m)^{n-1}[M, Y](v_0) = (M - m)^{n-2}[M, [M, Y]](v_0)$$
$$= \cdots,$$
$$[M, Y] = [g_{ij}X_iX_j, Y] = g_{ij}X_i[X_j, Y] + g_{ij}[X_i, Y]X_j.$$

Continuing to work out these iterated commutators with M, we see, since each X_i is a nilpotent element of $\mathbf{G}$, that $(M - m)^n Y(v_0)$ vanishes for n

sufficiently large. But, since $M - m$ is a Hermitian operator, this, for $n > 1$, forces it for $n = 1$. Hence, the eigenvectors of M with eigenvalue m are left invariant by **G**, hence also by G, hence, since G acting on V is irreducible, fill up all of V.

PERTURBATION THEORY AND GROUPS

We shall now discuss briefly the elementary material on perturbation theory that is in every quantum mechanics book. First, we recall what is involved here [following, for example, Wigner (1959)].

Let H_0 be a Hermitian operator, acting, say, on a Hilbert space ψ. Let $\psi_1^0, \psi_2^0, \ldots$ be its eigenvectors with eigenvalues $E_1^0, E_2^0, \ldots$ ordered by increasing value. Let

$$H = H_0 + \lambda V,$$

be the "perturbed" operator, with V also a Hermitian, and with λ a real parameter. This operator will have eigenvectors depending on λ:

$$\psi_k = \psi_k^0 + \lambda \psi_k' + \lambda^2 \psi_k'' + \cdots \qquad (k = 1, 2, \ldots),$$

with eigenvalues

$$E_k = E_k^0 + \lambda E_k' + \cdots \qquad (k = 1, 2, \ldots).$$

Inserting these into the eigenvalue equation and comparing coefficients of λ gives (in case of eigenvalues of multiplicity 1) the standard formulas

$$E_k = E_k^0 + \lambda V_{kk} + \lambda^2 \sum_{l \neq k} \frac{|V_{lk}|^2}{E_k^0 - E_l^0} + \cdots,$$

$$\psi_k = \psi_k^0 + \lambda \sum_{l \neq k} \frac{V_{lk}}{E_k - E_l} \psi_l + \cdots \qquad (k = 1, 2, \ldots),$$

with

$$V_{lk} = (\psi_l, V(\psi_k)) \qquad (k, l = 1, 2, \ldots).$$

We can look at this in the following way: Let G be the unitary group $U(n)$ considered as a compact Lie group. Let **G** be its Lie algebra, which we have seen can be identified with the Hermitian† matrices. Let **C** be a maximal Abelian subalgebra of **G**, which can be identified with the diagonal matrices in **G**. We can define a mapping of $G \times \mathbf{C}$ into **G** by sending (g, X) into Ad $g(X)$, for $g \in G$, $X \in \mathbf{C}$. The theorem that every element of **G** is conjugate to an element of **C** translates into the fact that this mapping of $G \times \mathbf{C} \rightarrow \mathbf{G}$ is onto.

---

† Strictly speaking, of course, it is the skew-Hermitian matrices. In quantum mechanics, one compensates for this by putting i in all the formulas.

Suppose now that $\lambda \to Y(\lambda)$ is a curve in $\mathbf{G}$, defined for values of λ close to zero with $Y(0) \in \mathbf{C}$. (In the application to quantum mechanics, this curve is $\lambda \to H^0 + \lambda V$.)

One may ask now if there is a curve $\lambda \to (g(\lambda),\ Z(\lambda))$ in $G \times \mathbf{C}$ whose image in $\mathbf{G}$ is "close" to the curve $\lambda \to Y(\lambda)$. Put

$$Y_1(\lambda) = \mathrm{Ad}(g(\lambda))Z(\lambda).$$

We want to see how $g(\lambda)$ and $Z(\lambda)$ can be chosen so that

$$Y_1(0) = Y(0) \qquad \frac{dY_1}{d\lambda}(0) = \frac{dY}{d\lambda}(0) \qquad \frac{d^2 Y_1(0)}{d\lambda^2} = \frac{d^2 Y(0)}{d\lambda^2}.$$

We can normalize the choice of $\mathbf{C}$ so that

$$Y(0) \in \mathbf{C},$$

hence may suppose

$$g(0) = \text{identity} \qquad Z(0) = Y(0).$$

Now, writing in terms of matrices, we have

$$Y_1(\lambda) = g(\lambda)Z(\lambda)g(\lambda)^{-1},$$
$$\frac{dY_1}{d\lambda} = \frac{dg}{d\lambda} Zg^{-1} + g \frac{dZ}{d\lambda} g^{-1} - gZg^{-1} \frac{dg}{d\lambda} g^{-1}$$
$$= \frac{dg}{d\lambda} g^{-1} gZg^{-1} + g \frac{dZ}{d\lambda} g^{-1} - gZg^{-1} \frac{dg}{d\lambda} g^{-1}$$
$$= [\dot{g}(\lambda),\ Y_1(\lambda)] + \mathrm{Ad}\, g \left(\frac{dZ}{d\lambda} \right),$$

where we have put

$$\dot{g}(\lambda) = \frac{dg}{d\lambda} g^{-1}.$$

$[\lambda \to \dot{g}(\lambda)$ is a curve in the Lie algebra $\mathbf{G}$ of G.]

$$\frac{d^2 Y_1}{d\lambda^2} = \left[\frac{d\dot{g}(\lambda)}{d\lambda},\ \mathrm{Ad}\, g(\lambda) \right] + \left[\dot{g}(\lambda),\ [\dot{g}(\lambda),\ Y_1(\lambda)] + \mathrm{Ad}\, g \left(\frac{dZ}{d\lambda} \right) \right]$$
$$+ \left[\dot{g}(\lambda),\ \mathrm{Ad}\, g \left(\frac{dZ}{d\lambda} \right) \right] + \mathrm{Ad}\, g \left(\frac{d^2 Z}{d\lambda^2} \right).$$

Suppose now that $\mathbf{G}$ is split up into $\mathbf{C} \oplus \mathbf{B}$, where $\mathbf{B}$ is a subspace of $\mathbf{G}$ such that $[\mathbf{C}, \mathbf{B}] \subset \mathbf{B}$. Suppose $\lambda \to Y(\lambda)$ is split up into

$$Y(\lambda) = Y^C(\lambda) + Y^B(\lambda) \qquad \text{with } Y^C(\lambda) \in \mathbf{C},\ Y^B(\lambda) \in \mathbf{B}.$$

Similarly, split up $\dot{g}(\lambda)$ into $W^B(\lambda) + W^C(\lambda)$. Then $(dY_1/d\lambda)(0) = (dY/d\lambda)(0)$ gives the conditions

(17–1)
$$\frac{dY^B}{d\lambda}(0) = [W^B(0),\ Y(0)]$$

(17–2)
$$\frac{dY^C}{d\lambda}(0) = \frac{dZ}{d\lambda}(0),$$

$$\frac{d^2 Y_1}{d\lambda^2}(0) = \frac{d^2 Y}{d\lambda^2}(0)$$

gives the conditions

(17–3)
$$\frac{d^2 Y^B}{d\lambda^2}(0) = \left[\frac{dW^B}{d\lambda}(0), Y(0)\right] + 2\left[W^B(0), \frac{dY^C}{d\lambda}(0)\right]$$

$$\oplus \left[W^C(0), \frac{dY^B}{d\lambda}(0)\right]$$

$$+ \left(\text{projection of } \left[W^B(0), \frac{dY^B}{d\lambda}(0)\right] \text{ on } \mathbf{B}\right).$$

(17–4)
$$\frac{d^2 Y^C}{d\lambda^2}(0) = \text{projection of } \left[W^B(0), \frac{dY^B}{d\lambda}(0)\right] \text{ on } \mathbf{C} + \frac{d^2 Z}{d\lambda^2}(0).$$

We can now discuss possible solutions of these equations. First, $Y(0) \in \mathbf{C}$, hence Ad $Y(0)$ maps $\mathbf{B}$ into itself. Now, $Y^B(\lambda)$ and $Y^C(\lambda)$ are to be regarded as given. Hence we must be able to solve (17–1) for $W^B(0)$. The condition that this can be done no matter what the choice of the left side is that:

Ad $Y(0)$ acting in B has nonzero determinant; i.e., the centralizer of $Y(0)$ in G is precisely $\mathbf{C}$, or, $Y(0)$ is a regular element of C.

Equations (17–2) also determine $(dZ/d\lambda)(0)$. Hence

if $Y(0)$ is a regular element of $\mathbf{C}$, and if one imposes the condition $W^C(0) = 0$, the first derivatives of the curve $\lambda \rightarrow (g(\lambda), Z(\lambda))$ at $\lambda = 0$ are completely determined.

Similarly, (17–3) determines $(dW^B/d\lambda)(0)$ and $(d^2Z/d\lambda^2)(0)$. $(dW^C/d\lambda)(0)$ can be chosen arbitrarily, e.g., equal to zero. Finally, then, we have an expansion of the form

$$Y(\lambda) = \text{Ad} \exp(W^B(0) + \cdots)\left(Y(0) + \frac{dY^C}{d\lambda}(0)\cdots\right).$$

For example, returning to the case of interest in quantum mechanics, $Y(\lambda) = H_0 + \lambda V, dY/d\lambda = V$; V^C is then the operator such that

$$(\psi_i, V^C(\psi_j)) = 0 \quad \text{for } i \neq j, \qquad = (\psi_i, V(\psi_j)) \quad \text{for } i = j,$$

while V^B is the operator such that

$$(\psi_i, V^B(\psi_j)) = 0 \quad \text{for } i = j, \qquad = (\psi_i, V(\psi_j)) \quad \text{for } i \neq j.$$

We see that we get the sort of expansion with which we began the section.

We shall leave these explicit calculations at this point.   The main point
is the qualitative one that the simple perturbation theory that has been
so successful in explaining the broad outlines of the applications of quantum
theory to atomic physics can be put into this purely Lie group-theoretic
setting, for possible use in more speculative areas where the framework
is not so well understood.   For example, in Weyl's book (1955) considerable emphasis is put on the fact that most of the successful applications
of quantum theory are based on general group-theoretic principles and this
first-order perturbation theory.

GAUGE GROUPS AND SUPERMULTIPLET THEORY

One of the current problems of mathematical physics is understanding
how to combine the $SU(3)$ internal symmetry and the Poincaré symmetry
in the classification of the elementary particles.   Of course, the first
approximation is to regard a multiplet of particles as described by irreducible representations of $P \times SU(3)$.   The Wigner supermultiplet idea
is to try to find a group G containing $P \times SU(3)$, say, whose irreducible
representations will tie together these multiplets into supermultiplets.
In this section, we shall describe† a geometric pattern that might be
useful in looking for this group.

Let $\pi \colon E \to M$ be a vector bundle over a space M; i.e., for $p \in M$,
$\pi^{-1}(p)$ is a vector space.   Let $\Gamma(E)$ be its cross sections.   Let H be a
Lie group that acts on E and transitively on M; i.e., for $g \in H$, $p \in M$;

g maps p into $gp \in M$, and maps $\pi^{-1}(p)$ linearly into $\pi^{-1}(gp)$.

Recall that this defines a representation of H on the vector space
$\Gamma(E)$.   For $\psi \epsilon \Gamma(E)$, $h \in H$, $p \in M$,

$$\rho(h)(\psi)(p) = h\psi(h^{-1}p).$$

Now, we have been dealing with one specific group H acting on E and M.
Suppose we define the *gauge group* of the vector bundle (relative to H) as
the set of transformations g of E into E such that

g maps each fiber $\pi^{-1}(p)$ linearly into a fiber $\pi^{-1}(p')$.   The mapping $p \to p'$ obtained in this way of M into M should be a transformation of H.

† These remarks constitute a "geometrization" of some observations made by Michel
at the 1965 Coral Gables Symmetry Conference.

Let G be this gauge group. It is clearly an "infinite-parameter" group. Let G_0 be the subgroup of gauge transformations g that act as the identity in M, i.e., such that

$$g\pi^{-1}(p) = \pi^{-1}(p) \qquad \text{for each } p \in M.$$

G_0 may be called the group of "pure" gauge transformations. It is an invariant subgroup of G.

By our construction, H is a subgroup of G. $H \cap G_0$ consists of those transformations of H that act as the identity on M. Note also that

$$G = H \cdot G_0.$$

Of course, this product is not "direct" unless $H \cap G_0$ is the identity.

Now we can pose in this language one of the main problems in Wigner's supermultiplet theory. Is it possible to find a finite-dimensional subgroup H' of G containing H which "mixes up" the action of H on the fibers of E? We shall now deal with one set of conditions that this be possible.

Suppose that the dimensions of the fibers of E is n. Choose indices $1 \leqslant i, j, \ldots, \leqslant n$ and the summation convention. Let (ψ_i) be a basis of cross sections of E; i.e.,

$(\psi_i(p))$ is a basis of the vector space $\pi^{-1}(p)$, for each $p \in M$.

Then, for $h \in H$;

(17–5) $\phi(h)(\psi_i) = A_{ij}^k \psi_j.$

In general, the (A_{ij}^k) are functions on M. If these functions are *constant* on M, we have an immediate way of choosing this larger group H'. In fact, choose H' as the set of $g \in G$ that transforms the ψ_i among themselves by such a *constant* matrix. Then, $H \subset H'$.

We can find such a choice of cross section if the following condition is satisfied:

(17–6) $M = H/S$, and H is the semidirect product of the subgroup S and invariant subgroup T.

We shall now prove the following fact. Let σ be the representation of S by transformations on the vector space U that determines the vector bundle E. A cross section of E can then be considered as a map $\psi \colon H \to U$, with

$$\psi(hs) = \sigma(s^{-1})\psi(h) \qquad \text{for } h \in H, s \in S.$$

Then, if $H = T \cdot S$, ψ is determined by its restriction to I. Let $\psi_i, \ldots, \psi_n$ be *constant* functions from I to U. Then, for $h \in H$, $t \in T$,

$$\rho(h)(\psi_i)(t) = \psi_i(h^{-1}t)$$
$$= \psi_i(h^{-1}th \cdot h^{-1}).$$

Suppose that $h = st'$, $s \in S$, $t' \in T$. Then

$$\rho(h)(\psi_i)(t) = \sigma(s^{-1})\psi_i(h^{-1}th \cdot t'^{-1})$$
$$= \sigma(s^{-1})(\psi_i)(t),$$

since the ψ_i are, by construction, *constant* on T. Then the ψ_i transform like (17–5), with (A_{ij}^k) that are *constant* on M.

For example, condition (17–6) is satisfied if H is the Galilean group and S is the semidirect product of the "spin" subgroup with the translation group. As Michel remarks, it is this group-theoretic fact that is responsible for the statement that $SU(6)$ theory can be made Galilean-invariant very easily, but different considerations are necessary to deal with Poincaré invariance, since the subgroup S of the Poincaré group which is semidirect product of the "spin" subgroup and the translation does *not* satisfy condition (17–8). However, at least this way of looking at this problem does pose a definite mathematical question. What is the minimal subgroup of the gauge group containing H, when H is the product $P \times SU(3)$ of the Poincaré group and $SU(3)$, S is the subgroup: spin group $\times$ translation group $\times SU(3)$?

CHAPTER 18

FURTHER TOPICS IN THE THEORY OF REPRESENTATIONS OF NONCOMPACT SEMISIMPLE GROUPS

It is becoming clearer that the theory of unitary representations of noncompact Lie groups will be of importance in physics. Of course, this has always been true because the Poincaré group is noncompact; however the Poincaré group is atypical, since its unitary representations can be constructed and discussed so simply and directly. For example, the proof of complete classification of the unitary representations of the noncompact simple Lie groups is, to the author's best knowledge, still incomplete.

One general scheme to explain how the representations of noncompact groups will appear in physics has recently been proposed by M. Gell-Mann and Y. Ne'eman. Suppose that K is one of the compact groups that have been used up to now in classifying states of physical systems, e.g., $SO(3, R)$ (angular momentum), $SU(2)$ (isotopic spin), or $SU(3)$ (unitary symmetry). Typically, an infinite family of representations of K will appear as "bands" in a single physical system. For example, in an elementary quantum mechanics problem with a spherically symmetric potential, the rotation group $SO(3, R)$ will commute with the Hamiltonian, hence the energy levels will admit a unitary $SO(3, R)$ representation. In certain simple problems of pion-nucleon interaction, families of representations of $SU(2) \times SU(2)$ (spin $\times$ isospin) appear. For the strongly interacting particles, the compact group seems to be $SU(6)$ or $SU(6) \times SU(6)$.

One simple scheme by which one might attempt to tie together these representations of K would be to propose the existence of a group G containing K and an irreducible unitary representation ρ of G which, reduced to K, contains precisely those representations occurring in the physical problem. Having "guessed" G correctly, one might try to identify the operators occurring in the noncompact part of the Lie algebra of G with physically relevant quantities.

To carry out this program, one must of course have some grasp of the type of mathematics needed to construct representations of noncompact groups so that the decomposition under compact subgroups can be obtained relatively simply. If we restrict attention to noncompact, semisimple G, with K the maximal compact subgroup, the general scheme presented in Chapter 9 for constructing representations of G can serve as a starting point in these investigations, particularly since most of the representations of the noncompact semisimple groups constructed up to now by Bargman, Gel'fand, Neumark, Graev, and Harish-Chandra fall into this pattern.

A basic role in all this is played by certain spaces M on which both a noncompact semisimple Lie group G and its maximal compact subgroup K can act transitively. Put another way, there is a subgroup H in G such that

$$M = G/H,$$
$$\dim(G/H) = \dim(K/K \cap H).$$

(It can be proved that this condition is also sufficient to guarantee that K act transitively on G/H.)

We can then consider vector bundles over E, and consider the representation of G on cross sections of the bundle, with multipliers to make the representation unitary. (G will not preserve a volume element on M.) The first question then is: How does the representation decompose under K? A particularly simple situation occurs when $K/H \cap K$ is itself a symmetric homogeneous space, i.e., when $H \cap K$ is a symmetric subgroup of K, and the fibers of E are one-dimensional. In this case, a theorem proved by Cartan asserts that each representation of K appears at most once in this decomposition. For example, in the example considered in Chapter 9, $M = P_n(C)$, $G = SL(n+1, C)$, $K = SU(n+1)$, and $K \cap H = U(n)$. We saw there that the decomposition of the action of K on the cross sections took a particularly simple and interesting form.

We shall now go into some of these points more systematically, with particular attention to Cartan's basic paper (1952d). Let K be a Lie group (not necessarily compact, for the moment) and let L be a closed subgroup. Let M be the space K/L, which again is not necessarily assumed to be compact. Let E be a homogeneous vector bundle over M. We shall assume that each fiber $\pi^{-1}(p)$, for $p \in M$, is a complex vector space, and that $(\ ,\ )$ is a positive-definite Hermitian inner product on it. Let dp be a volume element for M. We can then consider those cross sections $\psi \in \Gamma(E)$ for which the inner product

$$(\psi, \psi) = \int (\psi(p), \psi(p))^{1/2} \, dp$$

is finite. Until further notice, $\Gamma(E)$ will denote the set of these square-integrable cross sections, which then forms a Hilbert space. Further, we will suppose that the action of K on M preserves the volume element dp, so that the "natural" action ρ of K on cross sections defines a unitary representation of K in the Hilbert space $\Gamma(E)$. Recall the formula

$$\rho(k)(\psi)(p) = k\psi(k^{-1}p) \qquad \text{for } k \in K, p \in M.$$

We shall now investigate the relation between the action of K on $\Gamma(E)$ and the value elements of $\Gamma(E)$ take at points of M. Now, in general one cannot expect any reasonable relation between $\Gamma(E)$ as a *Hilbert space* and the values, since square integrability has no particular implication for values at any one point. However, we shall be considering a restricted situation where there is such a relation. To keep on a level of generality, we will suppose that V is a closed subspace of $\Gamma(E)$ that is invariant under K such that the following condition is satisfied:

(18–1) If $\psi_1, \psi_2, \ldots$ is a sequence of elements of V that converges in the Hilbert space norm, then $\lim_{i \to \infty} \psi_i(p)$ exists for all $p \in M$.

There are at least two situations of interest where this condition holds:

1. V is finite-dimensional as a vector space [this is the situation considered by Cartan (1952d)].
2. M is a bounded domain in complex Euclidean space, V consists of the square-integrable complex analytic functions in M.

[The proof that (18–1) is verified there is given by Helgason (1962), p. 293.]

Now, we can fix one point $p_0 \in M$. Let L be the isotropy subgroup of K at p_0; i.e., L is the set of $k \in K$ such that

$$kp_0 = p_0.$$

Let V_0 be the set of $\psi \in V$, such that

$$\psi(p_0) = 0.$$

Statement (18–1) then tells us that V_0 is a *closed* subspace of V, considered as a Hilbert space. Let $V_0^\perp$ be the orthogonal complement of V_0 in V with respect to the Hilbert space inner product. It, too, is a closed subspace of V. Let U be the fiber of E sitting over p_0, i.e., $U = \pi^{-1}(p_0)$. As we have seen, the action of G on the vector bundle E defines a linear representation σ of L in U:

$$\sigma(k)(v) = kv \qquad \text{for } v \in \pi^{-1}(p_0).$$

From the definition of $V_0^\perp$, we see that the linear mapping

$$\psi \to \psi(p_0) \text{ of } V_0^\perp \to U \text{ is one-to-one.}$$

Clearly also

$$\rho(k)(\psi)(p_0) = \sigma(k)(\psi(p_0)),$$

i.e., this one-to-one map $V_0^\perp \to U$ commutes with the action of L on V_0 and U. We can rephrase this as follows:

> V splits up into the subspaces V_0 and $V_0^\perp$ invariant under L.
> The decomposition of $V_0^\perp$ into subspaces irreducible under L is
> contained in the decomposition of the representation σ of L on U.

For example, suppose that σ is the identity representation, and that $\Gamma(E)$ consists of the square-integrable complex-valued functions on M. This remark tells us, if $V_0^\perp$ is not zero, that a given irreducible unitary representation of K *may* occur in the decomposition of $\rho(K)$ on V only if the representation contains a vector invariant under L. Such a "vector," as a function on K/L invariant under L, was called a "zonal spherical function" by Cartan (a "spherical function" by Helgason). We shall now show that in fact $V_0^\perp$ is nonzero.

Theorem 18-1

Suppose that (18–1) is satisfied and that U is finite-dimensional. Then $V_0^\perp$ is nonzero. In fact, suppose that $\psi_1, \psi_2, \ldots$ is an orthonormal basis of the Hilbert space V; i.e.,

$$(\psi_1, \psi_j) = \delta_{ij} \text{ for } i, j = 1, 2, \ldots.$$

Then

(18–2)
$$\sum_{i=1}^{\infty} (\psi_i(p), \psi_i(p)) = F(p)$$

converges for all $p \in M$, to a constant, nonzero value.

Proof:

That (18–2) converges is seen as follows. We have seen that V_0 is mapped in a one-to-one way into U, hence also is finite-dimensional, say equal to r. We can suppose without loss in generality that $\psi_1, \ldots, \psi_r$ belong to $V_0^\perp$, while the rest of the ψ_i belong to V_0. Thus, (18–2) is really a finite sum for $p = p_0$. But the same argument holds at any point of M.

Now, for $k \in K$,

$$\rho(k)(\psi_i) = \sum_j a_{ij}\psi_j.$$

Clearly, (a_{ij}) is a unitary matrix; i.e.,

$$a_{il}\bar{a}_{jl} = \delta_{ij}.$$

But then

$$\begin{aligned}
F(k^{-1}p) &= \sum_i (\psi_i(k^{-1}p), \psi_i(k^{-1}p)) \\
&= \sum_i (k\psi_i(k^{-1}p), k\psi_i(k^{-1}p)) \\
&= \sum_i (\rho(k)(\psi_i)(p), \rho(k)(\psi_i)(p)) \\
&= \sum_{ijl} (a_{ij}\psi_j(p), a_{il}\psi_l(p)) \\
&= \sum_{ijl} a_{ij}\bar{a}_{il}(\psi_j(p), \psi_l(p)) = F(p).
\end{aligned}$$

Since K acts transitively on M, F is constant.

Now, suppose $V_0^{\perp}$ is zero. Then $F(p_0)$ is zero, forcing $F(p) = 0$ for all $p \in M$, forcing $\psi_i(p) = 0$ for all $p \in M$, which is absurd. Q.E.D.

We can now, continuing to follow Cartan, prove the orthogonality relations. The simplest version goes as follows:

Theorem 18–2

Suppose V' and V'' are closed subspaces of V invariant under K in each of which K induces a different irreducible representation. Then, V' and V'' are orthogonal as subspaces of the Hilbert space V.

Proof:

Let θ be an element of V'. Consider the linear form $\psi \to (\theta, \psi)$ for $\psi \in V''$. Since a Hilbert space can be identified with its dual space (Riesz-Fisher theorem), there is a unique $\psi_\theta \in V''$ such that

$$(\theta, \psi) = (\psi_\theta, \psi) \qquad \text{for all } \psi \in V''.$$

This mapping $\theta \to \psi_\theta$ from V' to V'' is linear and continuous. It clearly also commutes with the action of K on V' and V''. Hence, the kernel is invariant under K. Since K acts irreducibly on V', the kernel is either all of V' or zero. If all of V', we are through, since then V' and V'' are orthogonal. Otherwise, the map is one-to-one. Similarly, the image in V'' is invariant under K. If zero, again V' and V'' are orthogonal. Otherwise, the map is onto V''. Hence, we explicitly exhibited a map from V' to V'' which establishes the equivalence of the representation of K on V' and V''. Q.E.D.

Now we turn to an analysis of which representations of K can occur in the decomposition of the representation of K on $\Gamma(E)$. Let ρ' be an irreducible unitary representation of K on a Hilbert space V'. Suppose that in decomposing the action of L on V', the representation σ of L on U occurs; i.e., there is a subspace U' of V' invariant under L and a unitary map $\phi\colon U' \to U$ such that

$$\sigma(l)\phi(\mu') = \phi(\rho'(l)(\mu')) \qquad \text{for } l \in L, \ \mu' \in U'.$$

(We say then that the representation σ of L occurs in the decomposition of ρ' under L.) Associated with each vector $v' \in V'$ we can associate a cross section ψ_v, of $\Gamma(E)$:

For $k \in K$, project $\rho'(k^{-1})(v')$ into U', follow by ϕ, obtaining a map. $\psi_{v'}\colon K \to U$ such that $\psi_{v'}(kl) = \sigma(l^{-1})\psi_{v'}(k)$. $\psi_{v'}$ is the associated cross section of $\Gamma(E)$.

It is readily seen that this map $V' \to \Gamma(E)$ commutes with the action of K, and is one-to-one. [Otherwise, if $\psi_{v'}(k) = 0$ for all $k \in K$, then $\rho'(K)(v')$ projected onto U' is zero, hence $\rho'(K)$ acting on V' is not irreducible.]

After this general remark, the next obvious step in the program is to analyze more carefully the decomposition of K on $\Gamma(E)$. To work further with noncompact K would involve us in considerably greater technicalities of functional analysis. From now on, we shall work with K compact. It will be assumed that the reader knows that an irreducible unitary representation of a compact group is finite-dimensional. We can then put together these facts to give a qualitative result.

Theorem 18-3

Suppose K is compact. A given unitary representation ρ' of K occurs in the decomposition of $\rho(K)$ of an $\Gamma(E)$ into irreducible representations if and only if the representation σ of L given by the vector bundle E occurs in the decomposition of ρ' under L.

Now, we need a sophisticated orthogonality theorem, usually called the Burnside theorem in group-representation theory.

Theorem 18–4

Suppose that V is finite-dimensional† and is the direct sum of subspaces invariant under K in each of which K acts with the same representation.   Explicitly, V has a set of elements

$$\psi_i^\mu, 1 \leqslant i, j, \ldots \leqslant n, 1 \leqslant \mu, v, \ldots \leqslant m$$

such that

(a) $\rho(k)(\psi_i^\mu) = \sum_j a_{ij}(k)\psi_j^\mu, 1 \leqslant i \leqslant n; 1 \leqslant \mu \leqslant m.$
(b) For each $\mu, \psi_1^\mu, \ldots, \psi_n^\mu$ are linearly independent, and the representation of K in the subspace generated by these elements is irreducible.   [Thus, $k \to (a_{ij}(k))$ is an irreducible matrix representation of K.]
(c) Every element of V can be written as a linear combination of the ψ^μ.
Conclusion: The elements ψ_i^μ are linearly independent, hence form a basis of V, or there is a relation of the form

$$\sum_\mu \lambda_\mu \psi_i^\mu = 0 \quad \text{for } i = 1, \ldots, n.$$

Proof:

We proceed by induction on m.   For $m = 1$, it is part of the hypothesis.   Suppose then that it is true for all integers less than m, but not true for m.   There are then constants λ_i^μ such that

$$\sum_{i,\mu} \lambda_i^\mu \psi_i^\mu = 0.$$

Recall now that the ψ_i are not abstract vectors, but cross sections of a vector bundle over M.   Hence

$$\sum_{i,\mu} \lambda_i^\mu \psi_i^\mu(p) = 0 \quad \text{for all } p \in M.$$

Consider the vector space Λ of all matrices (λ_i^μ) satisfying this condition. For all $k \in K, (\lambda_i^\mu) \in \Lambda, p \in M$:

$$0 = \sum_{i,\mu} \lambda_i^\mu \psi_i^\mu(k^{-1}p) = \sum_{i,\mu} \lambda_i^\mu k \psi_i^\mu(k^{-1}p)$$
$$= \sum_{i,\mu} \lambda_i^\mu \rho(k)(\psi_i^\mu) = \sum_{i,\mu,j} \lambda_i^\mu a_{ij}(k)\psi_i^\mu.$$

† We shall not consider the infinite-dimensional version (if any) of the Burnside theorem.

Thus, the matrix $(\Sigma_j \lambda_j^\mu a_{ji}(k))$ belongs to Λ. Let $(\lambda_{i,\alpha}^\mu)$, $\alpha = 1, 2, \ldots, r$, be the maximal linearly independent set of elements of Λ. Thus, the n-vectors $(\lambda_{i,1}^m), \ldots, (\lambda_{i,r}^m)$ form a space of n-vectors invariant under the matrices $(a_{ij}(k))$. By our construction they are linearly independent. Now, the matrix representation $k \to (a_{ij}(k))$ is irreducible. Thus, these n-vectors must be a basis of the whole n-dimensional vector space. In particular, $r = n$. We can also arrange a linear change of the (ψ_i^μ) so that

$$\lambda_{i,j}^m = \delta_{ij}.$$

Returning to general μ, there are relations of the form

$$\sum_j \lambda_{j,l}^\mu a_{ji}(k) = \sum_j b_{lj} \lambda_{i,j}^\mu.$$

Let $\mu = m$ now:

$$\sum_j \delta_{jl} a_{ji}(k) = \sum_j b_{lj} \delta_{ij},$$

or

$$a_{li}(k) = b_{li}.$$

Hence

$$\sum_j \lambda_{j,l}^\mu a_{ji}(k) = \sum_j a_{lj}(k) \lambda_{i,j}^\mu.$$

For fixed μ, the matrices $(a_{ij}(k))$ commute with the matrices $(\lambda_{i,j}^\mu)$. By Schir's lemma, there are constants λ_μ such that

$$\lambda_{i,j}^\mu = \lambda_\mu \delta_{ij}.$$

Returning to the original relation, we have

$$0 = \sum_{i,\mu} \lambda_{i,j}^\mu \psi_i^\mu = \sum_\mu \lambda_\mu \psi_j,$$

which finishes the proof.

Putting the Burnside theorem together with our previous remarks gives the *Frobenius reciprocity theorem*:

> If K is a compact group and σ is irreducible, a given unitary representation ρ' of K occurs in $\Gamma(E)$ as many times as the decomposition of ρ' under L contains the representation σ of L determined by the vector bundle.

Let us sketch the proof, starting at the beginning. Let V be a subspace of $\Gamma(E)$ on which $\rho(K)$ acts irreducibly. Let V_0 be the subspace of $\psi \in V$ such that $\psi(p_0) = 0$. Then, $\rho(L)(V_0) = V_0$; hence $\rho(L)(V_0^\perp) = V_0^\perp$, where

$V_0^\perp$ is the orthogonal complement of V_0 in V. The map $\psi \to \psi(p_0)$ defines a one-to-one map of $V_0^\perp \to U$ that commutes with the action of L on V_0 via ρ and the action on U via σ. Using Theorem 18–1, we have seen that $V_0 \neq V$. Since σ acts irreducibly on U, this map must be an onto unitary map. This shows that $\rho(L)$ acting on V_0, when reduced out, contains a representation equivalent to σ. We leave it to the reader to show that the construction of a subspace of $\Gamma(E)$ from the representation ρ of K just gives V back again.

To finish the proof, we must consider the following situation: ρ' is an irreducible unitary representation of K on the Hilbert space V', and there are orthogonal subspaces $U^1, \ldots, U^r$ of V in each of which ρ' acts by a representation equivalent to the representation σ. The construction used to prove Theorem 18–3 gives a family $V^1, \ldots, V^r$ of subspaces of $\Gamma(E)$ in each of which K acts by a representation equivalent to ρ'. Suppose that the V^μ, $\mu = 1, \ldots, r$ are split up into

$$V_0^\mu + V_0^{\mu\perp},$$

where V_0^μ is the set of $\psi \in V^\mu$ such that $\psi(p_0) = 0$, and V_0^μ is its orthogonal complement in V^μ. We see from the way that the subspaces V^μ were constructed that, in the identification of V^μ with V', V_0^μ corresponds to U^μ, for $\mu = 1, \ldots, r$.

We must show that each of the representations $V^1, \ldots, V^r$ occurs *distinctly* in the decomposition of $\rho(K)$ on $\Gamma(E)$. For this, it suffices to prove that the subspaces $V^1, \ldots, V^r$ of $\Gamma(E)$ are all independent of each other. Suppose, for example, that (v_i), $1 \leqslant i \leqslant n$, is a basis for V, and that (ψ_i^μ) is the corresponding basis of V^μ, $\mu = 1, \ldots, r$. We must show that *all* the elements (ψ_i^μ) are linearly independent. For fixed μ, the (ψ_i^μ) transform under $\rho(K)$ according to an irreducible representation. By the Burnside theorem, if the (ψ_i^μ) were not independent, there would be a linear relation of the form

$$\sum_\mu \lambda_\mu \psi_i^\mu = 0 \qquad \text{for } i = 1, \ldots, n.$$

We see that there is a contradiction with the way the $V^1, \ldots, V^r$ were constructed from V', and the fact that $U^1, \ldots, U^r$ are all orthogonal subspaces of V.

REPRODUCING KERNELS FOR REPRESENTATIONS

Let us return for this section to the case where K may be noncompact, but where V is a closed subspace of $\Gamma(E)$ invariant under $\rho(K)$ for which condition (18–1) is satisfied. Suppose that the bundle E is trivial, so that

$\Gamma(E)$ consists of complex-valued functions on M. We shall not even assume that the action of K on M preserves the volume element dp. Instead, assume that

$$\rho(k)(\psi)(p) = m(k, p)\psi(k^{-1}p),$$

where $m(k, p)$ is a scalar multiplier put in to compensate for the fact that K does not preserve the volume. We still assume, however, that the multipliers are chosen (for example, as a suitable power of the Jacobian) so that the representation ρ of K on $\Gamma(E)$ is unitary.

Let (ψ_i), $i = 1, 2, \ldots$ be any orthonormal basis of V. Consider the function $F(p, q)$ defined for $p, q \in M$ as follows:

$$F(p, q) = \sum_i \psi_i(p)\psi_i(q).$$

(Note that, following Theorem 18–1, this converges for all p and q. It is also rather clear that it is independent of the orthonormal basis chosen for V. It may be called the *kernel function* of the representation.) Also,

$$F(k^{-1}p, k^{-1}q) = \sum_i \psi_i(k^{-1}p)\psi_i\overline{(k^{-1}p)}$$

$$= \sum_i m(k, p)m(k, q)\rho(k)(\psi_i)(p)\rho(k)(\psi_i)(q)$$

$$= m(k, p)\overline{m(k, q)}F(p, q).$$

[In particular, note that $F(p, q)$ can never be zero.] This is one property of the kernel function: The second property, the *reproducing property*, follows just as easily. For $\psi \in V$,

$$\int_M F(p, q)\psi(q) \, dq = \sum_i \int_M \psi_i(p)\overline{\psi_i(q)}\psi(q) \, dq$$

$$= F(p).$$

This applies in particular if K/L is a bounded domain in complex n space and K consists of complex analytic transformations. $F(p, q)$ is then Bergmann's *kernel function*.

LINE–BUNDLE REPRESENTATIONS ON SYMMETRIC SPACES

The Frobenius reciprocity theorem reduces the problem of decomposing the action of K on cross sections of bundles over K/L to the purely algebraic problem of describing how often a given representation of K contains the representation σ of L defined by the vector bundle. However, when K/L is a symmetric space and the bundle is a line bundle (i.e., its fibers are one-dimensional complex vector spaces), there is a theorem proved by

Cartan that simplifies this analysis tremendously.   Namely, each representation of K on the cross sections appears *at most once*.

We shall now present proof of this fact.   Let s be an automorphism of K such that

1. $s = s^{-1}$.
2. $s(l) = l$ for all $l \in L$.
3. $\mathbf{K} = \mathbf{L} \oplus \mathbf{P}$, with $s(X) = -X$ for all $X \in \mathbf{P}$.

Let E be the line bundle on K/L determined by a homomorphism σ of L into the complex numbers of absolute value 1.   A cross section ψ can then be represented as a map from K to C such that

$$\psi(kl) = \sigma(l^{-1})\psi(k) \qquad \text{for } k \in K, l \in L.$$

Let $P = \exp(\mathbf{P})$.   Such a ψ is then determined by the restriction to P.

Let V be a Hilbert space of cross sections of E that satisfies condition (18–1) and that transforms by an irreducible unitary representation of K. For $\psi \in V$, define

$$\rho(s)(\psi)(k) = \psi(s(k)).$$

Because of condition (2), $\rho(s)(\psi)$ is also a cross section of the line bundle, although it does not necessarily lie in V.   Now, for $K_0 \in P$,

$$\begin{aligned}
\rho(k_0)\rho(s)(\psi)(k) &= \rho(k_0)\psi(s(k)) \\
&= \psi(k_0^{-1}s(k)) \\
&= \psi(s(s(k_0^{-1})k)) \\
&= \psi(s(k_0k)) = \rho(s)\rho(k_0^{-1})(\psi)(k).
\end{aligned}$$

Let V' be another subspace of $\Gamma(E)$ satisfying condition (18–1), transforming under $\rho(K)$ by the same representation as V.

Let $\psi_1, \psi_2, \ldots$ and $\psi_1', \psi_2', \ldots$ be an orthonormal basis for V and V', transforming by the same unitary matrix under $\rho(K)$.   We see that

$$F(k_1, k_2) = \sum_i \psi_i(k_1)\rho(s)(\psi_i')(k_2)$$

converges, and that

$$F(k_0k_1, k_0k_2) = F(k_1, k_2) \qquad \text{for } k_0 \in P.$$

Thus, for $k_0 \in P$, e = the identity element of K,

$$\begin{aligned}
\sum_i \psi_i(k_0)\rho(s)(\psi_i')(e) &= F(k_0, e) \\
&= F(e, k_0^{-1}) \\
&= \sum_i \psi_i(e)\rho(s)(\psi_i')(k_0^{-1}) \\
&= \sum_i \psi_i(e)\psi_i'(s(k_0^{-1})) = \sum_i \psi_i(e)\psi_i'(k_0).
\end{aligned}$$

Hence there is a linear relation between the elements of V and V'. Since K acts in both irreducibly, they must coincide. Hence Cartan's theorem follows: *Each representation of K [that satisfies (18–1)] appears in $\Gamma(E)$ at most once.*

As examples we refer to the representations of $SU(n + 1)$ and $SL(n, C)$ constructed in Chapter 9 by means of line bundles on complex projective spaces.

Now we turn to another theorem of Cartan's that severely limits the representations of K that can occur in the action of K on complex-valued functions on a symmetric space K/L. In fact, let K be a connected Lie group, L a symmetric subgroup, an automorphism of K such that

1. $s = s^{-1}$.
2. $s(l) = l$ for $l \in L$.

Now, let U be the complex numbers themselves, and let σ be the map $l \to \sigma(l) = 1$, so that the line bundle on K/L is just a product of K/L with the complex numbers, and $\Gamma(E)$ consists of the (square-integrable) complex-valued function on K/L. $\Gamma(E)$ can also be considered as the set of functions $\psi\colon K \to C$ such that

$$\psi(kl) = \psi(k) \qquad \text{for all } l \in L,\, k \in K.$$

Let V be a closed subspace of $\Gamma(E)$ satisfying (18–1), in which K acts irreducibly. Cartan's theorem can now be stated:

The representation of K in V is equivalent to its complex conjugate (or, since the representation is unitary, to its dual).

Recall that we found in Chapter 9 when analyzing the case $K/L =$ complex projective space, $K = SU(n + 1)$, that it was precisely this type of representation that occurred. (Of course, note that not all self-dual representations occurred, only those of a certain symmetry type.)

As we have seen, there is a *unique* $\psi_0 \in V$ such that

1. $\psi_0(e) = 1$.
2. $\rho(l)(\psi_0) = \psi$; i.e., $\psi_0(lkl') = \psi(k)$ for $l, l' \in L,\, k \in K$.

ψ_0, considered as a function on K/L, is what Helgason calls a *spherical function*. [Since $\rho(K)$ acting on V is an irreducible representation of K, ψ_0 is an eigenfunction for the Casimir operation of L. We shall follow Helgason's terminology.]

Again, define $\rho(s)(\psi)$ by the formula

$$\rho(s)(\psi)(k) = \psi(s(k)) \qquad \text{for } k \in K.$$

Thus, $\rho(s)(V)$ and $\overline{V}$ (the complex conjugate of each element of V) are subspaces in which $\rho(K)$ acts by an irreducible representation. One verifies easily by an explicit calculation that the spherical functions in each of these spaces is the same; hence $\overline{V}$ must be equal to $\rho(s)(V)$. But, the representation of K in $\overline{V}$ is just the complex conjugate of the representation of K in V; i.e., the representation is equivalent to its complex conjugate.

Let K be a compact semisimple Lie group, L a symmetric subgroup. We have seen that obtaining the decomposition of K acting on complex-valued functions on K/L is the same as finding the irreducible representations of K in which L admits an invariant vector, since each one of this type occurs once in the decomposition. We can now give a general method for generating these representations.

Suppose that s is an automorphism of G, and that

$$s(l) = l \qquad \text{for all } l \in L.$$

(For the moment, we shall not require that $s^2 = $ identity.) Let ρ be an irreducible representation of G in a finite-dimensional vector space V. Let ρ^* be the dual representation of G in the dual vector space V^* to V. Thus, if (v_i), $1 \leqslant i \leqslant n$, is a basis for V, and if

$$\rho(g)(v_i) = a_{ij}(g)v_j \qquad \text{for } g \in G,$$

then

$$\rho^*(g)(v_i^*) = a_{ji}(g^{-1})v_j^*.$$

Construct the following representation ρ' in $V \otimes V^*$:

$$\rho(g)(v \otimes v^*) = \rho(s(g))(xv) \otimes \rho^*(g)(v^*) \qquad \text{for } v \in V,\, v^* \in V^*.$$

Let

$$w = v_i \otimes v_i^*.$$

Now, for $l \in L$,

$$\begin{aligned}
\rho(l)(w) &= \rho(s(l))(v_i) \otimes \rho^*(l)(v_i^*) \\
&= \rho(l)(v_i) \otimes \rho^*(l)(v_i^*) \\
&= a_{ij}(l)v_j \otimes a_{ki}(l^{-1})v_k^* \\
&= \delta_{kj}v_j \otimes v_k^* = w.
\end{aligned}$$

Thus, if we decompose the action of G on $V \otimes V^*$ into its irreducible components, L will have an invariant vector in each of these components on which w has a nonzero projection.

As a final comment in this section, we shall try to state the basic existence theorem to be found in Section 6 of Cartan's paper on spherical functions (1952d). This is the most difficult part of this fantastic piece of work, and we cannot attempt here to give full details.

Start off with a compact semisimple Lie algebra **K** and an automorphism
s of **K** with s^2 = identity.   Let **L** be the subalgebra of elements of **K** fixed
under s, and let **P** be the subspace of **K** consisting of elements X with
$s(X) = -X$.   Then

$$\mathbf{K} = \mathbf{L} \oplus \mathbf{P}, \ [\mathbf{L}, \mathbf{P}] \subset \mathbf{P}, \ [\mathbf{P}, \mathbf{P}] \subset \mathbf{L}.$$

Let K be the (unique) simply connected group whose Lie algebra is **K**.
By general principles of Lie group theory, there is an automorphism of
K (which we also denote by s) such that s^2 = identity, which gives rise
to the given automorphism s of **K**; i.e.,

$$s(\exp X) = \exp(s(X)) \qquad \text{for } X \in \mathbf{K}.$$

Let L be the set of elements of K left fixed by s.   It is easy to see that the
Lie algebra of L is precisely **L** (as indicated by our notation).   Cartan
had already proved in an earlier paper the following general property of L:

L is connected, and the symmetric space K/L is simply connected.

Let **A** be a maximal Abelian subalgebra of **P**, and let X_0 be a fixed regular element of **A**.   Let $\sum_+$ be the set of roots of the symmetric space
that are positive with respect to X_0: Each $\lambda \in \sum_+$ is then a real-valued
linear form on **A**, associated with a pair (Y_λ, Z_λ) of elements of **K** such
that:

1. $Y_\lambda \in \mathbf{P}, \ Z_\lambda \in \mathbf{L}$.
2. $B(Y_\lambda, Y_\lambda) = -1 = B(Z_\lambda, Z_\lambda)$.
[$B(\ \ , \ \ )$ is the Killing form of **K**, which is negative definite.]
3. For all $X \in \mathbf{A}$,
$$[X, Y_\lambda] = \lambda(X)Z_\lambda,$$
$$[X, Z_\lambda] = -\lambda(X)Y_\lambda.$$
4. $\lambda(X_0) \neq 0$.
5. The elements (Y_λ, Z_λ) and $(Y_{\lambda'}, Z_{\lambda'})$ are mutually perpendicular with
respect to B for different $\lambda, \lambda' \in \sum_+$.
6. As λ runs through $\sum_+$, the (Y_λ, Z_λ) give a basis for the orthogonal
complement (with respect to B again) of the centralizer of X_0 in K.
Further, we can find a system $\lambda_1, \ldots, \lambda_r$ of elements of $\sum_+$ (r = dimension **A**) such that:
7. Every $\lambda \in \sum_+$ can be written as a sum of $\lambda_1, \ldots, \lambda_r$ with nonnegative integers as coefficients.
8. If $X_i = [Z_{\lambda_i}, Y_{\lambda_i}]$, for $1 \leqslant i \leqslant r$, then the $X_1, \ldots, X_r$ form a basis
for **A**.

Now, suppose that ρ is an irreducible representation of $\mathbf{K}$ on a complex vector space V. Diagonalizing $\mathbf{A}$ defines certain linear forms w on $\mathbf{A}$ that occur as eigenvalues, which we call the weights of the representation. Say that such a weight ω is *maximal* if $\omega(X_0)$ has its largest value among all weights of the representation. As in Chapter 8, one can then prove that for a maximal weight ω,

$$\omega\left[\frac{X_i}{-B(X_i, X_i)}\right] \text{ is an integer for } 1 \leqslant i \leqslant r.$$

Cartan then proves that for every such form satisfying this condition there is exactly one irreducible representation ρ of K whose maximal weight is precisely this form, and such that L admits an invariant vector, so that this representation appears among the representations obtained by decomposing the action of K on complex-valued functions on K/L. In particular, these representations of K† form a lattice. Every such maximal weight can be written as a sum with nonnegative integer coefficients of the fundamental maximal weights $\omega_1, \ldots, \omega_r$ defined by

$$-\omega_i\left[\frac{X_j}{B(X_j, X_j)}\right] = \delta_{ij} \qquad \text{for } 1 \leqslant i, j \leqslant r.$$

Any representation of this type determines, as we have seen, a unique set $\psi_1, \ldots, \psi_r$ of functions on K/L which transform on translation by K like this representation. There is then just one function of this set which is invariant under L, and which takes the value 1 at the identity coset of K/L. It is the "spherical function."

Suppose $\psi_1, \ldots, \psi_n$ and $\psi_1', \ldots, \psi_m'$ are two such sets of functions on K/L transforming according to two representations ρ and ρ' of K, with maximal weight ω and ω'. The products

$$\psi_{a\mu}'' = \psi_a \psi_\mu' \qquad (1 \leqslant a \leqslant n, 1 \leqslant \mu \leqslant m)$$

then transform according to a reducible representation of K.‡ However, there is precisely one such representation in these products with maximal weight $\omega + \omega'$.

These facts contain as special cases§ the facts about ordinary finite-dimensional representations of semisimple groups that Cartan had proved earlier; in fact, these results are used again here. However, these proofs for general symmetric spaces have new features.

† Helgason calls them "representations of class 1."

‡ This representation consists of those representations in the tensor product of ρ and ρ' that contain invariant vectors under L.

§ Choose K as $L \times L$, L as the diagonal subgroup.

Cartan also mentions that these general theorems are useful in the practical problem of determining all irreducible representations of K for which L has an invariant vector. Let us present a series of remarks along these lines. Let $\mathbf{B}$ be a maximal Abelian subalgebra of $\mathbf{L}$ that also commutes with $\mathbf{A}$: Hence, $\mathbf{C} = \mathbf{A} + \mathbf{B}$ is a maximal Abelian subalgebra of $\mathbf{K}$. Suppose $s = \dim \mathbf{C}$. The maximal weights of the irreducible representation of K can then be considered as real-valued linear forms on $\mathbf{C}$. By the results sketched in Chapter 8, there are s fundamental representations with maximal weights $\theta_1, \ldots, \theta_s$ such that the maximal weight of any other representation can be written as the sum of the θ's with nonnegative integer coefficients. Now, these fundamental representations will not necessarily have the property that L has an invariant vector. However, the fundamental maximal weights $\omega_1, \ldots, \omega_r$ of these representations having this property will be written as sums:

$$\omega_i = \sum_{j=1}^{s} m_{ij}\theta_j \qquad (1 \leqslant i \leqslant r).$$

Hence the problem of decomposing the action of K on functions on K/L is essentially the problem of finding the m_{ij}. This problem is particularly easy if K/L is a rank-1 symmetric space, of course, since then $r = 1$. For example, suppose that ρ is an irreducible representation of K on a vector space V that has highest weight ω_1 and that has a vector v_1 which is invariant under L. Let $\rho \otimes \rho$ be the tensor product of ρ on $V \otimes V$, and let $S(V \otimes V)$ be the subspace spanned by the symmetric tensors $v_1 \otimes v_2 + v_2 \otimes v_1$. Decomposing $\rho \otimes \rho$ acting on $S(V \otimes V)$ into its irreducible parts gives a representation of G of highest weight $2\omega_1$, which also admits an invariant vector. For example, the representations of $SU(n + 1)$ or functions on $P_n(C)$ that we calculated in Chapter 9 illustrate this behavior perfectly: ρ is the $(n + 1, n + 1)$-representation of $SU(n + 1)$, made traceless, with highest weight ω_1. Other representations of the "ladder" of representations that occur (the symmetric space is of rank 1) are obtained by taking tensor products, then symmetrizing, then decomposing into irreducible representations, i.e., making traceless, exactly as we found in Chapter 9.

Another general fact is useful in determining the maximal weights of representations of K that arise from the decomposition of K on functions on the symmetric space K/L. In fact, let $\mathbf{C} = \mathbf{A} + \mathbf{B}$ be the maximal Abelian subalgebra of $\mathbf{K}$ considered above, with $\mathbf{B} \subset \mathbf{L}$. Let ρ be an irreducible representation of K that occurs when the action of K on functions on K/L is decomposed. Cartan then proves that the maximal weight θ of the representation is zero on $\mathbf{B}$.

One final comment: Cartan's theorem about the lattice structure of these representations only holds for the simply connected model of the symmetric space $K/L = M$. Suppose that $K'/L' = M'$ is a symmetric space covered by M, with K covering K'. Then, M' is obtained from M by dividing out the action of a finite subgroup on M. Which representations of K' occur in the decomposition of the action of K' on functions on M' can be seen by analyzing the action of this finite group on the functions on M that transform among themselves reproducible representations of K. For example, the sphere S_n is $SO(n + 1)/SO(n)$, while $P_n(R) = SO(n + 1)/O(n)$ is covered twice by S_n. The group acting on S_n is generated by reflection through the origin. The representations of $SO(n + 1)$ arising from spherical functions on S_n also arise from spherical functions on $P_n(R)$ if and only if the spherical functions are invariant under the reflections.

REPRESENTATIONS OBTAINED FROM NONCOMPACT GROUPS ACTING ON COMPACT SYMMETRIC SPACES

As we mentioned in the beginning of this chapter, our goal is to show how certain infinite families of representations of a compact group K could be put inside of a single irreducible representation of a noncompact Lie group G containing K. Our method is rather indirect, but effective where it works: Find a subgroup L of K such that:

1. G also acts on the homogeneous space $K/L = M$, with isotropy subgroup H containing L.

2. There is a vector bundle E on M invariant under G whose fibers admit an invariant Hermitian inner product such that the given family of representation of K is obtained by decomposing the action of K on the cross sections of the bundle.

The first part of the program is then to determine the triples (G, K, L) with G noncompact, K compact, L a subgroup of K, such that G acts transitively on K/L. Of course, another way of posing the problem would be to ask, given G and K, in how many ways G can act on a compact space M such that K acts transitively on M? Unfortunately, this sort of problem is difficult, so we shall present instead one method for constructing such spaces.

Suppose that G is a connected, noncompact semisimple group, and let K be a maximal compact subgroup† of G. Consider the Cartan decomposition of **G**, namely

$$\mathbf{G} = \mathbf{K} \oplus \mathbf{P} \qquad \text{with } [\mathbf{K}, \mathbf{P}] \subset \mathbf{P}, [\mathbf{P}, \mathbf{P}] \subset \mathbf{K}.$$

† In addition, we suppose that G has only a finite center, so that the Lie algebra **K** of K is a symmetric maximal compact subalgebra of **G**.

Let X be an element of $\mathbf{P}$, and let $\mathbf{L}$ be the centralizer of X in $\mathbf{K}$, i.e., $Y \in L$ if $[Y, X] = 0$. Let $\mathbf{H}$ be the subalgebra of $\mathbf{G}$ spanned by the eigenvectors of $\operatorname{Ad} X$ for nonnegative eigenvalues. (Recall that all eigenvalues of $\operatorname{Ad} X$ are real, and the matrix corresponding to $\operatorname{Ad} X$ has simple elementary divisors.) Let H be any subgroup of G whose Lie algebra is $\mathbf{H}$, and let $L = H \cap K$. One sees from the Iwasawa decomposition of G that $\mathbf{L}$ is the Lie algebra of L (as our notation indicates) and that K acts transitively on G/H, with isotropy subgroup L; hence we have a compact space M exhibited two ways as a coset space, namely

$$M = G/H = K/L.$$

(In case X is a regular element of $\mathbf{P}$, we obtain the space some of whose properties have been investigated in Chapter 13. The more general space considered here shares these properties.)

There are certain remarks that can be made in a converse direction. Suppose that K is a maximal compact subgroup of a semisimple Lie group G, and that L is a subgroup of K so that G acts transitively on $K/L = M$. Since K is compact, there is an invariant volume element on $M = K/L$; we denote it by dp. However, suppose that this volume element is *not* invariant under the action of G on M. We shall now show that $\operatorname{Ad} L$ acting in $\mathbf{P}$ must admit an invariant vector.

For $g \in G$, recall that the Jacobian $p \to J_g(p)$ of the transformation g indices on M satisfies the condition

(18–3) $$\int_M f(g^{-1}p)\, dp = \int_M f(d) J_g(p)\, dp$$

for each function $p \to f(p)$ on M. This induces the transformation law

(18–4) $$J_{g_1 g_2}(p) = J_{g_1}(g_2 p) J_{g_2}(p) \qquad \text{for } g_1, g_2 \in G, p \in M.$$

The condition that the volume element be invariant under K imposes the condition

$$J_k(p) = 1 \qquad \text{for } k \in K, p \in M.$$

Now, suppose X is in the Lie algebra of $\mathbf{G}$. We have seen that X induces a first-order differential operator $f \to X(f)$ on functions on M (or, cross sections of any G homogeneous vector bundle on M, for that matter). In fact, we have

$$X(f)(p) = \frac{\partial}{\partial t} f(\exp - Xt)p \Big|_{t=0}.$$

The function $(p, t) \to f(\exp(-Xt)p)$ satisfies the first-order partial-differential equation:

$$\frac{\partial}{\partial t} f(\exp(-Xt)p) = X(f)(\exp(-Xt)p).$$

Let

(18–5) $$J_X(p) = \frac{\partial}{\partial t} J_{\exp(-X)}(p)\Big|_{t=0}.$$

J_X then measures infinitesimally how the one-parameter group generated by X distorts the volume element dp. In particular, we have from (18–3),

$$\int_M X(f)\, dp = - \int_M f(p) J_X(p)\, dp.$$

For $X \in \mathbf{K}$, $J_X = 0$. From (18–4) we have

(18–6) $$J_{[X,Y]} = X(J_Y).$$

Suppose $Y, \ldots, Y_n$ is a basis for $\mathbf{P}$:

$$[X, Y_i] = \sum_j A_{ij} Y_j.$$

Then

$$X(J_{Y_i}) = \sum_j A_{ij} Y_j.$$

We see that the functions $p \to J_{Y_i}(p)$ on M transform under the action of K like the representation obtained by letting Ad K act on $\mathbf{P}$. As a very special case of the Frobenius reciprocity theorem, we have then

Ad L acting on $\mathbf{P}$ has an invariant vector.

Continuing to suppose that G acts transitively on $M = K/L$, suppose that E is a G-homogeneous vector bundle on M, with G-invariant Hermitian inner product $(\ ,\ )$ on the fibers. This enables us to make the cross sections $\Gamma(E)$ into a Hilbert space:

$$(\psi_1, \psi_2) = \int_M (\psi_1(p), \psi_2(p))\, dp.$$

For $X \in G$, $\psi \in \Gamma(E)$, $X(\psi)$ is the following cross section of E:

$$X(\psi)(p) = \frac{\partial}{\partial t} \exp(Xt)\psi(\exp(-Xt)p)\Big|_{t=0}.$$

Let α be a complex number. We can define a representation ρ of $\mathbf{G}$ by transformations of $\Gamma(E)$ by means of the formula

$$\rho(X)(\psi) = X(\psi) + \alpha J_X.$$

The corresponding representation of G is

$$\rho(g)(\psi)(p) = g\psi(g^{-1}p) J_{g^{-1}}^\alpha.$$

The condition that $\rho(g)$ be unitary, hence that each $\rho(X)$ be skew-Hermitian, is that the real part of $\alpha = \frac{1}{2}$. We have seen that it is possible to describe in general terms how the representation ρ decomposes under K, by using certain general theorems. Of course, it is to be expected that the operators $\rho(X)$, for $Y \in \mathbf{P}$, will not preserve the subspaces of $\Gamma(E)$ that are invariant under $\rho(K)$, but will be "ladder" operators shifting one representation of K into several others. We can see this in a general way as follows. Let (Y_i) be the basis of $\mathbf{P}$ considered above. Then $[X, Y_i] = a_{ij}(X)Y_j$, for $X \in K$. Then, $X \to (a_{ij}(X))$ determines a representation of K, that is just, in matrix form, the adjoint representation of $\mathbf{K}$ on $\mathbf{P}$. Let (ψ_a), $1 \leqslant a, b, \ldots, \leqslant m$, be a collection of cross sections of E that transform in a given way under $\mathbf{K}$; i.e.,

$$\rho(X)(\psi_a) = b_{ab}(X)\psi_b.$$

Then

$$\begin{aligned} \rho(X)\rho(Y_i)(\psi_a) &= \rho([X, Y_i])(\psi_a) + \rho(Y_i)(\rho(X)(\psi_a)) \\ &= a_{ij}(X)\rho(Y_i)(\psi_a) + b_{ab}(X)\rho(Y_i)(\psi_b). \end{aligned}$$

Hence, the cross sections $\psi_{ia} = \rho(Y_i)(\psi_a)$ transform like the tensor product of the two representations $X \to (a_{ij}(X))$, $X \to (b_{ab}(X))$ of $\mathbf{K}$. However, the mapping of the tensor product of the representation spaces into the cross sections is not necessarily one-to-one; i.e., every representation occurring in the tensor product does not necessarily occur among the (ψ_{ia}).

GELL–MANN'S FORMULA

The formula in question expresses, in favorable cases, the noncompact operators of certain representations of a semisimple Lie group G in a very convenient form.

Let K be a maximal compact subgroup of G, and let H be a subgroup of G such that K acts transitively on the homogeneous space $G/H = M$. Suppose $L = H \cap K$. Let $\mathbf{P}$ and $\mathbf{M}$ be subspaces of $\mathbf{G}$ and $\mathbf{K}$, respectively, so that

$$\mathbf{G} = \mathbf{K} \oplus \mathbf{P} \qquad [\mathbf{K}, \mathbf{P}] \subset \mathbf{P} \qquad [\mathbf{P}, \mathbf{P}] \subset \mathbf{K},$$
$$[\mathbf{L}, \mathbf{M}] \subset \mathbf{M}.$$

Let E be a homogeneous vector bundle over M, with an invariant Hermitian inner product on its fibers, so that its space $\Gamma(E)$ of cross sections can be made into a Hilbert space, by the usual formula:

$$(\psi_1, \psi_2) = \int_M (\psi_1(p), \psi_2(p))\, dp.$$

Suppose that the volume element dp is invariant under K, but not under G. For $Y \in B$, let J_Y be the Jacobian function on M constructed using (18–5). (Recall that J_Y measures how the one-parameter group generated by Y changes the volume dp.)   Let $Y \to \rho(Y)$ be the representation of **G** by skew-Hermitian operators on $\Gamma(E)$ induced by the action of G on the cross section.   Let Δ be the Casimir operator in the universal enveloping algebra of **G**.   Gell-Mann's formula is now

(18–7) $\rho(Y) = [\rho(\Delta), J_Y]$ for all $Y \in \mathbf{P}$;

i.e.,

$$\rho(Y)(\psi) = \rho(\Delta)(J_Y \psi) - J_Y \rho(\Delta)(\psi) \qquad \text{for } \psi \in \Gamma(E).$$

We do not yet know the most general conditions under which this formula is true.   However, verification of the formula can be made to depend on a purely algebraic property of **G**, **K**, and **L**.   We shall now indicate briefly this reduction.

Note that both the left and right sides of (18–7) are first-order differential operators acting on the cross sections of E that transform under the action of K like the representation of K in **P**.   A first-order differential operator also determines a cross section of a vector bundle E' over M. E' is that K-homogeneous vector bundle over M associated with the representation

$$\sigma' = \sigma \otimes \sigma_1 \text{ of } L,$$

where σ is the representation of L determining the vector bundle E, and σ_1 is the representation of Ad L in **M**.   Thus, if this vector bundle has just one system of cross sections that transform under K like Ad K acting in **P**, we see that the left and right sides of (18–7) must differ by a constant; this constant can then be absorbed in Δ.   The Frobenius reciprocity theorem can be applied to give a sufficient condition for this.   Namely:

If each irreducible representation of L obtained by reducing Ad L in **M** occurs at most once in the reduction of σ' into irreducible components, then (18–7) holds.

Suppose, for example, that E is a line bundle, so that σ is a one-dimensional representation of L, and that K/L is a symmetric space, such that Ad L acting in **M** is irreducible.†   Then, the condition that (18–7) hold takes the form

† This will be true if **K** is simple, or if $K = L \times L$, with L the diagonal subgroup and L simple.

(18–8)   The representation of $\text{Ad}\,L$ in P contains as irreducible component the representation of $\text{Ad}\,L$ in M just once.

In principle, this reduces the question to one that can be answered completely using the classification of symmetric spaces. We shall not carry it out here. However, there is one large class of symmetric spaces for which this condition can be immediately verified. Suppose that $\mathbf{G} = \mathbf{K} + i\mathbf{K} = \mathbf{K}_C$, and that $\mathbf{K}$ is simple. It can be proved that this forces $\mathbf{L}$ to have a one-dimensional center. The possibilities can be read off from the list given by Helgason (1962, p. 354):

$$K/L = SU(p+q)/SU(p) \times U(q),$$
$$SO(p+2)/SO(p) \times SO(2) \qquad SO(2n)/U(n)$$
$$SP(n)/U(n) \qquad E_6/SO(10) \times SO(2) \qquad E_7/E_6 \times SO(2).$$

These are the "compact Hermitian symmetric spaces." Their dual non-compact symmetric spaces are the "bounded symmetric domains." Note that $K/L = SO(n+1)/U(n) = P_n(C)$ is of this type: Gell-Mann's formula can be verified by a direct calculation in this case. In fact, this is how it was discovered. Note that implicit in the formula are certain very strong and interesting algebraic conditions on the representation. These may be related to the sort of algebraic conditions one expects the representations to have on physical grounds.

REFERENCES

V. I. Arnold (1962), On the Classical Perturbation Theory and the Stability Problem of Planetary Systems, *Dokl. Akad Nauk SSSR*, **145**, 487–490.

L. Auslander and R. Mackenzie (1963), *Introduction to Differentiable Manifolds*, McGraw-Hill, New York.

V. Bargmann (1936), *Z. Physik*, **99**, 576–582.

V. Bargmann (1947), Irreducible Representations of the Lorentz Group, *Ann. Math.*, **48**, 568–640.

A. O. Barut (1964), *Electrodynamics and Classical Theory of Fields and Particles*, Macmillan, New York.

R. E. Behrends, J. Dreitlein, C. Fronsdal, and W. Lee (1962), Simple Groups and Strong Interaction Symmetries, *Rev. Mod. Phys.*, **34**, 1.

H. Boerner (1963), *Representations of Groups*, North-Holland, Amsterdam.

A. Borel and J. deSiebenthal (1949), Les Sous groupes fermés de rang maximium des groupes de Lie clos, *Commum. Math. Helv.*, **23**, 200–221.

R. Bott (1958), The Space of Loops of a Lie Group, *Mich. Math. J.*, **5**, 35–61.

F. Bruhat (1956), Sur les représentations induites des groupes de Lie, *Bull. Soc. Math. France*, **84**, 97–205.

E. Cartan (1952a), Les Groupes projectifs qui ne laissent invariant aucune multiplicité plan, *Oeuvres Complètes*, Pt. 1, Vol. I, pp. 493–531.

E. Cartan (1952b), La Géométrie des groupes simples, *Oeuvres Complètes*, Pt. 1, Vol. II, pp. 793–840.

E. Cartan (1952c), Sur certaines formes Riemanniennes rémarquables des géométries a group fondemental simple, *Oeuvres Complètes*, Pt. 1, Vol. II, pp. 867–990.

E. Cartan (1952d), Sur la determination d'un système orthogonal complète dans un espace de Riemann symmétrique clos, *Oeuvres Complètes*, Pt. 1, Vol. II, pp. 1045–1080.

C. Chevalley (1946), *Theory of Lie Groups*, Princeton Univ. Press, Princeton, N.J.

E. B. Dynkin (1950), The Structure of Semisimple Lie Algebras, *Am. Math. Soc. Transl.*, **17**.

E. B. Dynkin (1957a), Semisimple Subalgebras of Semisimple Lie Algebras, *Am. Math. Soc. Transl.*, (Series 2) **6**, 111–244.

E. B. Dynkin (1957b), Maximal Subgroups of the Classical Groups, *Am. Math. Soc. Transl.*, (Series 2) **6**, 245–378.

V. Fock (1935), *Z. Physik*, **98**, 145–154.

H. Furstenberg (1963), A Poisson Formula for Semisimple Lie Groups, *Am. Math. J.*, **77**, 335–366.

I. M. Gel'fand and M. I. Graev (1964), Geometry of Homogeneous Spaces, Representations of Groups in Homogeneous Spaces and Related Questions of Integral Geometry, *Am. Math. Soc. Transl.*, (Series 2) **37**, 351–429.

I. M. Gel'fand, R. A. Minlos, and Z. Y. Shapiro (1963), *Representations of the Rotation and Lorentz Groups and Their Applications*, Pergamon Press, New York.

I. M. Gel'fand and M. A. Neumark (1957), *Unitare Darstellungen der Klassichen Gruppen*, Akademie-Verlag, Berlin.

M. Gell-Mann (1964), *Physics*, **1**, 63.

M. Gell-Mann and Y. Ne'eman (1964), *The Eightfold Way*, Benjamin, New York.

S. G. Gindikin and F. I. Karpelevitch (1962), Plancherel Measure for Symmetric Riemannian Spaces of Non-Positive Curvature, *Dokl. Akad. Nauk SSSR*, **145**, 252–255.

F. Gursey and L. A. Radacati (1964), *Phys. Rev. Letters*, **13**, 299.

M. Hamermesh (1962), *Group Theory and Its Application to Physical Problems*, Addison-Wesley, Reading, Mass.

Harish-Chandra (1958), Spherical Functions on a Semisimple Lie Group, *Amer. J. Math.*, **80**, 241–310.

S. Helgason (1962), *Differential Geometry and Symmetric Spaces*, Academic Press, New York.

S. Helgason (1963a), Fundamental Solutions of Invariant Differential Operators on Symmetric Spaces, *Bull. Am. Math. Soc.*, **69**(1963), 778–781.

S. Helgason (1963b), Duality and Radon Transform for Symmetric Spaces, *Bull. Am. Math. Soc.*, **69**(1963), 782–788.

R. Hermann (1961), A Poisson Kernel for Certain Homogeneous Spaces, *Proc. Am. Math. Soc.*, **12**, 892–899.

R. Hermann (1962), Geometric Aspects of Potential Theory in Symmetric Spaces, *Ann. Math.*, Part I in **148**(1962), 349–366; part II in **151**(1963), 143–149; Part III in **152**(1964), 384–394.

R. Hermann (1964), Compactifications of Homogeneous Spaces and Contraction of Lie Groups, *Proc. Natl. Acad. Sci. U.S.*, **51**, 456–461.

R. Hermann (1965a), Compactifications of Homogeneous Spaces: I, to appear in *J. Math. Mech.*

R. Hermann (1965b), Compactification of Minkowski Space and $SU(3)$ Symmetry, to appear in *J. Math. Phys.*

E. Inonu and E. P. Wigner (1953), On the Contraction of Groups and Their Representations, *Proc. Natl. Acad. Sci. U.S.*, **39**, 510–524.

N. Jacobson (1962), *Lie Algebras*, Wiley (Interscience), New York.

D. Kastler (1961), *Introduction a l'electrodynomique quantique*, Dunod, Paris.

I. Kirilov (1964), Unitary Representations of Nilpotent Lie Groups, *Russian Math. Surv.*, **2**.

F. Lurcat (1964), *Physics*, **1**, 95.

W. D. McGlinn (1964), *Phys. Rev. Letters*, **12**, 467.

H. V. McIntosh (1959), *Am. J. Phys.*, **27**, 620–625.

G. W. Mackey (1963a), Group Representations in Hilbert Space, appendix to *Mathematical Problems of Relativistic Physics* by I. Segal, American Mathematical Society, Providence, R.I.

G. W. Mackey (1963b), *The Mathematical Foundations of Quantum Mechanics*, Benjamin, New York.

J. Mathews and R. L. Walker (1964), *Mathematical Methods of Physics*, Benjamin, New York.

L. Michel (1964), *On Relations between Internal Symmetry and Relativistic Invariance*, preprint, Summer Institute for Theoretical Physics, Madison, Wis.

C. C. Moore (1964), Compactification of Symmetric Spaces, *Am. J. Math.*, **86**, 211–218.

P. Moussa and R. Stora (1965), *Some Remarks on the Product of Irreducible Representations of the Inhomogeneous Lorentz Group*, preprint, Centre d'Études Nucléaires de Saclay.

E. Nelson (1959), Analytic Vectors, *Ann. Math.*, **70**, 572–615.

L. O'Raifeartaigh (1965), *Phys. Rev. Letters*, **14**, 575.

W. Pauli (1926), *Z. Physik*, **36**, 336–363.

L. Pontrjagin (1939), *Topological Groups*, Princeton Univ. Press, Princeton, N.J.

G. Racah (1951), *Notes on Lie Groups*, Institute for Advanced Study, Princeton, N.J.

F. Riesz and B. S. Nagy (1955), *Functional Analysis*, Ungar, New York.

B. Sakita (1964), *Phys. Rev. Letters*, **13**, 643.

A. Salam (1963), The Formalism of Lie Groups, in *Theoretical Physics*, International Atomic Energy Agency, Vienna.

E. Saletan (1961), Contraction of Lie Groups, *J. Math. Phys.*, **2**, 1ff.

T. Satake (1960), On Representations and Compactifications of Symmetric Spaces, *Ann. Math.*, **71**, 77–110.

I. E. Segal (1951), *Duke Math. J.*, **18**, 221.

D. Shale (1962), Linear Symmetries of Free Boson Fields, *Trans. Am. Math. Soc.*, **103**, 149–167.

R. F. Streater and A. S. Wightman (1964), *PCT, Spin & Statistics, and All That*, Benjamin, New York.

H. Trotter (1958), Approximation of Semi-Groups of Operators, *Pacific J. Math.*, **8**, 887–919.

L. Van Hove (1951), Sur certaines représentations unitaires d'un groupe infini de transformations, *Mem. Acad. Roy. Belg.*, **26**.

J. von Neumann (1931), Die Eindeutigkeit der Schrödingerschen Operatoren, *Ann. Math. Pure Appl.*, **104**, 570–578.

J. von Neumann (1955), *Mathematical Foundations of Quantum Mechanics*, Princeton.

H. Weyl (1955), *The Theory of Groups and Quantum Mechanics*, Dover, New York.

E. Whittaker (1944), *Analytical Dynamics*, Dover, New York.

A. S. Wightman (1960), L'Invariance dans la mécanique quantique relativiste, in *Dispersion Relations and Elementary Particles*, Hermann, Paris.

E. P. Wigner (1937), *Phys. Rev.*, **51**, 106, 149–204.

E. P. Wigner (1939), Unitary Representations of the Lorentz Group, *Ann. Math.*, **40**.

E. P. Wigner (1959), *Group Theory*, Academic Press, New York.

INDEX